Ballad of Calypso
Rhyme of the Modern Mariner

Ballad of Calypso

RHYME OF THE MODERN MARINER

by Dennis McGuire
Illustrated by Pat McGuire

Particulars:
    445 Quatrains
    88 Illustrations
    42 Photos
    13,000 word Ballad
    100,000 words Total

Fonts: Georgia, American Brewery Rough & Great Vibes

ISBN 978-0-5783505-4-7 (paperback)
ISBN 978-0-5789121-5-8 (epub)

First Edition
First Edition: January 2022

While Calypso's free fallin' in space
the mind's thinkin' "we're gonna leave no trace!"
A fifty or hundred foot wave the truth be told
"when we hit the trough she's gonna explode!"

Pat McGuire

CONTENTS

ILLUSTRATIONS

PHOTOS

PREFACE

Joshua Slocum, along with Howard I. Chapelle and Jack London are the early authors whose work influenced what follows in these pages. Their combined stories, knowledge and real life experience planted the seeds which grew into an insatiable yearning for a sailing adventure.

Slocum's real life account, "Sailing Alone Around the World" entertains the reader from the acquisition of a vessel to the completion of the first round the world, single-handed voyage. An ingenious, determined individual and lifelong creature of the sea, he imparts valuable wisdom in his fascinating tale of the journey.

Howard I. Chapelle's "American Small Sailing Craft" provides the reader with his intimate knowledge of "Traditional Small Sailing Craft, Their Development and Design." One could not help but cultivate an appreciation for the fine lines of the working vessels of years gone by. Their seaworthiness, a product of an evolution in design over several hundred years goes all the way back to old England and beyond.

Jack London's days as an oyster pirate in San Francisco Bay along with his "Voyage of the Snark" add comic relief with many truths embedded, applicable to this day. His story highlights the problems encountered in the building and sailing of a vessel, the results of the project learned in a most rude fashion, far out to sea.

Together with his tales of the inherent, adventurous spirit of the human being, London's stories blur the lines between truth and fiction with an emphasis on hilarity, preceding disastrous consequences. His tragic stories do nothing to discourage the sailor borne to the sea, rather, one is drawn further into its embrace.

Lastly, three authors, and the characters they created must be included with those individuals mentioned above. Joel Chandler

Harris, "Br'er Rabbit," Mark Twain, "Huckleberry Finn" and Mort Walker, "Beetle Bailey." Without them in the formative years of this author, in all likelihood this book would not have been written, nor the journey taken.

Dennis McGuire

Panama to Hilo
97 Days
5000 Miles

Hilo to Neah Bay
38 Days
3500 Miles

50°N

40°N

30°N

20°N

Hilo, Hawaii
6/3/81

6/8

6/1

5/23

5/16

5/7

10°N

Equator
130°

140°

120°

110°

100°

90°

80°W

0°
600 miles
150°W

600 miles

NE Trades

Neah Bay
10/27/81

strait of Juan de Fuca

Doldrums

Tehuantepec

4/11

1/30

4/4/80

Tavernier Florida
5/20/80

3/8/80

1/1/80
Panama Canal

Portsmouth, RI
9/26/79

PART I

Chapter 1

A JOURNEY BEGINS

March-September 1979

Herring Roe on Kelp Dive

Late March in Prince William Sound
icy snow covers the ground
Through glacial waters streaks the spring dawn
great schools of herring have come here to spawn

The Alaska spring of 1979 is a banner year for the herring stocks of Prince William Sound. A bumper crop of "herring roe on kelp" (*"kazunoko kombu"*), a Japanese delicacy, will be harvested from these waters this year. Untold numbers of these colossal silvery schools will wind their way through the fjords. The waters will cloud up with milt released by the males to fertilize the eggs. The females swim into the clouded waters and flutter their tails as they lay snow white eggs across the leaves of ribbon kelp which stream down over boulders then intertwine in the hollows. Sieve kelp stand like giant cabbages in patches alongside fields of "hair kelp." Hair kelp appears as sage brush before the arrival of the herring.

Ribbon and sieve fronds will receive a thick blanket of eggs. Layer after layer will flock the thin stranded limbs of the hair kelp thick as Christmas trees. The scene presents itself as a winter wonderland to the divers.

A circus atmosphere fills the air
as barges're loaded for this grand affair
Kelp buyin' stations these old wooden sleds
an' the place where divers make their beds

The village of Cordova, Alaska is a beehive of activity with crews making ready to be on the fishing grounds well ahead of this most important opening day of the season. Early spring fisheries are a great economic relief to Alaskan villages following the idleness of the winter months. Herring roe on kelp along with its associated "herring sac roe" seine and gillnet openings are the first of the spring fisheries, which will be followed closely by the homeward migration of the Alaska salmon. The salmon runs will continue throughout the spring, summer and into late fall.

Barges are loaded with processing equipment, which consist for the most part of pallets of hundred pound bags of salt and thousands of white, six gallon buckets. Hundreds of "kelp boxes" (four foot oblong wooden boxes) are stacked atop the barge alongside tall columns of buckets.

Weigh stations and processing tables fill out the working deck, shared only with a generous galley partitioned off for the processing crew and divers. The galley is well appointed, with tables to seat about twenty. An ancient oil stove, with heavy cast iron skillets, jumbo soup pots along with spatulas, spoons, forks and knives hang from a locally fashioned galvanized exhaust hood.

Above the processing deck and galley is the bunkhouse floor where the processing crew, divers and their tenders hot bunk in cramped quarters. Those unlucky to have no bunk make their beds under dripping dive suits and gear.

Japanese technicians, required participants in the operation, have a more comfortable room set aside. They are here to insure high quality and proper handling of the kelp as it comes aboard the barge.

Out on the grounds get their skiff ready
air compressor pumpin' steady
Waxin' zippers on the suits
checkin' for holes in bottoms of boots

The condition of the suit top notch throughout
gotta' protect the diver from freezin' out
Air hose coiled, kelp boxes stacked
with charcoal 'n cotton the air filter's packed

Working their skiff the crew had dubbed "Razzle Dazzle" in honor of Jack London's sailboat during his oyster pirating days, they are filling kelp boxes with Ribbon, Sieve and Hair Kelp which are heavily laden with herring eggs.

The pair had been invited to the fishery by "Smitty," a major kelp buyer who offered a skiff, with space in the bunkhouse and a seat at the galley table. The newlyweds, a commercial dive harvester between jobs and a wandering waitress with a boat, had met in Port Townsend a few months earlier. The diver promised the waitress an adventure in Alaska and the waitress gave the boat-less, unemployed vagrant, quarters from her tips along with a place to live on her 22' lifeboat, *Stella B*. They were married in short order by "Ferry Boat Hank," engineer on the local ferry, *Rhododendron*.

A compressor is pumping fresh air down to the diver on a "hookah" hose in the frigid waters of Valdez Arm. Ice bergs the size of a small house, calved from the Columbia Glacier are beached on Bligh Island,[1] Rocky Point and the shallows of Tatitlik Narrows. Bergs and bergy bits are floating free nearby in the deep waters of "The Arm."

Breathing in fresh glacial air while surrounded by the majesty of Prince William Sound, Pat is

---

1. It will only be ten years before this wonder of Nature, created over the eons, is destroyed by a reckless act committed by those in the wheelhouse of the *Exxon Valdez* on March 24th, 1989. This will be "ground zero" where herring and their eggs will be destroyed. The waters made toxic, eggs covered in crude oil.
The largest, most modern oil tanker in the world, fully loaded, will strike the reef a few hundred yards from where the *Razzle Dazzle* and crew are at work.

busy keeping an eye on the diver's bubbles and a worn out compressor. Cranking bags of kelp aboard, then sorting by species into the boxes, she learns the ropes of a "tender" quickly, a critical role in a tethered dive operation.

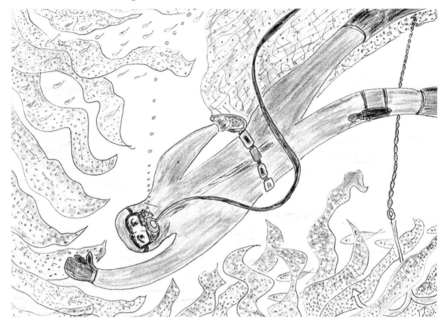

There's a new beauty down below
across the undersea landscape
a fresh herring spawn snow
The next generation springin'
to life here
on ribbon, hair 'n elephant ear

Ten or fifteen feet under the boat, thick schools of herring surround the harvester; their spawning uninterrupted by his thrashing flippers or the cutting and bagging of the kelp. Diving ducks are pecking along, busily competing with the diver for their share of the feast.

Steller's sea lions roam through the schools in herds, acting like unsupervised children in a candy store, gorging themselves as they run amuck. The animals appear without warning, their massive, agile bulk made even larger by the magnification of the diver's underwater vision. These gangs of beasts speed by gracefully, then are swallowed by the opaque herring milt, the visibility being only several feet.

Clams, urchins 'n cucumbers're fine
but herring roe kelp divin's really sublime
Swimmin' straight down into this
icy cold brine
fillin' our skiff with a product so fine

Divin' hard eight days in a row
we have eight grand to show
for that sailboat we'd been a wishin'
long before we started fishin'

The quality this season does entice
a very satisfying healthy price
Leavin' the grounds far astern
headed to town with money to burn!

Finding Calypso

Rode the Empire Builder to the eastern seaboard
beat the docks for boats our funds could afford
Lookin' aroun' an' whaddaya know
wound up at the Newport Used Boat Show!

T he crew discovers very inexpensive cross country tickets are available on "Amtrak." Rumors of cheap boats on the east coast combine with visions of sailing and diving warm waters offer an opportunity viewed as an open door to adventure.

On arrival in Connecticut, the search for a sailboat begins in earnest. Friends are a great help, having provided a vehicle for use in touring the coast. Walking the docks in a variety of harbors from Connecticut to Massachusetts, there are an abundance of sailing vessels found, however, limited funds narrow the possibilities substantially. The hunt alters course when an advertisement for the Newport, Rhode Island "Used Boat Show" is discovered on a harbor bulletin board. Without hesitation the crew makes a beeline for Newport, arriving late at night, before opening day.

Hop a fence middle of the night
'cause we spot a boat that looks just right
When mornin' comes an' the show's open
Calypso will be ours we're a hopin'

Gates are locked, however the fence is low: the crew hops over to get a closer look at one particular boat, blue in color, with a short bowsprit standing out among a long line of sailboats on the dock.

The excitement is tempered when the asking price is found to be $5900, just out of reach. A complete walk through proves there are an abundance of boats very well within reach, some showing wear in areas which are an indication of major disrepair, unseen, below decks. Buying a boat, "in the water" where the hull may not be thoroughly examined is risky business; the crew must be very careful when considering a purchase.

Only a few weeks earlier, they had turned down a potentially good deal on a fishing vessel in Alaska, which, had they purchased the boat, would have sent them off on an entirely different path of life. What saved them from that course of action was inspecting the interior hull below the floorboards, as the vessel was in the water, sitting in her slip. Reaching down, pulling out fistfulls of rotten wood from the keel and frames told a story, the whole idea was scrapped on the spot.

After a sleepless night the pair are up early, they gobble a breakfast sandwich, drink too much coffee, then set off for the boat show. They arrive early to find a sizable number of folks waiting at the gate.

The pair squeeze with the crowd through the gate as it opens. A quick, cursory tour of the show reveals a wide selection of wooden boats of every description, motor and sail, large and small. The interest in wooden boats here is self evident, noting the early birds in attendance.

One particular boat, which is free from worries of hidden issues is fancied by the would-be boat builder of the duo. A brand new, "clinker built" (lapstrake) twenty six foot double ender. A thing of New England beauty, from her lines to her meticulous construction, perfection. Dazzled by the view from the dock into her bare hull, as she has no decks or ceiling(interior planking) installed, the inner side of the frames and hull planks expose fine workmanship.

The builder is fussing with details, inviting the crew to take a close look. She is ballasted with rudder installed. Ready for engine, decks, cabin, mast and rig. The downside, although she could be had for a paltry $2000, the crew is well aware that would just be the beginning. Taking on this project will not have them sailing anytime soon.

The fellow is left shaking his head with the knowledge he had nearly closed a deal, and a very good deal it was, for the right person; if they were to be the new owners an income would need to be found, as well as a place to finish the boat.

If that was to be their decision, they would not have left their home in Port Townsend, the wooden boat capital of the Pacific Northwest.

Not to be discouraged, the crew returns to look once again at the little blue sailboat that had caught their attention the previous evening, and "lo!" The $5900 price tag has a red line slashing the price by one thousand dollars. The crew has the cash in pocket!

*Built by shipwright A.A. Bernard
nineteen fifty two in his backyard
A sturdy little ketch of twenty six feet
this boat deal's hard to beat*

Introducing themselves to Marie, the owner, the crew begins looking over the vessel. *Calypso* is a twenty six foot ketch-rigged pocket cruiser. She appears "turnkey" with a full compliment of sails; her standing rigging and two cylinder hand crank gas motor, a "Blue Jacket Twin" are in working order.

Stoutly built for her size, white oak frames are closely spaced, the planks clench nailed; solid, traditional New England construction. Her open cockpit is generous, due to the wide, raked transom stern. She has a shallow draft of three feet and carries iron pigs of inside ballast.

Down below, a bronze plaque with the inscription "A.A. Bernard, Woburn Massachusetts 1952" engraved is prominently displayed above the port berth. There is a head, of the joker valve design at which the crew looks askance. Should they buy this vessel, it will be replaced in short order with a five gallon bucket.

She will require the minimalist living of a pocket cruiser. No standing headroom, standard in this length and design, yet the living quarters below are quite comfortable with her generous nine foot beam.

Inside ballast makes her stable
we slap all our money on the table
Then Marie with tears in her eyes
to her little boat she says her goodbyes

The cursory inspection complete, the combination of intuition along with five thousand dollars burning in the pocket are an irresistible driving force. The wad is pulled out, a single one hundred dollar bill is plucked, the remainder placed on the engine cover.

Marie stares blankly at the wad. The pair seeing her hesitation, remain quiet. The pain is obvious as she ponders her decision. A decision not thoroughly thought through until this very moment, staring at the rolled up wad of hundred dollar bills.

A boat's value is not always measurable by way of money, rather by way of the heart. The pair hold their breath at her hesitation. Marie looks at them with tears welling up, her voice firm. "I'll do it. I'll sell my boat, I'll sell *Calypso*." With that, she takes the cash. There follows an emotional sigh. Tears and words of encouragement flow freely when Marie embraces the pair. She makes a very simple, not unexpected request to sail her boat one last time to Portsmouth where she has her slip.

A difficult decision she had wrestled with for some time, selling her boat. The new owners could relate, having both sold boats that had played major roles in their lives; they are happy to leave Marie with her boat for a final sail. Boats become living friends over time, a difficult parting is inevitable.

Portsmouth

The Stone Bridge Marina in Portsmouth we stay
start divin' for quahogs other side of the quay
Every day I go a clammin'
on Calypso Pat's a jammin'

Making their way to Portsmouth, the new owners waste no time moving aboard. *Calypso* is tied up at the Stone Bridge Marina, which happens to double as a major local buyer of quahogs.

As luck would have it, there is an active quahog fishery in the vicinity, which upon further investigation offers the opportunity to purchase a license to dive for the clams commercially. Dive gear is shipped out in short order as this fishery is viewed as a huge stroke of luck. One may go so far as to consider this an "omen."

Portsmouth is a tight knit community, with a large number of Portuguese quahog fishermen. Commonly referred to as "bull rakers," they can be seen standing in their skiffs working long, specialized rakes. The rakes have a basket with curved tongs incorporated to capture and collect the clams. They are limited in their optimum working depth, appearing to be most efficient in the neighborhood of about twenty feet or less. As the rakes are worked deeper, extra lengths must be added. The angle of the rake steepens becoming more inefficient as well as slower to haul back.

Only recently a dive fleet has developed around the fishery, creating intense conflict between rakers and divers. Having been a commercial fisherman long enough to be sensitive to fishing issues, it is easy to understand the problem, as well as the solution, for this diver to keep the peace. The more ambitious goal being to earn the respect of the raker fleet.

It is imperative, living at the dock on *Calypso*, to get along with everyone in this harvesting endeavor. There has been some nasty encounters between the two groups, however the disputes are taking place in relatively shallow water.

Quahogs

Rigging the eight foot dinghy, which the crew has dubbed the *Rinky Dink* with an air compressor and a hundred fifty feet of hose, the diver, wearing a simple wetsuit, is ready to go to work in a spot circled on the chart.

Typical of fishermen, the search begins where the legal fishing boundaries are placed by the authorities. The particular fishing spot chosen lies a mere two hundred yards from *Calypso's* slip.

The rakers are running much further down the Sakonnet River shoreline, where they work the shallows. Oddly labeled "pollution line," the selected location is just off the Fall River, Massachusetts shoreline and down river from Providence.

Locally known as "The Nuns," named for the convent on shore, the area is free of rakers, as it is fifty feet deep; undesirable for their gear. There are a couple negatives for the diver as well. The most obvious is again, the depth, which involves "diving the tables." This puts the diver in the ever present danger of the "bends" (decompression sickness).

The second issue is its location on "The pollution line." Working the legal side where, theoretically, the clams are clean, free of harmful contaminants, proves to be as bogus as one would expect. A political rather than scientific drawing of a fishing area. Throwing caution to the wind in favor of the potentially decent income, the *Rinky Dink* is rowed out between the two blown-out halves of the Old Stone Bridge to the far shore. Hurricane Carol had defeated this landmark structure in 1954.

Dropping onto a soft mud bottom, on the initial dive, the raking tool is abandoned almost immediately. Gloved hands are able to feel the size of the quahogs, laying a few inches deep in the mud.

A few days into the routine, which only involves roughly one hour of bottom time each day, production exceeded initial expectations. Working virgin ground, there were almost too many clams.

The size of the clams being a critical factor in the learning curve. Quahogs are chowder clams. The first clams delivered by the *Rinky Dink* were a mix of quahogs and "cherrystones." Quahogs fetch ten cents a pound where cherrystones bring ninety cents a pound. It does not take long to train the hands to locate the smaller clams which would pass through the sizing ring. Profits shot up as the smaller clams out outweighed the larger, less valuable clams by a large margin.

Loadin' the dinghy with cherrystones
workin' fingers to the bones
Scratchin' out a hundred bucks a day
from the bottom of Narragansett Bay

Eventually, after several days diving, the top raker in the quahog fleet shows up at "The Nuns." He gives a hearty wave, which is returned, signaling the game is on. The fleet had taken notice of the interloper's deliveries coming out of the Nuns and sent their best man to scout it out. Fishing has always been a competitive endeavor, the new arrival is welcomed for company and sport.

Surfacing from the third trip to the bottom, the overfull bag is hung off the port side of the dinghy, helping to balance the two bags hanging off the starboard side. Meanwhile, my neighbor is standing in his skiff, breaking down his gear. With another friendly wave, he motors away. Twenty minutes left on the sixty foot dive table allows for one last scramble across the bottom, a final bag will top off the load.

Rowing back to the buying station, *Rinky Dink* is taking water over the bow. Having put on a heavy load, due to an abnormally large number of big clams which had not been sorted out in the heat of the competition, now there is a real threat of sinking before reaching the dock.

Bailing water between strokes stays ahead of the flooding until tying up. The fleet is congregated, well aware of the match-up between diver and raker, and clearly curious of the result. Looking down from the dock at the *Rinky Dink*, loaded to the gunnels with her bags of clams, the result is obvious. Quahogs are tallied proving that the rakers in shallow water had out fished their friend who had left the fleet to work in competition with the diver at The Nuns.

A wide grin, his head shaking while staring down at the pitiful pile of clams he had produced spoke volumes. Earning the respect of the fleet for not intruding on their traditional quahog raking grounds assures life on the marina docks in Portsmouth will be quite pleasant.

Final Preparations

C *alypso* is readied for her journey throughout the summer. With Marie's help, encouragement and the many meals she shared, along with the support of so many local folks, preparations for the journey continue apace.

She is hauled out of the water, her hull cleaned and painted. The deck seams are reefed out and corked after a number of leaks are located. A tremendous summer deluge strikes during this process, an entire night is spent, sleeping in raingear and pumping many gallons of water out of the boat.

One particular old timer would stop by to observe the progress. After a time the crew became irritated with the fellow, as he would go through the same routine, every day. He would stand quietly for awhile, then walk away, pointing at the bottom of the boat saying "ya, but what're ya gonna do about those garboards?"

The "garboards" are the two planks on either side of the boat which fit into a groove, known as the rabbet, at the keel. This is a critical joint in the vessel and must be properly corked with oakum and cotton, then puttied with underwater seam compound or "bear shit" as it is known in the trades. The garboard planks look fine. The crew ignores the old fellow, launching *Calypso* as "mare's tails and fish scales" appear in the high altitudes of the Autumn skies.

Out of a woodpile appears a kitty
name him "Woody" 'cause it's kinda witty
Woody completes our crew of three
an' soon we'll be sailin' cross the sea

The "boatcat" arrives, not unexpectedly, appearing in the early hours one morning, wailing mournfully atop a pile of wood next to the boat. Some unknown person had thought to provide the crew with a cuddly companion, an irresistible tabby kitten.

In short order, the kitty is taken aboard, promptly and appropriately named "Woody." As cats go, this one is no exception, immediately finding a cozy, pillowed spot on a bunk then settling in.

Food and water are made available as well as a simple, handy cat box using a five gallon bucket with a hole cut in the side. Maintenance, a simple matter of removing the lid,dumping the contents then adding fresh sand, a readily available commodity.

Block Island Sound

Doesn't take long workin' on her steady
Calypso's gone through 'n made ready
An' when the moon's just a sliver
Calypso's sailin' down the Sakonnet River

Setting out from Portsmouth, motoring down the Sakonnet River, dusk has the light diminishing rapidly as *Calypso* approaches Sakonnet Point, where the river meets Block Island Sound. The crew are counting the seconds of intermittent red, green and white flashes partially obstructed by lights ashore while rain squalls pelt the helm sporadically. They strain to pick out the variety of markers playing hide and seek in the rainfog, on points of land or on mid water obstructions.

Calypso has a fathometer, the style where the zero and the sixty foot mark are in the same spot at the top center of a circular face. The indicator light makes a full sweep of the face, marked in ten foot increments from zero to sixty feet. One must pay attention, it is possible to read the sounder erroneously. The only remaining navigational tool aboard for inland navigation other than the combined wits of the crew, is a standard marine grade compass.

The voyage doesn't start out just right
nearly hit rocks very first night
Sailin' 'n bailin' I gotta say
Calypso's leakin' thirty gallons today

A bit of inattention to the depth sounder, added to some confusion reading the lights in the obscured visibility leads to the startling result of rocks making their unexpected appearance, breaking ten yards off the starboard beam. A ghostly, abandoned lighthouse, unlit and unseen until this very moment sits atop the reef. The hair rises on the back of the necks with the immediate realization the path to open water is blocked by the reef.

The gain automatically turns up on the crew's inner radar, all the senses are at peak alert. The compass and depth sounder are instantaneously scanned for clues. The compass points to open water directly through the rocks. The depth sounder throws the crew into confusion.

"Is it reading sixty feet? Or zero?!"

Had the indicator made a full sweep of the dial? A rock pile this close to the boat forces the assumption correctly or not, there is no water under the keel, just pinnacles lying in wait to stab through the bottom of the boat.

A most subtle clue to a possible way out is found in the slightest of swells pushing in from Block Island Sound. The helm is put down, hard. Counter-intuitively angling slightly toward the reef, the bow now greeting the gentle rolling swell of deeper open water. Breaths are held, waiting for that first bump, the first of many that will grind this beautiful little boat to pieces.

The bump never comes. The bow begins dipping and rising, responding to the deeper water she is entering. *Calypso* clears the dangers; the crew hugely relieved, set a course for Block Island. Going over the chart it is clear, had she turned away from the exposed rocks, she would have driven headlong into Sakonnet Point.

Block Island Sound's
our sea trial grounds
Where squally weather has plenty of fetch
we discover the nuances of sailin'
a gaff rigged ketch

Squally weather in Block Island Sound is an indication that *Calypso* is up to the task. She is well balanced, handy at the helm and exceptionally sea kindly. Her one negative is an irritating leak which has persisted since launching. The bronze hand pump at the rear of the cabin proves adequate in staying well ahead of the water coming in.

She had begun to dry out substantially while on the beach under the hot summer sun. The crew are not alarmed. They consider the leak temporary, expecting it to slow as the hull soaks and swells, tightening the seams.

Raise the mizzen 'n sheet 'er tight
Calypso holds in irons just right
Hoist the mainsail, throat an' peak together
while Calypso bobs obediently to weather

Backwind the mizzen, mainsail bellies out
raise the jib an' come about
Whooshin' 'n gurglin' a soothing sound
for the tropics, Calypso's bound

Calypso proves to be a forgiving vessel, allowing the new owners latitude in making errors as they develop efficient sailing practices. The mizzen sail, sheeted tight amidships, keeps her bow to weather which allows the crew to perform tasks on deck in a leisurely fashion. Setting the mainsail and jib is made easy with the boat held firmly "in irons." The crew, even with the gusty conditions found in Block Island and Long Island Sounds are quick to grasp the fundamentals. Credit must go to the vessel as well; her patient, steady bobbing under a lone mizzen sail gives ample time to sort out the operations.

Twenty to thirty knots blowing in from the northeast Atlantic produces a squally, fast passage to Block Island. The crew discovers the versatility of the ketch rig on this short jaunt.

Wind pipes up, the short choppy sea builds. The helm is put down, the jib and mainsheets thrown, the mizzen is sheeted tight on center. *Calypso* snaps to weather, the mainsail is dropped, the gaff and main booms are lashed together, securing the sail now sandwiched between them.

Very little time is lost before the jib sheet is hauled in, the mizzen let go slack. The bow falls off, the strong wind fills in the jib with a resounding, hardy slap. The mizzen sheet is hauled in, sheeted tight; *Calypso* is sent hurtling off on a beam reach. This jib and mizzen sail combination, with mainsail stowed, handles the miserable weather in relative comfort. There is a ton of wind blowing through the hole, where the mainsail once stood.

*Eighty gallons pumped this day
while Calypso's makin' excellent way
By the time we get to be good sailors
looks like we're gonna be real good bailers*

T he anchor is pulled at first light following an uncomfortable night in a cold, damp boat rocked by incessant traffic cruising by in an open roadstead. The previous evening the crew had made the questionable choice to drop the pick in a spot close by the Block Island Ferry dock. They are anxious to press on, as Long Island offers an abundance of bays and bights in which to seek shelter.

The mainsail is left secure as the wind has not let up overnight. *Calypso* works to windward out of the anchorage until she clears the mouth of the bay, where she tears off for Long Island to begin her second day, the wind abaft her port beam.

The weather is a continuation of the previous day. Cold, raining sporadically with a stiff breeze. Block Island grows smaller, melting into the grayness off her stern. The sailing is superb which keeps the real misery of the conditions at bay.

A quick passage is made to Montauk Point, leaving it well to port on her approach to Long Island. Before darkness closes in, her anchor is down in Fort Pond Bay, the first likely anchorage the crew comes upon in the shelter of the Island.

Off at first light on her third day, a very short run to Plum Island has her pick down early, in position to enter Long Island Sound proper.

The crew takes this opportunity to study information in the chart books as to where they might find a boatyard. The irritation of the leak, which has increased threefold since leaving Portsmouth must be dealt with. Port Jefferson, down island, appears to have several facilities to choose from. The weather has calmed considerably; the crew opts to sail through the light breezes of the night, tying up the following late afternoon in Port Jefferson, Long Island.

Port Jefferson

At Port Jefferson we haul her out
to see what this leakin's all about
There's small geysers squirtin'
our poor little boat's really hurtin'

When the story of their journey to date is related to the folks greeting the crew, punctuated with turns at the pump for emphasis, its all hands on deck to assist. To the expected question "where are ya headed?" The crew responds in unison with gusto: "Alaska!" It has not gotten past the pair, when word is out they are headed for Alaska, folks take a keen interest in them and their little boat.

In the same fashion a small village would gather to help a neighbor raise a barn, the marina and residents of Port Jefferson commence to stun the crew with their generosity.

Water's shootin' from her garboard
corked her tight port 'n starboard
Local folks helped in every way
till Calypso slides back into the Bay

Lesson learned! The old timer in Portsmouth knew there would be a problem with those garboard seams. A veteran boat builder jumps into *Calypso's* bilge armed with oakum, cotton and corking irons to tackle the leak. Rough waters had further loosened the corking material, increasing the leak substantially. Corking seams from inside the hull, while the boat is in the water is less than optimal by a large margin, however with a professional on the job, the work manages to slow the leak to an insignificant trickle. A haul-out is scheduled for tomorrow at the "Davis Island Boatyard." The garboard will receive further attention.

The morning following *Calypso's* arrival, local hospitality goes into high gear. A big hearted lady takes the duo under her wing for showers, laundry and dinner. She provides her car as well and chaperones the pair around town, further simplifying the whirlwind day of accomplishing a long list of tasks and shopping for items the crew has discovered are lacking aboard the boat.

The folks of Port Jefferson understand severe weather and its association with the month of September, further, "October it's over" is not always the case. "A late start for Bermuda, ya gonna take the Intracoastal?" is shouted to the crew from a passerby walking the dock. "Intracoastal? What's that?" The crew look quizzically back and forth from each other to the gentleman. "I have just what you need over on my boat, I'll be right back." With that he turns on his heel at a brisk walk, disappearing quickly among the boats in the marina.

The fellow returns in short order with a pair of coffee table size books. "Here, they are a bit dated, but plenty good for the passage to Florida."

The crew are familiar with the "Milepost" books for traveling by road as well as "chart kits" for boats on the "Inside Passage" through British Columbia and Southeast Alaska. This "Chart Kit" provides condensed charts in book form, covering a series of canals and waterways the pair have been, until this moment, unaware.

This two volume "kit" contains the detailed route to Florida from New York. They include information on key points of interest to the mariner. There are detailed insets of all the ocean entrances and harbors. Bridge heights, opening schedules, particulars on the various locks and waterways, as well as the complete numbering system, ala the "Milepost" of British Columbia and Alaska.

The Port Jefferson folks have *Calypso* repaired, loaded, and the crew fed by the end of the third day, saying their goodbyes that evening and encouraging the crew to get an early start; it's a long way to the Bahamas, and hurricane season is still on.

New York City

Distant thunder can be heard rollin'
New York City bells're tollin'
Long Island Sound this windless night
there's skyscrapers comin' into sight

The New York City skyline makes a ghostly appearance as the sun rises over Long Island Sound. The peaks of buildings becoming visible when the morning fog begins burning off. Bridges come into view as *Calypso* nears the southern end of the Sound, the low deep background noise which the crew has been only vaguely aware of now reveals itself. The thunderous, pounding heartbeat of a megalopolis.

The engine is cranked up, the sails lowered for this windless passage. The cute little putt putt putt of the two cylinder motor is lost in the cacophony which has replaced the fog that had been enveloping the boat. The sun's rays work their magic. Long heavy fingers of fog loose their grip on the water around *Calypso*. The roar of the city, no longer impeded by the fog blanket on this glassy calm morning, deafening.

Approachin' Hell Gate the fair wind dies
engine starts, sputters an' sighs
Crankin' on that "Blue Jacket Twin"
got bloody knuckles agin'!

Hell Gate, dead ahead. The East River carries *Calypso* along famously, passing under the Hell Gate Bridge, an arch which stands as the entrance to a most challenging navigational hazard for a low powered vessel. The crew has calculated the tide carefully for this long stretch of channel which runs through the watery hub of New York City. Currents running up to five or six knots in opposing directions meet at this fabled location.

A reputation evolving from a rich history of nautical disasters, the crew approach Hell Gate with apprehension. The name conjures visions of treachery around the bend. It does nothing to alleviate the tension within the crew, as their little boat passes under this ceiling of cement and steel blaring the sounds of the morning rush hour.

Under the "Triborough Bridge" where the Harlem River flows into the East River, the crew does not hear the engine quit, drowned out by the traffic noise above, over top of the general din of the city.

Without power, she is unresponsive to the helm. The crew leaps for the halyards, raising full sail for whatever help they may provide. Down below, the engine cover is torn off, cast aside, the hand crank then stuck in the flywheel. Cranking hard, repeatedly, while toying with the choke and throttle, nothing. Cranking ceases when the knuckles are bloodied and sore, with no more than a few pops punctuated by wicked shoulder wrenching backfires to show for the effort.

Calypso is spinning wildly out of control in whirlpools, boiling upwellings and the wakes of heavy, fast moving traffic. The sails are set, but without wind, useless.

---

*Jump to the halyards 'n raise full sail
broke down now with an engine fail
Under Hell Gate Bridge caught in whirlpools
Calypso's lookin' like a ship o' fools!*

*Helicopter takin' off on her right
blows poor Calypso right outa sight
At this point I could give a hill a beans
Calypso crashes in Jamaica Queens!*

Sails sheeted tight, she is drifting crazily through wild waters only to be spat out with the foam and flotsam in a most unflattering fashion.

Shooting out from Hell Gate she is then immediately flattened by a ham-handed punch from a helicopter at full throttle on take-off.

The chopper is leaving from a commercial heliport followed immediately by another, the morning rush hour at "the pad." Helicopters taking off in quick succession give the hapless little sailboat no space, appearing to relish in the havoc they wreak below, creating "Williwaws." (Downward spiraling winds.)

Fortunately, as powerful as the gusts are, they do not reach a catastrophic, boat sinking force. Stories are told in Alaska of anchored vessels being driven straight underwater when hit with big wind rolling down a mountainside into a bay.

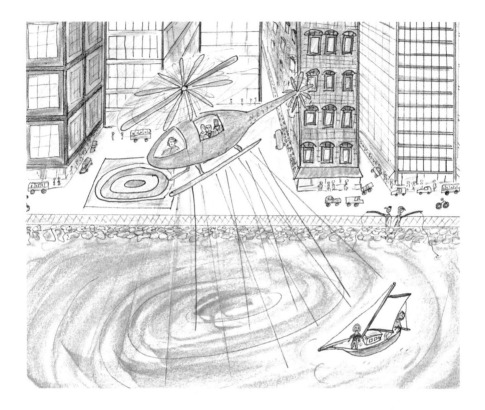

The staunch little boat takes the pummeling by the helicopters and continues on, only to be bandied about by more citified hazards. Her next challenge after being blown into relatively calm water, is to take a gale force broadside blast as she passes by a street with sky scraping buildings. The canyon funnels wind at *Calypso* and her crew, who's battered nerves are fraying fast.

Their hardy little vessel heels sharply to the venturi, then snaps upright in defiance. The crew drops and secures the mainsail, taking the next street under jib and mizzen. The mayhem of big traffic passing in both directions continues at a furious pace, until she arrives at an area protected from wind. The swift running tidal river takes command, sending *Calypso* careening into a barge berthed alongside the channel.

A wrap is taken around a cleat as she bumps alongside the old wooden slab. Fortunately, the barge is not built of steel, as severe damage most likely would have resulted from the collision. *Calypso* is whiplashed to a halt when the line comes taught on the cleat. The swift water wants to tear her away, while more lines are added to the beast until she is secure.

The crew takes this moment of relative calm, for the exception of rocking wildly to the wakes of passing traffic, to go below. The cabin is put back in order, the engine given a few half hearted cursory cranks. Spark is yellow and weak, the conclusion: The battery is toast, a simple fix.

We need a battery so go ashore
found a gas station 'n the fella says "Shore!
jess' gimme fifty bucks 'n have a cigar"
then he goes 'n rips off somebody's car!

⬤ ne must scale the high walls the barge, climb over a few fences and cross railways, before finding a circuitous route leading into Jamaica, Queens. Wandering around for a short time, a gas station is come upon where this jovial fellow stands smoking a big fat stinking cigar.

On explaining our boat is in need of a six volt battery, the fellow holds out a cigar. "You smoke?" Taking the cigar, while asking what a battery would cost, he replies "fifty bucks, but they're not here, sit down, relax and enjoy, it won't be long we'll have it delivered." The fellow disappears out the door. Before the cigar is half gone, he returns with a small, dirty box.

Proudly, he opens the box to reveal a greasy used battery, still warm. Without bothering to ask any questions, a crisp fifty dollar bill is exchanged, knowing someone's "V.W. Bug" won't be starting. The closest place to replace the missing battery is right here. That's the way things work in Jamaica, Queens.

Calypso is shoved off from the barge to the soothing putt putt putt of the Blue Jacket Twin. Tide and river whisk her, ironically, past the "Battery," a nationally known city park at the lower end of Manhattan.

Commercial traffic, while heavy at the narrow Hell Gate was orderly, as vessels carefully negotiated the passage. The Battery has an altogether different character. The number and speed of a wide variety of vessels on intersecting routes increases exponentially. *Calypso* is motoring on a course for Sandy Hook, New Jersey.

*Makin' our way through New York City
sailin' right by the Statue o' Liberty
Sailin' through that thunderous roar
Calypso's course set for the New Jersey shore*

Calypso's sails are raised to increase visibility, she holds a steady compass in the face of chaotic traffic, which quickly diminishes as Manhattan is left behind. She passes close by that most impressive icon of the New York Harbor; the "Statue of Liberty."

Chapter 2

INTRACOASTAL WATERWAY

Fall -Winter 1979

Atlantic Ocean

The anchor is dropped at Sandy Hook, New Jersey as darkness falls. The *Rinky Dink* takes the crew to shore for a pizza, where they return with full bellies, all set for a good nights sleep after a trying passage through New York City.

Even with exhaustion, sleep is elusive for the crew. *Calypso* is straining on her anchor like an anxious pony, prancing at the end of a hitching post. The Atlantic Ocean holds mystery for the pair, having only a sense of its immense presence when the swell pushing into Block Island Sound worked up.

This is their moment. The occasional sighting of schooners, cutters, sloops, ketches and yawls sporting clouds of sails, heading for destinations over the horizon had whetted their appetite for the adventure. There are the ocean going vessels, long at sea, arriving with streams of kelp, barnacles, mussels and a host of critters congregated at the waterline. These visions of hearty, weather-beaten old wooden salts with their enchanting stories from years of traveling the globe on the sea lanes, compliment the boat's pitching and rolling in the open roadstead.

On pulling the pick, *Calypso* drifts out of the anchorage under full sail, helped by a glassy smooth ebb tide and greeted by a crisp October dawn. Passing by the Sandy Hook Lighthouse, a moderate northeasterly freshens. She responds, putting a bone in her teeth on a broad reach along the New Jersey coast, roughly a mile off the surf line.

The swell increases, her bow dips into the Atlantic, a deep genuflection in respect of the vast ocean she is entering for the first time in her twenty five years. Her twenty six foot length is cradled comfortably in the trough of the relatively short North Atlantic seaway. The generous fantail stern, buoyant on the steep face of  an ocean wave, mimics that of a seabird, negotiating one swell at a time. *Calypso's* mainsail fills, her roll to port slows, she is in perfect harmony with her environment. At the Shark River Inlet the wind switches, rather abruptly, to the southeast. An option to duck in to shelter close at hand is considered and abandoned, in favor of beating to weather another seven miles for Manasquan Inlet and the northern terminus of the Intra-coastal Waterway (ICW).

Calypso sails right up to the Shark River jetty, an intimidating turmoil of ocean swells crashing against a solid man made rock pile. A pusher tug and barge appear to take up the entire channel between the jetties. Three foot standing waves guard the entrance where she tacks seaward, 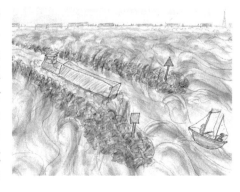 putting the surf line a couple miles distant as night falls.

Manasquan Inlet

The Shark River Jetty and the building swell have the crew on edge, anticipating the coming challenge of Manasquan Inlet, in uncertain conditions. The squally night is spent working against an adverse tide under jib and mizzen, tacking back and forth from the beach. The sound of pounding surf or the flashes of white water breaking on riprap turns *Calypso* back to open sea until well clear, then she returns to the Manasquan tack.

This goes on through the dark hours, with the added challenge of spotting Manasquan Inlet Light. The light is buried in an array of lights ashore, making positive identification difficult, and near impossible to maintain.

As dawn approaches, there is no mistaking Manasquan Inlet. Like its neighbor to the north, a violent display of ocean swell smashing rocks, the attending standing waves appearing as spikes, daring vessels to attempt passage.

Calypso had spent the night beating against a tide flooding into Ambrose Inlet, filling New York Harbor. Now the tide has turned and with daylight the approaches to Manasquan Inlet are clearly visible.

Her jib and mizzen are sheeted tight, helm is put down, the jib let fly, her bow hauls directly into the southeast wind and choppy waves she had been beating against in the darkness. The mainsail is set, the throat halyard made off followed by the gaff peak. The mainsheet left slack, the mizzen is let fly while the jib sheet's hauled in, the bow falls off downwind to starboard. The mainsheet is hauled until the mainsail fills, followed by the mizzen. Slacking the jib a bit, *Calypso* feels the press of wind off her stern quarter to port. With a gentle heel to starboard she scoots briskly along on a broad reach with a following sea, directly toward an ebbing Manasquan Inlet.

The crew is well aware they may have to turn *Calypso* on her keel should her progress be inadequate, as the stage of tide and river combined will produce an adverse current she may not overcome.

Headlong, she crashes into the confusion of standing waves. Tossed violently, she breaks through the first wall of resistance. She works slowly against a strong current then passes between the points of these two menacing rock piles to port and starboard.

The broad reach serves her well, she has the power to make a knot or two headway upstream in the relatively calm waters between the jetties. The wind chop and colliding swells have ceased to worry her, yet the surge continues to shove heavily at the stern.

There is the eerie illusion when looking down at the muddy water rushing by the hull, of excessive speed, then looking up at the rocks nearby, her progress is barely perceptible. There is a tight knot in the gut, the body rocks forward, trying to physically push the little boat upstream. The anxieties recede as she inches her way past the red and green markers at the inner ends of these elongated rock piles jutting out into the Atlantic Ocean.

Breaking free of the venturi, she gains hull speed, then veers off to starboard, ceding the right of way to the mass of wood and metal coming at her in the form of a push tug and barge. It consumes the entire channel while making the turn which will bring it into alignment with the inlet, in preparation to ride the ebb out to sea. *Calypso* is fortunate to not have met this beast between the jetties.

There is a collective sigh of relief as the danger passes when she slams her bow into the mud shallows at the edge of the channel. She drives up hard under full sail, shuddering to full stop.

With the tide receding the crew wastes no time; sails are doused, the main anchor is rowed out in the *Rinky Dink* where it is dropped in deep water. Kedging off is a laborious task, *Calypso's* advantage is her shallow draft and inside ballast. There is no heavy metal buried in the mud, the wood keel, shallow at the bow moves several inches or a foot with every heave ho and bight on the bitts. Timing the line hauling with the wakes of passing vessels assists the combined efforts of the crew who achieve the desired result in short order. Underfoot, she is felt bobbing free in deep water, clear of the bottom where she grounded. An extra couple wraps are taken at the bitts securing *Calypso's* anchor.

Order returns to the deck, the sails stowed, as they lay all askew where they were dropped when she struck mud. The deck and lines are squared away. Once the crew is satisfied they retire below, settling in to study charts, rest, and make a plan.

The Coast Guard arrives to inform the crew they are not allowed to anchor in this spot. Dutifully, the pair respond, pulling the hook amid some grousing under the breath, raise sail, and as she sails off the Coast Guard returns to say its fine if the boat is anchored there.

The mizzen is sheeted tight, the helm is put down. The main and jib sheets let go, *Calypso* spins neatly into the wind, she is allowed to drift back with the breeze until clear of the channel fairway; the anchor splashes for a second time. The crew makes quick work of the deck chores then settle down to the task at hand. Navigation.

Two bridges stand between *Calypso* and the official start of the Intracoastal Waterway. Beyond these, both of which are low clearance bascule bridges which will require timing the passage with the published opening hours, the channel makes a hard turn to port at the entrance to the Point Pleasant Canal. Once through, she will enter the northern reaches of Barnagat Bay.

Chatting up folks at the pizza joint back in Sandy Hook the crew had been made aware of this short stretch of canal. It is decided to take these first two bridges this first day, then transit the canal the following day.

A couple of hours are spent hovering before a railroad bridge. Having been early on the opening, *Calypso* waddles and rolls deeply now as she holds her position in the middle of a fast growing pack of power vessels, muscling their way into the crowd.

When the bridgemaster toots his intentions, he opens on schedule; engines roar, black smoke pours out from the boats which have congregated. Size, power and speed take precedence over rules of the road. *Calypso's* throttle is pressed up against the stop, knuckles are bone white on the spokes of the wheel.

The fleet roars past her, port and starboard, the noise is deafening within the confines of the bridge halves and steel truss work. The herd tightens up to pass through the narrow, forty-eight foot opening. Eyes dead ahead, jaws set, the crew stand as stone as they slip slowly through.

The wait is very short at the next bridge, only a couple hundred yards distant; the traffic, however, has built up substantially. Fortunately this highway bridge carries ninety feet of clearance in width, allowing for heavy traffic of every persuasion to pour into the funnel.

Once beyond the bottleneck, *Calypso* pulls off to starboard, throttling down to allow vessels to pass. When the traffic has cleared, a beeline is made for the preselected anchorage, a penciled-in anchor on the chart directly cross channel. The pick is dropped with less than a mile progress for the day. She is now however in perfect position to choose her stage of tide for the next obstacle. Two miles farther down the channel is the entrance to the Point Pleasant Canal.

Point Pleasant Canal

Mile Post # 1

Dawn finds her swinging on the hook with the tide. Nearby stands a piling with a square green marker, a lone cormorant atop, the number "one" plainly visible. The first of hundreds ahead with a variety of shapes, colors, marks and meanings.

The sound of air sucking into the bilge pump at twenty or thirty strokes tells the crew the boat has taken on ten gallons or more since last pumped the previous night in the ocean, when a few gallons were sloshing around under the floorboards. The pump, located in the cockpit next to the hatch is an old bronze hand pump that moves a gallon or so in two or three pumps. Tossing around in the Atlantic then slamming the sandbar appear to have reopened *Calypso's* leak.

The crew have familiarized themselves with the route, markers and immediate navigational concerns, specifically, the tidal stage when *Calypso* will arrive at the "Pt. Pleasant Bridge," a bascule bridge mentioned back at the pizza joint and noted specifically on the chart: "NOTE D ... Boat operators should exercise extreme caution when approaching and passing through the bridges across Point Pleasant Canal. The waters are turbulent."

Fair warnings, the "Blue Jacket Twin" is cranked up. With the leak having returned, the crew is happy to be off the ocean in protected waters, even if it does involve a lot of motoring. *Calypso* makes her way past the first marker, traveling with the flood tide that carries her to Point Pleasant Canal. The favorable current is lost shortly after making the turn and is now running against her as she makes her way toward the Point Pleasant Bridge. The strength of this opposing current continues to build, seriously slowing forward progress. The throttle is kicked up to maximum, the Blue Jacket responds with a few extra putts in her usual cadence of cruising putts. Putt Putt Putt Putt Putt Putt becomes PuhPuhPuhPuhPuhPuhPuhPuhPuh.

The plan is to arrive at the bridge before high water, passing through on schedule as the current begins to go slack for the change of tide. They will then ride the ebb through the remainder of the passage. Being narrowed to less than fifty feet from the one hundred thirty foot wide canal, the crew is wary of the expected venturi effect. The ideal will have the current change direction just prior to *Calypso's* arrival.

A fine Saturday afternoon has a large crowd of locals on the banks watching boats pass in the canal. This should have been a hint as to what was about to occur here at the bridge, but the crew is paying close attention to the shoreline, gauging her progress, which is slowing considerably as she closes in on the open span where power boats of every description are pouring through.

Street traffic is lined up on the bridge, both sides, adding to the tension of not wanting to be the boat the slows things up any more than they already are. The bridge gives a toot on its horn letting the boaters know the bridge will be closing in a matter of minutes.

This warning signal comes as *Calypso*, early on the tide, is just entering the main force of the venturi between the two bridge halves. She comes to full stop then begins to lose ground while simultaneously the last rush of power cruisers converge on the gap from both directions. *Calypso*, knocked aside by heavy rolling wakes, slams into the bridge abutment, careens off and is taken by the current, spun by whirlpools, then crashes into a small cement outcrop downstream.

Coiled lines are let fly with long sweeps of the arms. They uncoil neatly in the air and spectators standing on the outcrop jump to action in a choreographed leap, grabbing lines as they fly overhead then hauling her up close.

A chilling scream is heard coming from the flying bridge of a sixty foot, twin screw power boat. The vessel is in great distress as it slams into the bridge stern first right at the same spot *Calypso* had just struck.

"We ... NO STEERING!" a broken high pitched, panicky voice is heard above the roar of the fleet. The jumbo power boat is spinning off the bridge, straight at *Calypso*, being held to the cement outcrop by the hands of three young boys. The crew abandons ship to the relative safety of the outcrop. The woman has turned to stone. Her mouth agape, she stands with a face frozen in time.

A great relief to watch the skipper stay cool on his fly bridge, gunning two or three thousand horsepower in reverse and forward, working those twin propellers to spin away from *Calypso* with every revolution that could be rung out of those screaming diesel engines.

The boys could not keep a grip on the lines against the thrust from those big motors when the skipper slams the controls forward. With nothing available to secure her, she rips the lines out of their hands. The crew and boys alike hop aboard as she is torn away from the outcrop, throttled up, and makes her way to the back eddy of the bridge, where two anchors are set to hold her.

The crew learns from Eddy and his buddies that this is regular weekend entertainment in the neighborhood, hence, the crowd we had noticed as we came up on the bridge.

The boys are enchanted with our story and give us some fishhooks and line for the trip. The crew spend time some chatting about Alaska, diving and sailing until the current lets up considerably, when the anchors are pulled and the boys dropped off at the outcrop with many thanks for their timely assistance. The bridge is opening for vessels again.

Calypso, still early on the tide, charges once more at the Point Pleasant Bridge, taking advantage of the back eddy before grinding against the main flow of the canal between the bridge sections. The throttle pushed full ahead, the bridge wide open, she makes her move into swift water. She struggles to make headway, creeping along as the bridge sounds its first warning. Desperation has a heavy hand on the throttle, demanding every ounce of power the little Blue Jacket will deliver.

Progress is painfully slow, the final frenzy of vessels stampede, *Calypso* is about half way through when impatient cars start a honking fest. The Bridge Master gives a series of irritated blasts in return, then steps out where the cars cannot see him giving a thumbs up, a big grin and a hearty wave. Returning the gesture with great relief, the crew work past the choke point where they gain speed, freeing their boat from the iron grip of rushing water.

Sailin' & Bailin'

T he anchor is dropped at Bay Head Harbor, where a dizzying display of pleasure boats running through the anchorage will not allow the crew a badly needed rest. The following morning *Calypso* moves a few miles down channel to Swan Point. A peaceful anchorage in unseasonably warm weather is enjoyed while the crew pours over charts. A calm having settled in, a second day on the hook is taken.

The predicted north wind pipes up on the third day, the well rested crew take full advantage. Raising the mizzen pulls *Calypso* into the wind followed by a slackly sheeted mainsail. Held in irons, the anchor is pulled, the jib raised. *Calypso* falls off to a powerful broad reach, heeling deeply at the press of wind on the mainsail which has filled taut.

Far more breeze than required for hull speed, the crew respond. They haul up into the wind, drop and secure the main, then fall off, back on course making hull speed under jib and mizzen. This combination was discovered to be balanced and powerful while the boat is easily handled.

Calypso sails briskly, protected from the Atlantic Ocean by a long arm of land labeled "Island Beach." The sailing is exhilarating with the strong northwest breeze cutting across the ICW channel. This allows for top speed and easy maneuvering. A light following chop laps at her stern, a bone is held firmly in her teeth.

The crew makes a habit of giving the old bilge pump a few pulls when passing from the cockpit to the cabin. The leak is fairly steady now, almost predictable, until it gets worse, then for no apparent reason, appears to slow somewhat. "Ya, but what're ya gonna do about those garboards?" has become a little ditty translating to roughly six pumps, or about two or three gallons of water over the side.

Down Barnegat Bay *Calypso* makes her way, dropping the pick well off the channel as the light fades, however, the wind does not. The wind gains strength in the dark hours, she is swinging wildly with the current opposing the stiff northerly breeze. The anchor fails to hold her as it is worked loose from the mud.

Dragging anchor, a mariners nuisance. "Anchor drill" as it is commonly called, involves rolling out of the bunk in the middle of the night with no time to dress; tear off the engine cover, turn on the battery switch, attach the handle to the front of the motor and commence cranking hard and fast. A backfire bloodies the knuckles on the engine bed. but it's a good sign she's going to start. The anchor pulls easily as the boat is drifting into the deeper water of the channel. She is repositioned, anchor dropped, the bilge given a couple dozen pumps; the crew goes back to bed, with hopes they will not be repeating the routine.

Calypso makes quick work of Barnegat Bay scooting past Barnegat Inlet to the protection of Long Beach, another narrow strip of land stretching to Beach Haven Inlet and providing the same conditions we had been experiencing, easily negotiating the twists and turns of the ICW with the ideal vector of the wind.

Atlantic City

Sailin' 'n bailin' I gotta say
Calypso's makin' fifty miles a day
Into Atlantic City we scoot
do some gamblin' 'n make some loot

Calypso passes by Beach Haven Inlet then quickly puts Little Egg and Brigantine Inlets behind her, arriving in Atlantic City, where shedrops the pick.

A decision is made to go ashore with the last five dollars and change. The small amount of money we left Rhode Island with is nearly exhausted. The stop in Port Jefferson took very little cash as the folks there were extremely generous and sympathetic, however the battery in Queens and the pizza, beer and jug of gas at Sandy Hook, had nearly wiped out the funds.

The crew will attempt to parlay it up to a more usable amount for food and fuel. At present *Calypso* is not hurting for the necessities, she has been well stocked with very little fuel required to this point.

Woody sits on the cabin top, observing the city's glittering casino lights, but acting very disturbed by the noise, having been accustomed to the quiet sail down the ICW. Curling up in the lap of the person at the helm or laying in a favorite spot in the sun, out of the wind; that's Woody, the boatcat.

The crew tie off the *Rinky Dink* at a spot on the beach, scramble up a bulkhead of pilings and rip rap to a sidewalk, but there are no glittering lights here. They appear to be several blocks away, beyond the darkened streets nearby.

Walking up Baltic Avenue, through an extremely poor neighborhood toward the bright lights of the casinos, folks we passed would smile andsay hello. The two worlds collide when the crew reaches the Boardwalk. People are elbowing, shoving, yelling and throwing their money away.

The crew wanders into a glitzy gaudy hotel and the five dollars goes away in a few pulls of a one armed bandit. Unimpressed and now totally broke, nothing to do but return to *Calypso* and move along.

Boardwalk 'n Park Place don't treat the crew well
left Atlantic City no money 'n nothin' left to sell
Blew our shot at gettin' rich
back to sailin' this muddy little ditch

"Muddy little ditch you say?
this is the Intracoastal Waterway"
An engineering marvel tucked away from the sea
Calypso sails in peace and tranquility

Having retreated to *Calypso's* cozy cabin, insulated from noise and lights, the crew pour over the charts to Cape May, their next port of call. Eighteen bridges will be encountered along the ICW between their present position and Cape May. The channel snakes its way through marshlands totaling many more miles and difficulties than the ocean run alternative.

Considering the cranky Blue Jacket Twin, never knowing if she will start when needed, the switchbacks, many turning straight upwind and bridges, where conditions and timing must be near perfect to open under sail, the decision is made to sail to Cape May via the ocean route.

A moderate offshore breeze with the ebb tide finds *Calypso* under full sail, scooting down Absecon Inlet at one a.m. for the forty mile run to Cape May.

She covers the distance in sixteen hours of exhilarating sailing and negotiates the Cape May Inlet jetties with a series of upwind tacks. The pick is down in Cape May Bay well before nightfall.

C & D Canal

Caught a fresh breeze up the Delaware River
November winds givin' us a shiver
In the C 'n D Canal shelter's found
alas, lotta commercial traffic runnin' around

This has been a long week on the hook at Cape May; difficult and quite depressing. *Calypso* had been anchored three days among a number of vessels transiting the ICW when the crew was awakened in the night to shouts and banging on the hull. Scrambling up on deck to a scene of boats and searchlights cruising slowly around the anchorage. The Coast Guard is there, searching the waters near the anchored vessels. A person has been lost off a neighboring boat, the searchers are asking for everyone to post a lookout.

From the silty nighttime waters a sense of dread accompanies the sadness. The crew offers to set up the dive equipment to aid in the search, however it is obvious an underwater search in dark waters, shallow as it is, would most likely be unproductive. The gesture is appreciated; the crew spends the rest of an eerie night sitting on deck, standing by, chilled by a cold November wind.

Several hours after daylight the search of the immediate area is called off. The crew return to the business at hand; preparations to make progress south ahead of winter.

Tugs 'n barges big 'n strong
Chuggin' by all night long
through the darkness they pull their load
Rockin' 'n rollin' our tiny abode

alypso swings on the hook to a brisk southeast breeze blowing upriver, perfect sailing conditions for making her way upstream to the Chesapeake and Delaware Canal (C&D Canal). The charts provide a challenging picture of the way ahead, however the crew are not intimidated, anxious to get a move on. Commercial traffic is heavy, so the crew opt to navigate the Cape May Canal under power with the tide. Where the canal joins Delaware Bay, they hoist sail. A hard charge across the bay under jib and mizzen continues until conditions become problematic about halfway to the C&D Canal.

Calypso will not cover the fifty miles to the Canal before dark. An excellent anchorage is available as light is fading, however, *Calypso* must make haste, as oyster beds are partially blocking access. The twenty knot wind has her pole bending through a maze of beds, getting the pick down in a cove at the mouth of the Cohansey River, clear of obstructions as darkness envelops the scene.

The anchor is up early to take advantage of wind and current, the plan being to hit the flood tide into the C&D Canal. The crew negotiates their way back through the maze of oyster beds to the main channel where commerce is a bustling array of tugs pushing barges, freighters small and large as well as the Oystermen working from their skiffs in the shallows.

Rising above a low hanging, dirty smog layer, a nuclear power plant dominates the scene, lording over a gray drizzly day and intensifying the prevailing somber mood of the crew aboard *Calypso*.

Chesapeake Bay

Autumn colors fill Chesapeake Bay
as Calypso sails along her way
Back n' forth into the wind we tack
find another cove, anchor 'n kick back

Crossin' the Potomac at night's a fright
Calypso put up one hell of a fight
River and wind throws everything at her
till she safely drops anchor in the Wicomico Spider

T hey succeed in catching a favorable tide entering the quiet waters of the C&D Canal. The surrounding Autumn colors are stunning, evoking a serenity that beckons them to drop anchor in a neat little cove, a comfortable distance off the Canal.

Widely known for its heavy traffic, they are treated to one miserable night on the hook. The keyhole anchorage *Calypso* settled in funnels the heavy wakes from pusher tugs and their barges straight into the venturi, where the wakes pick up speed and height, then slam *Calypso*, anchored directly in their path. The waves have not far to go after entering the anchorage before hitting the circular shoreline, the resulting rebounding waves stand up, hitting her from all directions.

A premium anchorage is found the following morning a little further down the Canal where the water is undisturbed by passing vessels. The warm afternoon sun, catfish jumping around the boat along with the park-like setting keeps the anchor planted for another day of rest.

Calypso is off at first light, wallowing her way down the remainder of the Canal under power; a continuous train of commercial traffic passes, knocking her about. There is no relief when the Canal dumps into the Elk River in the upper reaches of Chesapeake Bay. as the narrow channel continues through a delta system stretching for many miles in all directions.

The Elk River drainage joins with the Bohemia River drainage, which after passing Turkey Point, continues through the Susquehanna and Sassafras River deltas. The world is afire with Autumn color. The crew is accustomed to the colors of the Northwest and Alaska where there are smatterings of burnt orange, yellows and reds in a variety of shades among the evergreens. The Chesapeake, with its largely deciduous populations is a cornucopia of color, where the crew revels in finding secluded coves to drop the pick.

Small issues keep them on their toes, primarily the leak averaging thirty or so gallons a day, occasionally quite a bit more, or a little bit less. The propeller shaft too is a nuisance, when it pops out of the transmission, jamming the rudder. The Blue Jacket is showing the wear from its many years of service. A good motor, even in her cranky old age. All told, *Calypso* is proving herself a forgiving vessel.

The crew continues to enjoy the Chesapeake until the weather comes up from the south. The game now becomes cat and mouse, ducking hard wind and rain by making short hops, or staying put and exploring ashore for a day or two.

After a couple days anchored in the Patuxant River, which marks *Calypso's* five hundredth mile from Rhode Island, the weather window the crew has been waiting for arrives; the breeze backs to the East, springing up in the pre-dawn hours with stars winking through scudding clouds.

The anchor comes aboard after a hearty egg burrito breakfast. Excitement is in the air; today *Calypso* will cross the Potomac River. This storied river, steeped in the country's early history, is another milestone, signaling the conclusion of the Chesapeake experience is near. *Calypso* will again pick up the ICW trail at Hampton Roads.

A day long sail in fluky wisps of air and warm sunshine finds *Calypso* off Point No Point. The very light puffs drop off to a glassy zero; the crew make note of another point in Puget Sound of the same name, and its neighbor, the aptly named, Foul Weather Bluff. The discussion is cut short when skies darken over the boat.

"SUCKER HOLE!" The words blurt out simultaneously, a light wispy breeze springs up, glassy water ripples. By dark, it's blowing a full gale, the wind having veered to the south then strengthened steadily over the course of a couple hours.

The prevailing weather the crew has been dodging for the past several days has returned, *Calypso* now finds herself in the thick of it. Wave heights increase and have no order about them. Confused seas pop up from every direction at this convergence zone of the Chesapeake Bay and the Potomac River.

Calypso is not able to make headway under reefed jib and mizzen. Rather than turn tail and run with it, the crew is in a stodgy mood, dousing all sail, the Blue Jacket Twin is cranked up.

For the next five hours she is beaten mercilessly, the light on Smith Point, twelve miles distant, her only friend. The intended passage to Hampton Roads in one hop is abandoned for the closest shelter available. Eight miles beyond the precious Smith Point light is a complex system of drainages at the mouth of the Great Wicomico River referred to as the Wicomico Spider.

Once she clears Smith Point Light she makes the turn to starboard; running in the trough, choppy waves slap her port side, snap rolling bilge water through the floorboards and up the sidewalls in a harmonic slosh. Fortunately, she has picked up substantial speed on this fresh course; the way is clearly marked with

a light at the next course adjustment at Great Wicomico River, followed by less than two miles of lighted channel to the selected anchorage behind Sandy Point. Two more hours of misery after the turn at Smith Point, she passes into the protection of the estuary, anchoring in a quiet cove, the wind howling ineffectually high above the mast. A hearty meal of rice and lentils, fiercely spiced and loaded with cheese soothes the exhausted crew.

Several days are spent drying out, hiking and exploring while the crew waits for favorable weather. When a light northerly breeze arrives on a crisp pre-dawn morning, they set off under power for Hampton Roads.

After a couple hours running, the Blue Jacket putts become uneven, then with one final long wheeze, sputters into silence. Knuckles are bloodied; the spark, a sickly yellow says it all. The Blue Jacket Twin will not be running anytime soon.

Peace and quiet have returned. Full sail is set against a blue sky amid the blazing colors of Chesapeake Bay. The breeze, a gentle ten knots on her stern, provides tolerable headway. The absence of engine noise is welcome, the crew is relieved of its wearisome distraction from the magnificence of the scene which surrounds them.

Rappahannock Spit juts out into the Chesapeake less than ten miles downwind. Once *Calypso* clears the buoy marking the spit, eight miles further on, an inviting anchorage waits behind Stove Point Neck at the mouth of the Piankatank River.

Well before dark, the anchor is down in Fishing Bay, a spot every bit idyllic as the crew had imagined from its location on the chart. It does not go unnoticed by the crew, once the engine died, the quality of the passage, and life itself, had greatly improved.

With Hampton Roads a day sail away, the crew is well aware, they are about to end these days of abundant, quiet anchorages. A couple days are spent savoring the last of the Chesapeake. They are soon to be replaced by noisy city streets belching exhaust from buses and autos, heavy commercial marine traffic rolling *Calypso* at all hours; grimy buildings and bridges will replace the trees. The trees will be missed.

The crew takes stock. Supplies are low, cash is gone, the battery is dead, the generator is in need of repair. The fact *Calypso* is leaking like a sieve does not even make the list at this point, the leak is more like a companion than a problem. The water coming in serves a function; it keeps the crew alert, day and night. A glance at the list of shortages and necessary repairs dictates a stop where all issues may be remedied in one fell swoop.

The late November weather has turned mild. An extremely light to non-existent breeze out of the north prevails. The early morning is crisp, the decks glisten with frost. *Calypso* glides silently on wisps of air out of her cozy bight into the expanse of the Bay. This day wears on without wind, she drifts or catches light airs coming out of Mobjack Bay. Sunrise the following day finds an estimated fifteen miles made good for twenty four hours. Night falls for a second time on a still, starlit scene. Dawn finds the crew working every puff of air with Old Pt. Comfort coming into view.

With full daylight comes a glassy calm, not as much as a zephyr to be had. As *Calypso* drifts around the point into Hampton Roads proper, the crew takes advantage of the favorable tide, employing the *Rinky Dink* as tug boat.

Phoebus, Virginia

Phoebus, Virginia makes a handy anchoring target. With the help of the current and the *Rinky Dink* assisting with steerage, two miles of this effort has *Calypso* anchored tight to the city; nearby a small tributary labeled Jones Creek. The thirty five mile passage ends after fifty four hours. The same distance could have been covered in half the time at a walk.

Straightaway the crew makes their way ashore, priority is given to the battery for which a kindly service station offers to put on a deep charge. At the State Employment Office, they secure food stamps and a recommendation for work at a local fish processor. This all appears, on the surface, as a huge stroke of luck.

First things first, the crew loads the boat with necessities purchased with the food stamps. The stores replenished, the crew then makes their way to the fish plant, conveniently close to *Calypso's* anchorage.

Filleting fish! A perfect fit for a couple of fisher folk from the "far north." The crew leaves the clean and tidy office of the plant, being directed to the break room where they are issued aprons, knives and an oversize beard cover.

They begin work in the afternoon, cutting fish in separate areas, one for the men, one for the women. Piles of headless monk fish lay on the cutting tables.

The crew had never seen a monk fish, and could not help but wonder what they actually look like. That mystery is cleared up when the first tote of heads roll by. Wolf eel looking critters, mouths agape, eyes wide open staring blankly in all directions with that familiar look of aston- ishment.

A predictable half day of cutting fish; tiring, standing on a cold, wet cement floor. No surprise to the crew, they are in familiar territory, a typical fish processing plant. The day done, the crew returns to the comfort of their tiny floating home, chilled to the bone. A wonderful collard greens soup, leftover from their Thanksgiving dinner warms them as they discuss the events of the day.

It is notable, they are the only white folk in the processing room. The office had no people of color. It also could not go unobserved, that *Calypso* had crossed the Mason Dixon line.

The following day, the crew reports to work. There is a no- ticeable hostility which was not apparent the previous day. The employees are grumbling, agitated with the appearance of the new hires, nagging and nit picking their work all morning long.

The morning break bell goes off, the crew meets for coffee aboard the boat. The anchor comes up; aprons, knives and a beard cover on the cutting tables, as well as paychecks in the office, are left behind.

Great Dismal Swamp

The Blue Jacket coughs, sputters back to life with several jubilant cranks. The battery is freshly charged, the generator cleaned and working. *Calypso* returns to the ICW trail with a light heart. The crew revel in the full effect of freedom; the ability to just pick up and move "lock, stock and barrel" at the drop of a hat.

Leaving Hampton Roads, the little wood sailboat is dwarfed by an impressive line of war ships, standing at the ready. The Walls of grey steel, guns raised, may induce a sense of patriotism in some. The crew only feel a deep foreboding. The blood drains with a sense of dread as they pass by.

An intimidating ten bridges now stand in her way before she will enter the Great Dismal Swamp. The Blue Jacket is running flawlessly, the early start pays off handsomely, as the entire series of bridges is put behind her well before nightfall. With her anchor down, a hearty bean burrito dinner fills out this cold first day of December.

In the Dismal Swamp
Calypso's engine breaks down
'bout the same time we run her hard agroun'
"Rinky Dink" to the rescue now
kedgin' anchor off the starboard bow

Grunt 'n groan, pull with all ya got
gotta' get Calypso offa' this shallow spot
With every purchase ya' take another bight
Calypso moves ever so slight

Off the bottom she finally goes a bumpin'
an' we get that ol' motor a thumpin'
Drop anchor 'n get some rest
for tomorrow may be another test

Wispy winds have *Calypso* gliding silently through the Dismal Swamp. Surrounded by waterborne cypress trees, their twisted shapes, ghostly in the light morning fog. A thick patch rolls in, obscuring the way ahead. *Calypso* sails out of the channel into the cut bank where she buries her bow.

Smoke is pouring out of the hatch. The crew dash below where it is immediately obvious, steam, not smoke is coming out of the engine compartment.

On close examination the source is found to be the salt water intake, a copper tube cooling the exhaust had given out to corrosion. Salt water is spraying the precious generator forcing a shut-down. The *Rinky Dink* is now sent out to drop the main anchor in deep water, where the crew begins the arduous routine of kedging off. Another

of *Calypso's* forgiving attributes, being light and of shallow draft, she pulls out of the mud with the combined efforts of the crew.

North Carolina

Anchors aweigh on this frozen dawn
through swamps 'n byways Calypso glides along
Layin' her wake on a mirrored pond
sailin' in silence with grace of a swan

Albemarle winds chill the air from the north
Calypso continues to sally forth
The Alligator-Pungo has stories to tell
of the Underground Railroad
'n people runnin' from Hell
Calypso glides quietly on these waters of mystery
cypress standin' silent witness history

Coinjock provides a brief rest before the ICW drops *Calypso* into Currituck Sound, North Carolina. The first of a series of Sounds which adjoin the Outer Banks, stretching to Cape Hatteras, continuing south to Cape Lookout and further, almost to the South Carolina border.

A shopworn book residing in *Calypso's* library comes off the shelf here. Howard I. Chapelle's "American Small Sailing Craft" is one of the most influential in the boat's library that has brought the crew to this point in the journey.

Chapelle's wonderful drawings and descriptions are beautiful examples of working vessels found all along the East Coast. The Chesapeake Skipjacks now give way to the Carolina Shad boats, another traditional shallow draft, sailing fishing craft.

The pace of travel has slowed considerably with the arrival of an offshore weather system. Days of remaining anchored in a backwater nook off the channel or sailing a few miles, eight or ten, to another cold spot down the line are the norm as a mild November has given way to December winds.

Crossing Albemarle Sound, the decision is made to avoid the northern reaches of Pamlico Sound, following instead the ICW route inland, up the Alligator River. Several anchorages are taken along the way, the crew huddles in blankets during the very cold evenings. *Calypso* is a summer day sailer having no heat source on board. Florida beckons.

Calypso ducks out of Albemarle Sound into the Alligator-Pungo River Canal and her next stop, Bellhaven, North Carolina. On arrival, the grocery store for provisions is given priority.

The ground feels good under the feet as the crew takes a brisk walk through town. There is an eerie sense of walking with one foot in each of two worlds. This uneasiness continues into the grocery store, where these two sailors from the other side of the country, naive to a degree, are snapped rudely out of their innocence.

At the check-out with a basket chock-a-block full, the pair offer an elderly colored lady behind them with only a handful of items to go ahead. The shock on her face and refusal to move knocks the crew off balance.

They find themselves in an awkward situation with this simple gesture of politeness. The mutually stunned reactions freezes everyone within earshot. Turning back to the white cashier, they are met with an ice cold stare. The crew hurry through the check-out business, making fast tracks for the boat, acutely aware now of the scene on the street. People passing by each other as though they are ghosts, no acknowledgment of the others existence.

The discomfort at this scene is interrupted where *Calypso* is tied up. A ninety foot yacht is pulling up to the dock, the little man on the bridge is screaming at his wife and folks onshore, demanding lines be taken. Dwarfed by his vessel, he appears as a marionette puppet, bouncing around on unseen strings.

Obligingly the crew put down the groceries and grab lines as the wife tosses them to the dock. Immediately upon being secured, a much larger, mega-yacht steams by; the little puppet goes ballistic. "That's my next boat! That's my next million!"

The crew waste no time, tossing groceries onto the boat and cranking up the Blue Jacket; the plan to stay the night is abandoned. The crew are eager to find a quiet, secluded anchorage; they have had their fill of Bellhaven, North Carolina.

Sail on

Inside Cape Hatteras 'n the Outer Banks
give that ol' motor fifty cranks
Cursin' 'n cajolin' to no avail
Pamlico Sound sees Calypso set sail

An' sail she does with so much heart
Calypso's happy that ol' engine won't start!
For she's a sailor true as can be
a hardy little vessel 'n her crew of three

Gettin' right down to the nitty gritty
Calypso sails into Morehead City
Make repairs on that Blue Jacket Twin
Calypso's up 'n runnin' agin'!

Calypso makes passage down the Pungo River, dropping into the Pamlico River which carries her to Pamlico Sound. The long fetch from an ocean breeze benefits *Calypso* when the carburetor spits out flame with a loud backfire, the motor sputtering into silence.

Sails are raised, the crew make their way down Pamlico Sound on an exhilarating beam reach. The leak having increased substantially, the crew is pumping the bilge several times more than usual each day. They have become quite comfortable with her propensity for taking water, the amount always seems manageable and concern remains at a minimum.

Cape Hatteras and Cape Lookout are two more milestones left behind. A boarded-up Morehead City provides an opportunity to rebuild the carburetor to a degree, enough at least to bring the Blue Jacket back on line, albeit, its dependability is questionable.

Bogue Sound, the next body of water on leaving Morehead City provides a continuation of the excellent sailing found in Pamlico Sound. The pick is dropped in front of a small town as darkness falls.

The crew is just serving up a bowl of spicy beans and flour tortillas when they sense a disturbance near the boat. Popping out of the hatch, they discover a wonderful parade of vessels coming directly toward them. A giant Christmas tree mounted on a houseboat leading the procession swings dangerously close by, then comes Rudolf, a herd of Reindeer and finally Santa on his sleigh boat.

All the floats are packed full of folks, singing and waving. The parade circles *Calypso* and returns to town. There follows what appears to be a solemn ceremony of setting rafts afloat with lighted candles from a dock loaded with children. A  moving finale to a delightful evening in Swansboro, North Carolina.

Calypso is off with first light, motoring her way down the narrow channels of the ICW, with the usual number of groundings and engine failures while pumping thirty to fifty gallons a day.

Near the bed keep a potato handy
for a bilge alarm it's a dandy
Toss the spud 'n hear a splash
for the bilge pump you must dash

Pumpin' the bilge a daily chore
this ol' girl's leakin' more 'n more
'Bout the time ya can't take the stress
Calypso starts leakin' less 'n less

Over a thousand miles she's motored 'n sailed
an' as many gallons we certainly have bailed
Through the Carolinas sailin's sublime
runnin' wing 'n wing cross the Georgia state line

Saint Simons Island

Winter Solstice arrives the day Calypso logs one thousand miles. A quiet anchorage is found in the Cape Romain National Wildlife Refuge, South Carolina. The crew spends a few days surrounded by large numbers and varieties of birds. Scores of pelicans dominate the area along with Louisiana herons, blue herons, egrets, hawks, kingfishers and terns. The crew may have spent more time lingering here, however the onset of a cold front has them pushing on. The marshlands provide excellent fetch for sailing the narrow, twisty channels.

Fort Sumter comes into view as *Calypso* breaks out of a narrow causeway leading to Charleston. A short provisioning stop includes a day ashore, celebrating Pat's birthday, before moving on to Port Royal. Here the crew makes a decision to continue along the back-waters to St. Simons Island, Georgia, then head out into the Atlantic for a sail to Florida.

We're catchin' onto this sailin' life very well
an' find ourselves yearnin' for the oceans' swell
One more bridge we have to pass
then for the ocean Calypso will dash

Many bridges 'n locks negotiated along the way
but the tide's ebbin' hard in Frederica River today
Start crankin' on that Blue Jacket Twin
got bloody knuckles 'n broke down agin'!

Bridge is closed blockin' her way
total destruction now just yards away
Hoist sails, crank the helm harda' port
'cross the river lay St. Simons resort

Caught in the grip of a mighty stream
winds' comin' down river abaft her beam
Across this river lies a dock
where a number of folks have begun to flock

Close hauled on the last tack
fightin' ebb tide 'n bridge back to back
When Calypso makes her final turn
the Saint Simons Bridge's right off her stern

The cold northwest breeze proves to be an asset on approach to St. Simons when the old Blue Jacket, almost predictably, breaks down at this most critical moment; an ebbing tide in Frederica River, less than a half mile upstream of a closed bridge with only eight feet overhead clearance.

The mizzen sail is set, sheeted tight amidships. The bow swings up river, into a gusty twenty five plus knots sweeping across the marshland. Racing downstream stern first, the jib is set, partially sheeted in. The helm is put down to port when the mizzen is let fly. The jib snaps with the "wollop" of authority, the bow falls off, the mizzen is sheeted in tight. The jib now sheeted in for balance.

Calypso responds, racing downwind, downstream at breakneck speed, heeling smartly on a sizzling broad reach cross-current, the wind off her starboard sternquarter.

A marina dock is available across the river to port, a hundred yards or less ahead of the bridge. A second option is a hard turn to starboard, ram her into the shore then toss anchors. *Calypso's* heel steepens uncharacteristically to the extreme press of wind against jib and mizzen, her speed downstream increases dramatically.

C losing in on the bridge, yet still upstream of the dock, a moment is stolen to assess what comes next. First glance is directed to the mizzen mast and boom. There is a nasty gybe coming to make the dock. The turn will be timed early to avoid overshooting the mark which could find *Calypso* being swept out of control into the bridge. The mast must withstand the crash of mizzen sail and boom to starboard when they come through the hard wind. If there is a weakness, the mizzen could go by the boards and all will be lost.

When the chosen moment comes, the gut tightens, the jaw sets the teeth. White knuckles on the spokes put the helm down hard to port. *Calypso* responds instantly, heeling sharply, the mizzen takes the wind on the backside, the boom slams hard to starboard and is brought up short by the sheet. She shudders right through to the frames, but the mast and rigging survive the gybe.

Her stern swings through the wind. She is rocked to the tune of a loud "whack" forward, as the jib slams full on the port tack. With her bowsprit pointed upstream of the dock, *Calypso* is committed. The surge of power triggers adrenalin in the crew. The race against certain destruction is on.

They strain to gauge progress against the shore. It will be close. Very close. This is evidenced by the crowd of observers swelling on the dock. They are alert, probably from experience, to the peril *Calypso* is in.

Midstream it is easy to ascertain, the battle is being lost. The bridge, looming larger by the minute made more threatening with the sounds of vehicle traffic and the rushing water boiling around the boat. The mizzen sheet is hauled tighter out of desperation, the bow pointing just upstream, but not so much as to point too high upwind, as that would spell disaster in short order.

Calypso is fifty yards from crashing into the bridge, just beyond the downstream end of the dock, when her speed across the current carries her out of the center stream. She passes into water slowed by the resistance of the bridge structure; her headway increases, which does not go unnoticed by the crowd of people gathered on the dock. A cheer goes up as they can see *Calypso* has escaped disaster.

She labors back upstream, easing to starboard; when she comes abreast the dock, the mizzen is slacked, the bow falls further off toward the dock, where the mizzen sheet is taken up, the helm put down gently to port. *Calypso* presents a nice finish when she sidles neatly up to the dock. The crew, with great relief, hand lines off to waiting hands.

Plenty of handshakes 'n hugs all around
people're happy we're safe 'n sound
This scene has played out before
while folks watched standin' helpless on shore

On St. Simons Island we find respite
celebratin' late into New Year's night
Islanders help out the followin' day
eager to lend a hand in every way

Repairin' the Blue Jacket 'n haulin' provisions
helpin' with navigation decisions
When St. Simons Bridge opens at six o'clock
Calypso lets go her lines from the dock

When the exuberance of the landing subsides, folks help the crew with provisioning, providing transportation while the Blue Jacket's carburetor is taken into the marina shop and cleaned of gunk; the culprit in this most recent fiasco. Local knowledge of the way ahead convinces the crew St. Simons is indeed a great spot to leave the ICW for Florida.

The St. Simons visit proves delightfully friendly and a good time. Dancing and bar hopping on New Years Eve caps the evening followed by a relaxing day making final preparations. *Calypso* will continue south in the morning with the six a.m. scheduled opening of the bridge which coincides nicely with an ebb tide. The ebb will carry her through St. Simons Sound to the Atlantic Ocean.

The Gulf Stream

A strong ebb tide pullin' her free
Calypso's bow tastes the salt of the sea
Icy bowsprit sparklin' in sunlight
a twenty knot nor'wester with its freezin' bite

Out the inlet 'n down to its mouth
Calypso stands to the south
A few hours sailin' under jib 'n mizzen
the crew's pleased with their decision

An invisible warm wall Calypso sails through
under her bow the ocean turns blue
Sargasso Seaweed floats abeam
Calypso sails the mighty Gulf Stream

The decks are icy. The morning coffee is on for a crew eager to be off and through the bridge that was such a headache a couple of days ago. They bundle against a cold twenty knot northwest breeze. The Blue Jacket chugs patiently at idle and as the bridge opens, sails are raised, lines tossed by several folks wishing the crew well and a safe journey.

Calypso motorsails through the bridge and out to the ocean. Sailing under jib and mizzen several hours into the morning, she passes through an invisible curtain. The temperature climbs forty degrees, while the water loses its silty green character, turning a bright aquamarine. A seaweed appears, similar to the macrocystis kelp of the west coast and Alaska. This kelp is free floating in deep water, rather than anchored to the bottom.

The Sargasso Sea, a thing of story books to the crew. *Calypso* sails on through this rolling garden of golden leaves into the night. She is greeted by whiteside dolphins appearing as long streams of fiery phosphorescence running alongside and criss crossing at her bow.

The Gulf Stream is teeming with life, an enchanted sea under this stunningly clear blanket of stars. The four foot swell running on the stern quarter with a light chop is a comfortable tack. Harmony reigns.

Phosphorescence streamin'
off dolphins leapin'
Calypso 'n crew watch with glee
acrobats on this moonlit sea

Night Raid

A ship's lights appear late in the night
then a Coast Guard Cutter comes within sight
Calypso's boarded 'n searched bow to stern
while the crew's tempers begin a slow burn

This marvelous evening is interrupted by the sight of red and green lights bearing down on *Calypso* at a high rate of speed. The vessel veers slightly as it approaches, relieving the crew of the worry of not being seen. They hear the engines cut back, slowing the mysterious visitor, then are startled by a powerful searchlight sweeping the entire deck and ocean around *Calypso*.

The searing white light blinding the crew, destroying their night vision, leaving no doubt, this is the Coast Guard. A welfare check on the little boat? No.

A red Zodiac launched from the mothership appears at *Calypso's* side. A half dozen heavily armed Guardsmen clamber aboard; without a word, they begin searching, bow to stern, inside and out.

Let those sheets 'n halyards drop
lay in the trough 'n let Calypso flop
Cross the deck that main boom comes a sweepin'
duckin' for cover these Coasties're a leapin'

The crew sits at gun point, fuming silently to themselves. The sailing, to this point has been perfect. As evening came on, the breeze had dropped to about fifteen knots, allowing for the mainsail to be set. The swell and chop, leftover from the stronger breeze during the day, are still respectable. *Calypso* is held in irons as the search below progresses when a furtive flick of the wrist slips the mainsheet off its cleat. A heavy roll of the boat swings the main boom, now loose, outboard. When she rolls sloppily to starboard, as the wave passes, she drops into the trough and the boom makes a wicked sweep of the decks. The "Coasties" standing guard on the crew don't see it coming.

Driven violently by sea, sail and rolling boat, the boom slams into the three overloaded guards with their guns, life preservers, ammo, pack sacks and paraphernalia. It is all the crew can do, angry as they are, to not break out laughing at these young men, who are ducking and scrambling clumsily, trying not to be batted in the head or shoved overboard by the wayward chunk of wood.

*Back to their boat they scatter for safety
their retreat very hasty
Didn't know Calypso's sails lay a flappin'
on account of an angry Capn'!*

The short Atlantic seaway and chop are *Calypso's* friend this night. The search ends abruptly, our unwelcome guests hurry back aboard their Zodiac cussing "is it always like that?" among themselves, appearing to not have a clue as to what had just happened.

UFO

*The follwin' night there's a strange sight
off to the west appears an odd light
Darted left, darted right
then stood still shinin' bright*

This third night out of St. Simons, the warm clear weather holds, the wind lays down, a glassy, gently rolling calm settles in, with the occasional light wispy breeze filling the mainsail. The sky, a plethora of stars reflected in a sea alive with phosphorescence.

Dead reckoning has *Calypso* making slow progress, having sailed offshore about ten miles into the Gulf Stream, seeking the safety of sea room. A rough estimate with available information, as the crew have not, as yet, mastered celestial navigation. All the necessary tools and books had been acquired, a "Davis" plastic sextant, "Universal Plotting Charts," tables ("HO249") and workbook however the time has not been right to get down and study the technique and calculations.

The northward flow of the Gulf Stream may be running four knots or better, resulting in the decision to sail back near shore. There *Calypso* will encounter less current, possibly catching a counter current, to carry her south much faster. Navigation too, will be much more accurate, using the "Coast Pilot," charts and aids to navigation along the coast.

Space travelers seem quite curious to know
'bout little Calypso bobbin' below
The light disappears without a sound
for outer space they are bound

The course is set to the southwest, where late in the night a light appears due west, first observed as a planet, with its steady light, rather than the twinkling of a star. Something is not right it seems, as one tries to determine which planet it could be; Venus or Jupiter being the two obvious choices due to its size and brightness, however, Venus is not seen until the early morning. Jupiter is just not that bright. Before another planet comes to mind, the light darts south twenty miles or more and just as quickly, shoots back to its original position. This is repeated to the north, again, almost instantly, taking up its station off *Calypso's* starboard bow. Before one is able to shout out the excitement of the observation, the light whooshes straight away, making an instantaneous exit out of sight.

Calypso is in her fourth night out when she has a second encounter with the Coast Guard. This visit however does not have the heavy handed armed boarding party, rather three gentlemen arrive to do a courtesy inspection of the vessel. The crew is asked right away if they know where they are, as *Calypso* is still out of sight of land. The answer comes quickly, with authority from Pat.

"We're off St. Augstine." Brilliant! "Off St. Augustine;" a vague response which not only satisfies the inspectors, it confirms to the crew where they actually are. The Coast Guard completes their inspection of required safety equipment, and satisfied, return to their mother ship, standing nearby.

The following day finds *Calypso* picking up the northwesterly along a now visible coast with a clearly defined breaker line to follow. Ponce de Leon Inlet offers the next available entrance to the ICW. The sailing goes well until the choppy northwest buffeting throws a crew member into a fire extinguisher.

Located in a handy position next to the companionway it had been in the hands of the boarding party the previous night for inspection. The obvious question for the crew, "why the heck did they pull the pin?!" "Was it payback?" The galley and crew took the full effect of the explosion of white powder. Suspicious, at a minimum.

Ponce De Leon Inlet

*Two days more
sailin' the Florida shore
Cape Canaveral off the starboard bow
turn for land an' the Intra-Coastal now*

Ponce de Leon inlet with the flood tide
the rules of the road a boat must abide
Traffic can be heavy 'n hairy at times
Calypso's a sailin' 'n tackin' on dimes

C *alypso* stands off Ponce de Leon Inlet awaiting the flood tide. The sail on a beam reach between the jetties appears challenging, if not altogether intimidating. The traffic is dizzying, tugs pushing their barges, weekend boaters en masse.

The crew is well aware, sailboats under sail have right of way, however this is a typical situation where the gray area of the rule becomes obvious. Limited maneuvering room, excessive speed, tugs taking up half the channel, unable to change course, and drunken party boaters combine to conceal any clear path.

The crew tacks hard to starboard on the tide change. *Calypso* charges the jetties, crammed with weekend spectators. Nothing to do but join the melee and hope for the best. Tugs and power boats ignore the tide change, racing at *Calypso*, hogging the channel. Vessels waiting for this moment are now inbound as well, passing a three knot *Calypso*, port and starboard.

The turn has *Calypso* head on with a tug pushing an empty barge. The wheelhouse of the tug can just be seen above the barge, which appears to be taking up more than its share of the channel.

The main and jib sheets are slackened some, the bow falls off, gaining speed and pointing at the narrow gap between the barge and seaward end of the jetty. The turn is made big, signaling to the tug *Calypso* intends to pass, port to port while sailing full tilt at the jetty to give right of way, or rather, get out of the way! There is a crowd of people on the jetty now waving, laughing, and having a generally great time, unaware, the crew are puckered.

The low tide scent is strong coming off the jetty when the crew can see daylight, albeit, crowded with pleasure boats, between the barge and rocks. A narrow passage with everything moving, as well as vessels continuing to pass, all shooting for the same narrow gap.

Calypso manages to scoot out of the way of the fast moving behemoth, so close its wheelhouse is no longer visible. The mizzen already sheeted tight, the helm is put down hard, jib and mainsheets are thrown as her bowsprit is nearing to kiss the rock jetty. *Calypso* spins obediently, the crowd raises a collective gasp as she neatly clears the rocks. She is back on collision course with the barge.

Squeezed between barge and jetty, jib and main sheets are immediately hauled tight to grab air, get up some speed, put down the helm, toss the jib sheet, spin back toward the jetty, sailing again right up to the rocks. Another gasp from the crowd as the helm is put down, sheets tossed and again, she neatly avoids crashing head on, right at the feet of the spectators.

These aggressive evasive maneuvers being forced as power boats are eating up every inch of available space, throwing huge wakes, tossing *Calypso* as they pass. The crew can only ignore the fast moving plastic, concentrating solely on the space between the barge and jetty.

Quick succession tacks continue until *Calypso* can point her bowsprit at the pusher tug's stern. The captain pops out of his wheelhouse giving a hearty wave and shouting unheard words, muted by the surrounding thunder of powerful engines.

With the passing of the tug and barge, sailing is relatively easy now, the remaining wall of power boats almost magically open clear water lanes on her approach.

Beyond the inside points of the breakwater, the channel opens wide, congestion is relieved, allowing the crew to set *Calypso* on a direct course to the "ICW."

Chapter 3

FLORIDA

Winter-Spring 1980

Indian River

Florida Keys lay just ahead
pockets're empty gotta' make some bread
A few more inlets 'n bridges to pass
maybe get some dough 'n buy some gas

Ponce de Leon Inlet is *Calypso's* introduction to the Indian River. To the delight of the crew, a restful anchorage is taken where the canal passes through an orange grove.

Surrounded by heavily laden fruit trees on a warm January afternoon, no longer rocking to the ocean swell, the crew spends an extra day here.

Ashore, a fruit stand beckons. The crew loads up with oranges, grapefruit, limes and lemons. Pleasant weather allows for lounging on deck, winter clothing no longer necessary.

The crew studies charts, finding the way ahead is choked with bridges. Notes are made on scheduled opening times as well as those that are opened with a toot from the air horn. The course is arrow straight, stretching roughly a hundred fifty miles with wind driven currents, as the Indian River is more accurately described as a lagoon.

Rested from the ocean travel, *Calypso* continues on her way, the protected open water sailing her reward, topped off by the route taking her inside Cape Canaveral where a rocket stands tall, waiting in the launch gantry.

Melbourne Causeway

A Melbourne bridge presents the crew with adverse conditions to make passage. The wind has veered to the southeast from our extremely favorable northeast quadrant. The resulting twenty knot breeze off the ocean is on the nose, pushing water through the narrow bridge opening. For three days the crew sits at anchor, the Blue Jacket, silent, having left knuckle scabs bleeding again. Either the generator or regulator has failed to keep a charge on the battery. Checking conditions at each scheduled opening, impatience sets in on the fourth day. The wind has come down to about ten or fifteen knots, a pattern which has been consistent in the morning, before puffing up in the early afternoon.

The crew calculates that the wind driven current will slacken overnight with the expected drop in wind speed. The added advantage of sailing right up to the bridge well in advance convinces the crew, *Calypso* will be perfectly positioned for the most advantageous tack well ahead of the scheduled opening.

Calypso works back and forth into the wind toward the bridge in the same manner a racing boat would approach a starting mark, wasting time as needed to hit the mark right at the desired moment.

In this case, the crew intends to tack hard to port from the starboard side of the bridge when it is just half open, ahead of full clearance. A sharp eye is kept for ruffled water in the lighter airs near the structure, steering clear of glassy patches on her approach.

The bridge master toots his warning, gates are lowered, the traffic comes to a halt on Melbourne Causeway and appears to stretch miles in either direction.

(1) *Calypso* makes her move, tacking to port well before being caught in the airless lee of the bridge. The turn is snappy, her sheets hauled tight for the upwind jog to a point at the center of the span on its east side. At that point she will tack back to starboard. If all goes well, she will clear the structure on the west side, upwind of the bridge with no further maneuvers necessary.

She makes surprisingly good headway cross current with what wind is available, arriving at her intended point, mid-span under the roadway as the bridge reaches its full open position. Some ground is lost at the center of the stream then regained as she approaches the far side of the span.

(2) The helm is put down to starboard, sheets are thrown as the bowsprit comes about, dangerously close to the sidewall of the structure. *Calypso* spins sharply to the port tack. Jib, main and mizzen are hauled in a hurry as her bow passes through the eye. The loss of headway on this port tack is easily gauged against the opposite wall, watching *Calypso's* bowsprit slide downstream as she crosses the center flow.

Once through the midstream current, headway is seen to be regained; again, gauging by the bowsprit against the sidewall. If she can hold this course, she will still clear the opposite side of the bridge, allowing her to sail into the open water south of the causeway. Without warning, the gaff peak gybes wildly to port by a fluky gust of wind swirling around and through the girders. *Calypso* spills air, losing her grip on the course taking her to freedom. She begins a downstream sideways slide; the mainsail is twisted with main boom to starboard while the gaff boom waves awkwardly to port.

Another gust rocks the boat as the gaff boom slams back to starboard; the mainsail untwists as headway is lost. Her bow now points downwind, downstream. The jib is let fly as the helm is put down to starboard. The timbers shudder, the port shrouds drawn violin tight when they take up the shock of the hard gybes of the main and mizzen.

This chaotic turn has *Calypso* repeating the crossing of the midstream current, however, she has lost ground. She must make it up in the slower moving water near the sidewall.

(3) Reaching the east side for the second time, she spins again to the port tack at the wall to begin another attempt at the tedious crossing of the span.

Horns begin honking as the little boat fails to appear in a timely fashion on the other side of the bridge. The crew cannot see the bridge master, however glaring eyes can be felt on the back of the neck.

It would be a simple matter to let the current pull *Calypso* free of the bridge, abort the passage and allow traffic to flow. The crew however, have spent so many days waiting for this moment, they are not about to give up the effort.

Calypso crawls painfully across midstream, again losing some ground, then gaining some on approach to the side wall. Sheets are hauled tight as possible, the mizzen leaned on to gain leverage, coaxing *Calypso* to the course which will allow her to escape.

The bridge master joins the cacophony of horns with his own series of long, angry, ear splitting blasts. The crew digs in. *Calypso* edges her way upstream at a snail's pace, bowsprit pointing just clear of the final obstruction to open water.

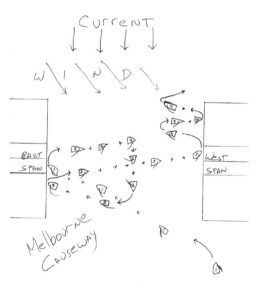

(4) When the attempt to make her mark to freedom fails, the crew forces *Calypso* into a series of lightening quick tacks, between the downwind side of the center stream of current and the west sidewall of the bridge. Progress is painfully slow, however she eventually succeeds in clearing the bridge structure, immediately moving out of the channel into open water.

On the slowly closing bridge, well behind her now, cars are stopped as far as the eye can see in both directions, a blue cloud of exhaust gases and heat waves rises off the lines of traffic. Horns are still sounding off with the bridge master tooting his anger, now most definitely directed at the smoldering traffic.

Two more days and *Calypso* is fifty miles further down river, anchored on the north side of the Fort Pierce Causeway. Another bascule bridge with a twenty eight foot clearance has her waiting again for conditions to make passage.

The crew are losing patience with the rigors and routines of the ICW. The charts show another series of bridges must be opened south of the Fort Pierce Inlet, as opposed to a hundred fifty miles of clear ocean sailing to Miami.

The morning of day three the crew wake to a sweet fifteen knot breeze. The wind has backed from southeast to northeast overnight, affording perfect conditions to open the bridge and head out the inlet.

Calypso is underway at the first daylight opening. The gentle wind off her stern quarter carries her through the North Causeway with ease, becoming a beam reach when she turns to port, heading out the Fort Pierce Inlet.

Calypso's bowsprit bobs a greeting to the ocean as she passes the end of the jetties at the inlets' mouth. The helm is put down to starboard, the mainsheet slackened and the jib worked over to port.

Running wing and wing now, balancing her on an easy four foot following sea, her course is set south, following the breaker line. A perfect day of sailing ends with *Calypso* moving offshore, dousing the main to the freshening twenty knot northeast breeze and continuing through the night under jib and mizzen. This routine is repeated the following day and night, moving inshore to assist with navigation, then offshore with reduced sail for comfortable sea room.

Fort Lauderdale offers easy access to drop anchor for a night. Another busy inlet is negotiated by trusting the traffic, mostly fast moving powerboats who abide the rules and give way to the little sailboat. Hair raising as it is, the passage is made without incident and anchorage is taken inside the protection of the jetties.

Rocking to the incessant boat wakes of a city partying all night, followed by a horde of sport fishermen in the pre-dawn hours, is way more uncomfortable for the crew than the nights spent on the ocean.

The crew wastes no time at first light getting *Calypso* under way. Anchor up, full sail set to the persistent northeaster, she joins the herd of fishermen, heading out the Inlet.

Last Bridge

Skirting by Miami, *Calypso* rounds Key Biscayne, into Biscayne Bay. Sailing the length of the bay, she approaches Key Largo through a twisty channel in a mangrove swamp. Her final bascule bridge will be opened by a toot of the air horn. Fluky light breezes must be contended with, deep in the mangrove. The current, however is favorable at a respectable knot and a half or so.

Calypso is several hundred yards from the bridge, drifting with the current as well as catching the occasional puff of wind from one direction or another. The crew sounds off ahead of a blind corner with one long and one short blast of the air horn.

The bridge master responds instantly from the unseen bridge around the bend with five short blasts. This stuns the crew who are expecting a long and short signal in response; five short blasts is the signal for "do not pass."

There is little the crew can do, carried swiftly by the current with only wispy breezes to steer her by. The bridge comes into view as she rounds the bend. It is open, however, only slightly. The port half remains closed with *Calypso* dead on a collision course. Her way ahead blocked, she is about to lose her mainmast in slow motion.

The helm is put down hard to starboard, the main sheeted in slightly to fill the sail with the little bit of downstream breeze. Her bowsprit swings obediently, pointing just clear of the corner of the port span, which threatens to take her mast.

The starboard span fails to reach full open, requiring *Calypso* to make a sharp turn back to port at the corner of the port span. Only a tiny slot is available to slip through, the slot itself being of questionable height. From the angles involved, sighting the top of the mast against the lowest girder of the bridge, the way is appears blocked by the starboard span.

The wheel is spun to port the instant her hull can pivot the mast around the corner of the port span. Too wide in the turn and the starboard spanwill do in *Calypso's* mast as well. The main is sheeted out simultaneously, filling with the breeze which has strengthened a bit as it is funneled under the bridge.

The bridge master running out from his control room, turns to stone. The crew, frozen, stare at the top of the mainmast, its slender, delicate form silhouetted against the black rusting hulk of bridge. The tip of *Calypso's* mast slips under the forward girder.

The bridge master becomes animated, running to the down-stream girder. Even from his better vantage, it must be difficult to gauge clearance when there are only inches involved.

The crew are not breathing as eternity passes. The helm clutched by a hand tight with stress, pressing down on the spoke, keeping the mast close to the port span, where maximum height of the downstream girder must be found. Mouths agape and silent as *Calypso's* mast narrowly passes under and clear of the danger.

The bridge master pops back to life shouting a hearty "Whoop! You done real good! We lost two masts this week!" The crew, returning the wave and shouting their relief, continue on their way, drifting downstream, ghosting along with an occasional puff of air for steerage. Their adrenalin subsides in the warmth of the sun and realization they have entered the enchanted world of the Florida Keys.

Key Largo

Key Largo's close at hand
Calypso drops anchor in white sand
Ballyhoo seinin's what we chose
to cure those money woes

Calypso drops the pick in Sunset Cove off the town of Key Largo, resting and reviewing the journey to this point. The leak has been consistent for weeks, the crew have lost all cause for concern. It remains manageable, only covering the floorboards if the pumping has been ignored for a day or so. Finances are a real concern. *Calypso* is beginning to run low on rice, beans and spuds, among other staples. The crew gets along fine on simple foods supplemented with fresh fish, keeping the travel expenses to an absolute minimum. A decision is made to remedy the situation in Key Largo. Beating the docks. A tried and true method of job hunting over the years. There are pitfalls, as with any job search, fishing being no exception. The key to landing a job on a fishing boat is not so much finding a job, rather, finding a job on a good boat. This accomplished, it is then up to the prospective crew member to prove him or her self to the skipper and crew.

There are times, as now, where the pair are desperate for immediate cash. In short order a job as crew on a ballyhoo seine boat is landed. The captain, referred to as "Hallyboo" on the docks, is quick to hire the duo. The pay will be 7 1/2%, abnormally low for commercial fishing, especially since he's getting two bodies for less than the price of one. The crew are a bit too desperate which results in agreeing to this arrangement.

Curiosity as well, a factor in the decision. Hand pulling purse seine, an ancient form of fishing still happening in the modern age; here in a world where fishing technology continues to make advances in equipment and techniques.

The crew, having been involved in a variety of fisheries are excited by the opportunity to take part in this unique operation. The gear is light, built to catch schools of fish at a shallow depth. The boat is small and fast. Designed to drop the end of the net with a large buoy attached off the stern while circling the fish, trapping them at high speed.

The net is suspended from the cork line, the lead line takes the web to the bottom, sealing off all escape routes. One member of the crew handles the cork line the other pulls the lead line in. The fish are locked in a circle of net which gets smaller with every heave on the gear.

When the end buoy is retrieved, the cork and lead lines are stacked separately. Lead line to starboard, cork line to port, the light web flaked between the cork and lead piles. When all but the "bag" is back aboard, fish are scooped from the pool described by a small ring of corks next to the boat. They are transferred live to a holding tank on board. When cleared of fish, the remainder of the net is let go from the boat then stacked on deck, ready to repeat the operation.

---

*Miniature swordfish complete with a snout
'round colorful corals small schools swim about
Hand pullin' purse seine makes the back sore
'cause these folks don't know
that's what hydraulics're for!*

Captain Hallyboo collects his new crew well before dawn, driving a dozen miles back to Key Largo where his fishing boat is tied up. *Calypso* had moved down island to Tavernier, where a tidy little harbor was found at a reasonable rate.

The crew's happy to hop aboard a shipshape little speedboat, rigged with a neatly stacked seine net on the stern. The throttle pushed, a couple hundred horses jump to life, excitement boiling in the crew with the thrill of taking part in an altogether new and unfamiliar fishery.

On the run to the grounds they learn this is the captain's first trip out since taking over the operation. He had been crew, now the responsibility is his. This is no cause for the concern by the crew, we have all been there.

Our captain races to and fro, at high speed for almost two hours searching for his quarry. The crew strained to spot fish, however in unfamiliar waters looking for fish they had never seen, were of little help.

At long last Hallyboo yells "let 'er go!" The end buoy is tossed, dragging the web and leadline off the stern when it hits the water. The little boat, traveling at top speed is brought into a tight circle, The lead line is sinking out of sight as it pours off the back of the boat. A trail of white corks is left floating in the wake, forming a perfect circle around a dark spot at its center. An old fashioned "round haul," always gets the blood moving when executed at high speed with the perfectly stacked net ripping off the deck.

To the untrained eyes of the crew from the far north, the net appears to have surrounded a substantial school of fish. The crew are familiar with the sight of large schools of salmon or herring swimming in shallow water and this looked to be a perfect set of the gear. The dark spot could be made out in the center of the net, presumably, the school of ballyhoo.

The end buoy is retrieved, Hallyboo jumps to the cork line while the crew handles the leadline and web. The gear is lightly built, but for the sheer size and resistance, is hard work hauling it back aboard, particularly, the lead line which is heavy and dragging across the bottom. The circle of corks grows smaller as the net is pursed. Only about a quarter of the net is aboard when corks start sinking at the opposite end of the circle from the boat. Hallyboo goes into a tirade, cussing up a storm, throwing a mask and snorkel at a dumbfounded crewman. "We're snagged down, get out there and clear it!" Punctuated with a boatload of expletives coming out of a small hole between flopping jowls, hanging from an angry crimson face.

"A screamer" was the first thought rolling over the side, splashinginto the water on the outside of the net. Diving around fishing gear is scary work, extra caution is exercised.

With a tank of air, there is the danger of getting dive equipment tangled in fishing gear. Freediving, the diver has only one breath of air to rely on, entanglement is deadly. Approaching the snag will be much safer from the outside of the net, where one will not get caught up from behind with the light gear waving around.

The water is murky, not clear as it appears from the surface, with visibility only about twenty feet. Swimming hard for the sunken corkline, twenty five or thirty yards from the boat, the familiar sting of a jellyfish slashes across the ankle.

Looking up and around, the little purple gas bags the crew had observed in the Gulf Stream are everywhere, tentacles streaming down to the depths. The swim intensifies with the maze of man-o-war to work around. In these numbers, avoiding getting stung, impossible, one can only minimize the torture.

This creepy swim through the jellies in clouded water conjures up visions of tiger sharks and barracuda, lurking just out of sight in the murk, looking for the moment to tear this struggling creature to pieces. Not being accustomed to warm water diving, the mind is working overtime.

Stroking and kicking harder than ever now, feeling naked and vulnerable without the comfort of a wetsuit. Fear is niggling the back of the mind, it tries hard to take control and start a panic. This struggle in the mind is distracted and subsides where the corkline disappears from the surface, pointing down toward an unseen bottom.

A series of slow, deep breaths are begun, while allowing every muscle in the body to relax. The hyperventilation necessary for a prolonged freedive, preparing to follow the corkline to the spot where it is snagged down.

One last breath, lungs filled, blood now oxygen rich, a good pull on the corkline and Hallyboo's screaming gives way to the quiet wilderness below. Ten feet down the water clears substantially revealing a much greater issue than the "snag" visualized when the corks went down. Descending alongside staghorn and brain corals, draped in seine net it occurs to the diver that captain Hallyboo has no more idea what a school of fish looks like than the green crew from the frozen north.

What he had determined to be a school of Ballyhoo was a small, round, reef system. Now decorated with his net and presenting the problem of retrieving it. The reef, a colony of living critters with scores of little fish darting about, is fragile, easily damaged. The net, draped over brain corals, wound through the staghorn branches threatens to do a lot of harm.

Returning to the surface, waving arms wildly and making the slashing sign across the neck, Hallyboo at least reacts correctly, cutting loose the end of the net. The tension relieved, it is now a matter of making a series of dives, carefully removing the net from the corals, little by little.

The process takes a good portion of the morning before the net is back aboard, ready to fish again. More time is spent running around searching the waters for fish before the order to let 'er go is shouted out. A tight circle is made, much smaller than the previous set. The end buoy is retrieved and pursing begun in earnest. Again, the corks sink. An irritated diver hops over the side, happy for the opportunity to get off Halyboo's boat. Chuckling at the sting of a loose tentacle, he'd rather be diving in a herd of man-o-war than spend any more time on the boat with Hallyboo.

Following the corkline to the bottom, the fix is simple, the lead line only wrapped around a lone brain coral in a sandy area. The remainder of the net is clear. On the completion of pursing and hauling the corkline aboard, no fish are swimming in the bag. Another water haul receives a tirade, gunning the engine and waving the bird at the ocean. He slams the motor into gear nearly knocking the crew off their feet.

The search is on again, however it is short lived, when Hallyboo hollers "let 'er go!" The buoy goes flying, the gear ripping off the back deck is only half gone when the boat is back at the end buoy, which is gaffed and brought aboard. The tight little circle over clear sand produces no snag as the net is pursed. The bag of web beside the boat when finished pursing has a sizable number of what appears to be miniature swordfish. Iridescent blues and silvers scooting about, sporting handsome bills, a third as long as their bodies.

The crew were so busy examining these curiosity's they did not hear the quiet approach of a second boat, which rafted up, asking if we had bait for sale. Hallyboo was prepared for the question with a scoop net in hand. Price agreed, cash in hand, the fish are scooped out of the holding tank and the fishermen race away, in search of a wide variety of sport fish offshore in the deep blue waters of the Strait of Florida.

Hallyboo, now in a jolly mood with his pocket full of cash, races around in circles, searching for more fish, shaking a fist and loudly boasting at the ocean of his prowess. The crew is quietly counting up their share of cash in his pocket.

Several more sets are made with a variety of results from water hauls to small handfuls of fish. A few more snags required clearing, however, Hallyboo succeeded in not wrapping entire reef systems any longer. A huge improvement.

The light is fading when Hallyboo docks his boat at the buyers station to offload a pitiful catch, which draws snickers and snide remarks from his competitors, eyeballing each others fish holds as the fleet ties up, one by one.

The catch brings in a little over four hundred dollars. The crew is well aware, the bait sold to the fishermen on the grounds easily doubled the amount being sold to the buyer for a fish ticket. Hallyboo also got top dollar out of the fishermen, who paid extra for the convenience and the lively baitfish. The retail fish the buyer sells are more lethargic and not as "fishy" as those right off the boat. Hallyboo effectively stole the buyer's profits and avoided the tax man in one fell swoop.

The crew remain quiet, aware Hallyboo's secret pocket cash will sweeten their paycheck. Seven and a half percent of about four hundred dollars only amounts to thirty bucks. The added cash in the pocket changes the equation substantially, the crew figuring they have about a hundred dollars or so coming to them. Almost worth the grief.

Hallyboo drives the crew back to Tavernier, where on arrival he pulls out thirty dollars saying "here's your seven and a half percent." Then, keeping the ten spot, hands twenty dollars to the crew. "I'll keep the ten for driving." Nearly in unison the crew retorts, "what about the fish you sold on the grounds?" "Grounds money goes to the boat" with a tone of finality that set the man-o-war welts throbbing. "A piddling twenty bucks!" A wise wife started shoving an extremely irritated diver out the car door with a calm "Not worth it" which could be heard under a loud string of expletives and a door slam, essential in venting the welt driven anger.

Tavernier

Tavernier is a lively little community and more work is found in short order. Having some fiberglass work experience, a job patching the bottom of a houseboat is found, the owner offering five dollars an hour for each of the crew. A guaranteed low wage sounds good, after the fiasco they had endured out fishing.

The Florida weather; hot. Catalyzing fiberglass in eighty plus degree heat, a new element to the crew, having worked on fiberglass in the northwest during the Fall and Winter months. The houseboat is about two feet off the ground, presenting a twenty by forty foot rusted steel surface to cover.

The owner's thirteen year old son is hired as well, however, not without great argument and fuss. The son finally agrees, reluctantly, his work being conditional. The crew missed a clue here, when the father agreed to his sons demand that he be paid every five minutes.

The plan for the job is to create a waterproof shell on the entire bottom of this leaky rust bucket, in an effort to get it floating again. The crew got straight to work, being careful not to add too much catalyst, as the reaction will take off fast in the hot weather.

Tricky business, the three are working on their backs with four by six foot panels of fiberglass roving and a pan of hot resin kicking off. Tacking one end of the panel to the bottom of the boat with a swipe of the resin coated paint roller holds that spot in place. All free hands are used to hold the rest of the panel flat against the hull. The roller is dipped in the pan again and another spot is tacked in place. The kid lets go, his five minutes up. He leaves to get paid with the shorthanded crew left to struggle with the unfinished panel which begins peeling itself back off the bottom of the boat. More resin is added franticly to the panel to make up for the lost pair of hands, but the resin, too lightly catalyzed, is not kicking off yet. Unable to hold its weight, the entire panel lets go, covering the hapless duo in a sticky, hot resin blanket.

Pasted to the ground, the crew wrestles their way out from under the goo, crawling out onto hot black asphalt. With resin kicking off fast on hot pavement and in the direct sun, the crew dashes for the acetone to wash the hardening resin off bare skin and out of the hair.

If one were to choose, swimming in a herd of man-o-war would be preferred over bathing in acetone in the Florida sunshine. Undeterred and not wanting to appear unprofessional the crew cleans up, returning to tackle the job once more. They noted it must have been about five minutes cleaning up, as the kid is over with his dad, getting paid again.

A repeat of the previous performance is avoided by adding catalyst and cutting smaller panels, small enough that when the kid leaves to get paid, the remaining crew will not lose control.

Progress is slow, but with the improvement in technique, is progress nonetheless. The adjusted catalyst kicks off quickly. Being smaller, lighter and chemically "hotter," the panels quit pulling away when tacked to the hull.

The day is finished out, without much help from the kid, always busy looking at his watch and running off to his dad. At days end, the crew went to the owner to get paid, and were put off until the next day, as the kid had taken all of his immediate cash.

They had no problem with this, until returning to their boat where folks on the dock warned them about the owner. Rumor had it that a fellow in the Bahamas had been shot because he was this guy's dopelganger. That together with the kid getting paid every five minutes, the crew sensed, they'd been had.

The following morning an effort to get paid failed to the excuse that someone had sabotaged his work skiff. All his tools and boat were on the bottom at a neighbors dock. He had no immediate cash, whereby the crew refused to go back to work on his houseboat

Since divin' is my forte'
I embark on a salvage divin' sortie
Raise a boat to get some cash
but the owner he tries to dash

Demanding to be paid immediately, without success, the owner's boat, which has been sunk, is quickly salvaged. The diver takes possession, holding it hostage for payment. On this, a loud angry exchange ensues between the two. The diver claims salvage rights, which he does not actually have; the owner storms off.

Late in the afternoon the diver is looking over his treasure trove of tools and ski boat. Mostly, a load of junk and garbage with a few cheapo tools mixed in. The boat, a beat up junker is ready for the crusher.

He sneaks out from behind a trailer
an' with a crowbar whacks this sailor
I take his weapon 'n throw it willy nilly
then commence to slap this coward silly

The cops, they arrive on scene
an' of course they intervene
Agin' for money we've come up short
lookin' for work we abort

At a minimum, a bargaining chip was the last thought before nearly passing out from a blow across the back of the head and shoulders. Spinning to face his attacker who is poised to strike again, the next swing is stopped with a defensive move, then the weapon, a crowbar, is ripped out of his hands and tossed.

A crowd gathers quickly as the diver wonders what to do with this little worm. If he hits him with a closed fist on the jaw, it may very well kill him. A better course of action is taken, a backhand slap across the face is followed up by series of quick hard open hand slaps, the diver getting in a few for Hallyboo as well. Sirens, lights and screeching tires put a halt to the festivities, the crowd now turns angrily on the police for their reckless entrance. The police bark a few harsh, unintelligible words, quieting the onlookers. Addressing the two combatants, the police explain to the diver he must use small claims court to settle the issue. Departing with a wry smile, an officer says "good luck with that."

The Last Straw

To rent the Rinky Dink we get an offer
a hundred bucks goes into the coffer
It's a few days later when we know
never again the Rinky Dink we'll row

Desperate now for cash, what appears to be a stroke of luck, the trusting crew are offered a hundred dollars to rent the *Rinky Dink*.

A very pleasant, engaging fellow on a sixty foot motor yacht had lost his skiff, towing it across from the Bahamas. Fifty dollars a day for the weekend was more than fair, the crew not using it while tied up in their slip. Accustomed to doing business with a simple handshake, the deal is done. With the windfall the crew puts the two previous endeavors behind them, making straight for the grocery store to stock up.

The weekend passes without incident, however, the crew begins to worry on Sunday evening when the dinghy is not returned. They shrug it off, assuming the big yacht will be back the next day.

Monday comes and goes as does Tuesday. On Wednesday the crew are resigned to their fate. *Calypso's* sidekick has been stolen. The trusty little Rinky Dink had served them so well, she will be very difficult to replace. The hundred dollars long gone now, the crew sees no future in working. This is a different breed of folks from what they are accustomed to up north. Classic; two little fish in a pool of sharks.

Another failed attempt to raise money
I say "let's sell the engine Honey!"
We say good-bye to the "Blue-Jacket Twin"
Calypso sails on, no more bloody knuckles agin'

The old adage states, "Desperate times call for desperate measures." Taking into consideration the pain, anguish and cost of keeping the Blue Jacket Twin running, the crew puts it on the chopping block, along with anything of value in the boat that is deemed unnecessary.

Calypso is a handy little vessel under sail, able to maneuver in harbors, easy to dock and much faster than the motor when she has a good breeze behind her. Recalling incidents where engine failure and the subsequent sailing out of danger are a testament to her abilities, makes the decision an easy one.

Word gets out on the motor which sells in short order for one hundred dollars. There is no use for a battery now, *Calypsos'* running lights are kerosene, the only electrical device is the depth sounder, which brings thirty dollars with the battery thrown in. The depth sounder is replaced by the ancient lead line method.

The crew is delighted with the extra space afforded by the missing engine, extra water jugs are brought on board as well as a sealed five gallon bucket of rice, flour and beans.

It is now early May. The quality of life has deteriorated considerably since our arrival in Florida in general, and Tavernier in particular.

When a couple on a houseboat moves in next to *Calypso*; an alcoholic abusing his wife, beating his kids in fits of rage, the crew decides it is time to move on. Preparations are made to sail for the Bahamas, then follow the chain down to Jamaica. The crew has had their fill of Florida.

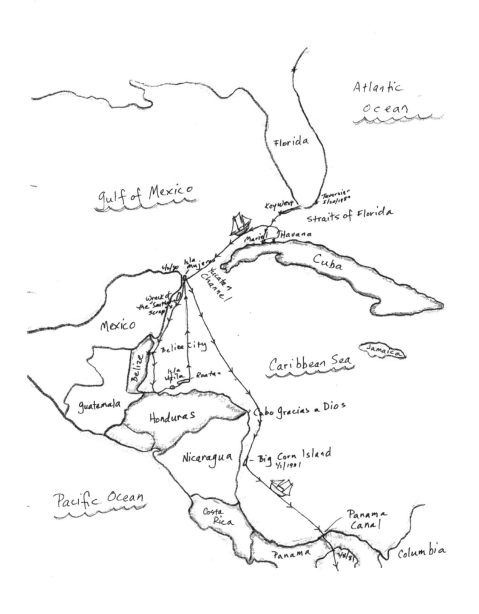

Chapter 4

CUBA

April 1980

Mariel Boat Lift

Calypso lays at anchor off Lignum Vitae Key. A radical change of plan occurred the previous morning, when the crew decided on a restaurant breakfast, celebrating their final day in Tavernier.

The day had begun with an early morning row in their newly acquired *Rubber Ducky* dingy. A drug store purchase and embarrassing replacement for the hardy little *Rinky Dink*. However, a vessel of some sort will be absolutely essential for transferring supplies from shore to anchored boat. The $39.99 price took a large portion of their cash, left over from money spent on preparations for their sail to the Bahamas.

When broke, the crew has a tendency to splurge what little money is left, this day being no exception. The prospect of leaving the country with a little over a hundred bucks does not despair the pair, giddy with the prospect of the great adventure before them.

Ashore, on the walk up to the Overseas Highway, it is apparent something has changed overnight. There are trailered boats of every description jamming parking lots and choking the highway. The crew is lucky to get a seat in the packed restaurant where a TV news station is showing breaking news in the Florida Keys.

The headline is "Mariel Boatlift" with the reporter talking about Fidel Castro allowing an exodus of refugees to the United States. There are chaotic scenes of boats overloaded with people to the point of near foundering. The Coast Guard is out in force, escorting a stream of vessels as they cross into U.S. waters.

The crew is caught up in the excitement when the chatter in the restaurant reveals that for each person brought out of Cuba, the family will pay one thousand dollars. Seeing the heavily loaded little boats, the crew is calculating; at a minimum, *Calypso* has room for a dozen people.

*Set sail for Cuba we're gonna make a lotta' hay
the "Mariel Boatlift's" underway!
By the way did I forget to say?
Calypso's still leakin' thirty gallons a day!*

*A thousand bucks for every soul we put aboard
we'll come back to Florida with a whole horde!
Unfortunately it does not happen
becalmed with sails loosely flappin'*

The "Gold Rush" mentality kicks into high gear as the crew gobbles their breakfast, racing to join the fleet. The promise of big bucks and a circus atmosphere energizes the pair. Such good fortune, an opportunity has arisen which falls perfectly within the current plan to leave Florida. Calypso is prepared for an extended sail to the Bahamas, nothing to do now but row back to her and set the course for Cuba.

Visions of financial freedom whirl in the heads of a crew as they board their boat and set sail without delay. A light breeze has *Calypso* working to the west where she finds excellent anchorage at Lignum Vitae Key, adjacent to Indian Key Channel where she will debark for Cuba.

The necessary navigational tools, still in the box where they were stored in Portsmouth are not bothered with at this point. There are many boats, mostly speedy little sport boats, anchored here as well, waiting for a morning start; the run, roughly a hundred miles to Mariel Cuba. The crew will simply follow the fleet.

A restless night is spent in anticipation. When at the very first hint of light, well before the sun is up, powerful engines are growling to life and boats are roaring out of the anchorage. The race is on!

The crew wastes no time getting under way, charging out into the Florida Straits at a respectable three or four knots. Within a matter of minutes they are left quite alone as the fleet disappears to the south over the horizon. Their compass course noted as the last of the boats fade out of sight, a key piece of information for dead reckoning navigation.

Sailing to fluky winds has Calypso far offshore, with the mass of vessels seen on TV nowhere in sight. Squally weather at times forces the crew to shorten sail for an hour or so, breaking up the calm periods and keeping the crew on their toes. The third day is airless which holds her on a glassy drift, powerless. Dead reckoning, with the current and unsteady winds taken into consideration has Calypso off course to the northeast.

Content to enjoy the peace and quiet, confident the wind will return, the drift continues through the night and into the following afternoon when a lone vessel is sighted, steaming directly toward them.

Cuban Fishing Boat

Out front of Havana on this windless day
a fishin' boat comes steamin' our way
Side by side, rafted together
fishermen all we're birds of a feather

An imposing sight growing larger from its initial appearance, it becomes apparent from the rigging, this is a fishing trawler. Even better, it is Cuban flagged. *Calypso* is in Cuban waters! The crew has no idea where exactly in Cuban waters, having been drifting and sailing in the Florida Strait for three days. Regardless, spirits soar, with only a slight headwind of trepidation.

The vessel sidles up cautiously, a jolly crew and captain laughing, waving and shouting greetings in Spanish and English. What little apprehension the crew had initially felt, evaporates as they raft up together and are invited aboard.

The five young fishermen and two sailors fall into excited conversation in broken languages. Big hugs and laughing, an instant bond of friendship is forged, not tempered an iota over current and past political issues. The two crews knowing intuitively, this moment is special, one to be cherished.

Fishers from Alaska joining with Cuban fishermen. The language barrier, rather than a problem, encouraged animated, often hilarious conversation, describing each others fishing techniques and big hauls, with much exaggeration, as is common among fisher-folk everywhere.

The crew is treated to a wonderful tour from fish hold to engine room and wheelhouse, winding up at the large galley table where there is plenty of room for everyone to sit and enjoy a sumptuous, spicy fish stew with fresh baked bread and sweet black Cuban coffee. Seven people laughing, making all kinds of large gestures in effort to convey their contribution to the conversation which naturally winds around to the Mariel Boatlift, for which this boat had been taken off the fishing grounds and put on patrol.

The belly laughs are contagious describing the hordes of people let loose from the jails to become the refugees. Comic interpretations of the scene eliminated the need for words with this jovial crew.

Our friends had been dutifully rotating a watch in the wheelhouse while the remainder visited in the galley. A wonderful time that would have continued for hours comes to an abrupt end when the watch jumps down from the his post, breaking in to the conversation. Our hosts jump up at once, excitedly rushing the two sailors back to their boat, tossing lines, cutting *Calypso* loose.

On the horizon, a plume of black smoke can be seen, soon taking the shape of a large, speeding gunboat. With a bone in her teeth, white spray explodes from her bow as she dives headlong into waves at twenty knots.

Cuban Gun Boat

---

*Just havin' lunch 'n to our dismay
there's a Cuban gunboat comin' outa' the bay
Our fishermen friends must say goodbye
no time for mango pie*

◆ur friends, laughing and waving, steam off in the opposite direction; with not a breath of wind, the crew sits, waiting for what comes next.

The gunboat, closing in, menacing by its very nature, makes a wide sweeping arc around *Calypso*, slowing considerably as if preparing a boarding when a puff of heavy black smoke and deafening roar from her engines startles the crew.

Having made a complete circle around *Calypso*, the vessel now takes a starboard turn, tearing off in the direction from which it had come. The crew notes the compass course of the gunboat appears to coincide with their dead reckoning as to the location of Havana. The tour of the wheelhouse had included a helpful look at the fishermen's charts, showing *Calypso* to be about fifteen miles out of Havana. Mariel lying about thirty miles down the coast to the west. Our dead reckoning proved relatively accurate.

Calypso returns to the windless drift on low glassy swells, the crew shying from the heat with an awning fashioned of canvas stretched over the mizzen boom, shading the cockpit.

Land still not visible, the crew retires for the evening, wondering what the morning will bring. They are now close enough to Mariel, a good breeze may just put them in port before night falls again.

Sometime during the night, while the crew slept, *Calypso* found a favorable current. With dawn, land is plainly visible, the hills behind Mariel are identified by the elevation sketch in the "Sailing Directions".

Havana is off the port bow, where the crew spots the now familiar black smoke pouring from the stack of a gunboat. The vessel growing larger is coming out of Havana Bay, directly toward them.

Big grey warship headin' our way
passin' too close 'n tears off a stay

Driftin' on that starboard tack
Calypso gets sideswiped with a whack

With only a sporadic breeze for maneuvering, the approaching vessel appears to be on a collision course at very high speed. A starboard tack is forced to some degree, signaling intentions to the speeding vessel. The gunboat adjusts course to intercept. The crew works to steer clear of its path with the intermittent puffs of air available. The fast moving menace maintains its speed, continuing to bear down adjusting course as needed to intercept, dead on.

The vessel is very close now, still moving at a high rate of speed, the decks lined with a crew of maybe fifty men in bikini shorts. From the vantage point of *Calypso's* deck, it appears collision is imminent, unavoidable. The crew braces for impact.

Calypso shudders at the strike, tossed violently by the bow wake while the half naked sailors look down from the rail. A few of the crew are tall blonde men, Russians! The captain, standing in the flying bridge, animated, is screaming at his helmsman. The bulwark crushed in, a mainstay torn loose is whipping wildly as *Calypso* continues to be thrown by the stern wake. The main and jib are dropped to gain control of wildly swinging booms. The gunboat comes about, returning at a much reduced speed.

They swing back 'round 'n throw us a line
But they do not ask if we'd like to dine
Cigar smokin' sailors line the rail
Starin' down at this little boat under sail

We tell 'em "we're Alaska bound!"
The Captain thinks our minds unsound!
"We're kickin' crazy people outa' Cuba today
an' you are not invited to stay!"

The crew scrambles to get bumpers out, protecting their wooden hull as the steel wall comes alongside. Lines drop from the vessel to their deck, which the crew quickly gather up and make off. A boarding ladder drops as well and two individuals climb the fifteen feet to *Calypso's* deck. It is difficult to ascertain whether the captain is stern, embarrassed, or possibly a bit of both. The crew brush off the damage as inconsequential with a wave of the hand, easing his discomfort; they welcome the captain and first officer aboard, inviting them below decks.

Down below, following the formality of checking passports the captain asks "*casa matrimonial?*" To which Pat, familiar with sufficient Spanish to understand, instantly responds with a hearty "*Si!*"

All tensions immediately dissipate with her answer. It appears the fact the crew are married and this is their home plays a major role in the conversation which follows. The very next query is the expected "*a donde van?*" to which in unison, the crew explode, "Alaska!" with great gusto. The two gentlemen light up.

Predictably, our prepared answer to the question elicits the immediate expected response from our guests. "Alaska! Ahh!" The conversation now becomes all about Alaska, border issues go on the back burner.

The four engage in spirited broken dialogue covering a wide range of topics, from bears to snow, ice and igloos. Bear stories always fascinate, and like fishing stories, lend themselves to fabrication. Exciting bear encounters acted out, more than spoken, prove to be an effective diversion from discussing *Calypso's* encroachment and reason for entering Cuban waters. Water has been whooshing past the hull all this time, telling the crew they have been underway while the conversation has been taking place. Where they are bound for, a mystery, as below decks, there is no easy way to get up and have a look, without disturbing our guests.

The first officer, an alert young fellow, beaming a wide toothy grin, points to *Calypso's* bilge saying *"mucho agua!"* This further lightens the conversation as it turns to sailing to Alaska in a sinking boat. The antics of the two officers has everyone in stitches.

The crew eventually broach the subject of Mariel and their intention to stop there, to which our guests bristle. The response is immediate, coming in the form of a direct order; *Calypso* must leave Cuban waters immediately, without landing in Mariel, or anywhere else for that matter.

The conversation now tapers off quickly, the two officers politely taking their leave. On deck, the crew observe they have been towed right up to a main boulevard running along a sea wall.

Music blaring from bars and the general big city bustle leaves no doubt, *Calypso* is out front of downtown Havana. The crew finds it disconcerting, not being allowed ashore, the lively Caribbean music and delicious aromas emanating from the busy street, beckon. The captain and his accompanying officer scramble back up the side of their ship on the rope ladder, which is immediately retrieved. The vessel does not slow to allow the crew to toss the ship's lines, and there is no signal from the captain, now on the bridge, to cut loose.

Calypso's let go on a lee shore
clawin' her way off as so many times before
With the streets of Havana in plain view
Calypso sets her course anew

A fierce squall blows in, of the sort the crew has been experiencing since they made their way into the Strait of Florida. The roar of the warships engines dies off to a low, deep rumble as they are throttled back. The captain gives *Calypso's* crew a wave to toss their lines, allowing them to break away from the tow.

Mizzen and Jib halyards are in the hands of the crew instantly. For whatever reason *Calypso* had been towed right up to the seawall, now a lee shore with potentially disastrous consequences.

Sheeting the jib and mizzen combination tight, *Calypso* begins edging her way along the riprap jutting from the base of the seawall. A heavy chop of standing waves caused by the swell coming in from the strait, hitting the seawall, rebounding, slamming back into the oncoming seas adds exponentially to the stress of working to get clear of rocks that will grind her to death in short order.

An eternity, one of many the crew has experienced on the journey thus far is passing as *Calypso* somehow finds the inner strength to tack to weather, each time bearing a bit further from disaster into open water where the seas are steep, topped with a nasty chop but clear of dangers.

I-Ching Navigation

nce clear of the seawall and sailing out of Havana Bay, the crew must decide, which course they should now take. The three simple options are east to the Bahamas, north, back to Florida, (which is eliminated without hesitation), or west, to Mexico.

The crew weighs the pros and cons of the two remaining destinations. Although the Bahamas are closer and the prevailing current is favorable, the dominant northeast winds may have *Calypso* working to weather at times. Mexico's most obvious negatives are its greater distance and it lies upstream against the current, with a venturi at the Yucatan Strait.

The plus sides of Mexico are threefold. First, it lies down wind to the prevailing northeast winds. The crew is of the mind their strength and consistency will offset the adverse current. Secondly, nearly all sailboats leaving the Keys were headed east; Mexico and points south appear to be "the road less traveled."

The final reason is the I-Ching. When faced with a dilemma, the crew occasionally resorts to this ancient Chinese book of changes for some clarity. One oddity contained within its pages is found among its conclusions. Never once will it give "go east" as an instruction, rather, the suggestion, if a direction is stated, is invariably "go west."

For Mexico we'll now sail!
an' with that we continue to bail
Cause the water's still comin' in
an' if we stop it'll surely win!

Off to the west Mexico lay
nearly three hundred nautical miles away
No longer sailin' with a map's details
an empty chart Calypso now sails

---

alypso sets a compass course, angling off toward the Dry Tortugas, the nearest landfall she may make should the desire or need arise. Squally weather is cause for concern for good reason. The seas have become very rough, pushed by gusty winds, entering the Gulf of Mexico. Calypso reduces sail to jib and mizzen as darkness is falling. This sail combination has become her hard weather mainstay. The two sails, fore and aft balance well, provide ample power, easy steerage and can take a surprising amount of weather. Waking on the sixth day out of Tavernier, having been tossed through the night, Cuba has disappeared from sight, replaced by the heaving deep blue of the Gulf in all directions. The seas remain rough, still choppy on top from the previous evening of strong winds.

Three more days of taking turns at the helm covering all twenty four hours, holding a course, is beginning to take a toll on the crew, along with the uncertainty of their true position.

Celestial Navigation

*Pat learns quickly what it's all about
when those celestial navigation tools're brought out
Sextant measures angles to the sun, moon 'n stars
soon we're friends with Aldebaran 'n Mars*

ow the crew is presented with something new. Up to now they have used charts with much detail, backed up by the "Coast Pilot" and a variety of written materials.

The box that had been so carefully packed in Portsmouth is now dug out of the bow. The time has come, out of necessity, to find our position by identifying and applying mathematical calculations to a variety of celestial bodies as they travel through the sky.

Celestial navigation is that mysterious method of finding one's position by measuring the angles of the sun, moon, planets and stars, noting the exact time while doing so.

The crew had been careful with cash in Portsmouth when fitting *Calypso* out for the journey. Limited finances had them seeking out bargains on supplies and a local marine swapmeet provided the perfect opportunity to acquire the necessary navigational tools.

At one booth in particular, the proprietor, a crusty weather beaten character is eyeing shoppers with obvious suspicion, guarding the wealth of bronze items hanging everywhere. A large box labeled with the bold letters NAV catches the immediate attention of the crew, as this is the most important item on their list. It is not just a single item, but a massive collection of charts, books and tools which must be accumulated from a variety of sources.

Upon seeing the crew's interest in the box, the old fellow's beady blue eyes light up. "You folks going for a cruise?" The crew responds to this ancient sea-worn face, breaking out in a wide wrinkled grin when in unison they announce "Alaska!"

This is the canned response the crew had cooked up, preparing themselves for this exact question. They actually have no idea where they are going, however, regardless where in the world they are, the crew knows, people love Alaska. The mere mention of "Alaska" conjures up images in people's minds instantly, inevitably opening a plethora of the usual questions. Alaska is the perfect conversation starter, world wide.

The old salt, after the usual barrage of queries, changes the subject, pointing to his NAV box, saying "that'll get you to Panama. Everything. Both routes, east and west." "And that box there, got all the tools. Even got a sextant 'an a Almanac. My days of adventure are done, you can have the works for fifty bucks!"

Pawing through the mass of paper charts, books and paraphernalia, it is obvious to the crew this collection is very valuable. Dated, but well cared for and in excellent condition, the purchase is a no brainer, one stop shopping crosses navigation tools and charts off the list.

A second barrage of questions along with a boatload of tips and suggestions, many from a curious crowd which had gathered around the booth. At length, the crew says their goodbyes to this generous fellow, who had literally turned over to *Calypso* his most prized possession, containing the memories of his life's adventures at sea.

Learning the calculations required for navigation proves to be a much more difficult task than at first perceived. The puzzle of celestial navigation is not so easily solved, with so much time fighting the sea sickness brought on when attempting to study the required material.

The "Universal Plotting Charts" are in jumbo pamphlet form. For the exception of a light blue grid of very large proportions and a central compass rose, they are blank. With her knack for solving problems in general, and mathematical in particular, Pat takes up the challenge of absorbing the material.

Along with the chart sheets are a "Nautical Almanac," three volumes of the "HO 249" covering the entire northern hemisphere from the equator to eighty nine degrees north latitude, and a simple "Davis" plastic sextant. For accurate time, *Calypso's* entertainment center is key.

A "Zenith Trans Oceanic" short wave radio has the ability to pick up "WWV"[2] out of Colorado. Tuning in to the continuously broadcast "Coordinated Universal Time" fulfills this essential

---

2 "WWV" is a high frequency radio station located at Ft. Collins Co.

element in the process of finding longitude, for which an accurate source for Greenwich Mean time is necessary.

The radio bongs time, angles're measured
then turn to the books so treasured
Sight reduction tables n' almanac
keep Calypso 'n crew on the right tack

Among constellations Calypso travels
when navigation's mysteries Pat unravels
An empty blue Gulf at first hint of light
the crew of Calypso takes the morning sight

After three days alternating between the books, practice sights and time spent barfing over the side of the boat or curled up in the bunk, lines of position are solved. The first line of position drawn, the crew felt was accurate in every detail from time and angle of the sight to the final calculation leading to a line drawn on the blank page leaving the the crew with the simple question, "what's that?"

This puzzle is soon solved as additional sights are added to the page. Then "Lo!" The following lines of position begin intersecting the original line on the page. The evening sights continue the pattern, solving the final question. *Calypso* lies along the lines of position at points of intersection.

The lines of position describe a record of travel, nearly parallel to the estimated compass course ("great circle") which had originally been drawn from Havana Bay to the tip of the Yucatan Peninsula, Mexico. The crew begin a routine of morning sights as some planets and stars are still showing when the horizon becomes visible. These are followed up with the morning sun sight. The traditional noon sight gives the crew fits, as the sextant finds the sun directly above her. There are four distinct sights, each with a different angle registered. The noon sights are dispensed with in favor of sights made as the sun is low on the horizon. The stars, moon and planets begin to appear, presenting a variety of potential sights. The navigation day ends when the horizon gives way to the darkness.

Big Weather

Even when weather is calm 'n fair
storms appear out of thin air
Cumulonimbus risin' thousands of feet in the sky
hard wind 'n lightning bolts as the storms pass by

Race to the halyards 'n drop sail
tie the jib off at the rail
Lash everythin' on deck real good
with Mr. Nimbus in the neighborhood

Easterly winds prevailing in May, veering intermittently to the southeast are favorable in general for *Calypso*, although there are frequent calms associated with the pattern. A fascinating event becomes quite a common occurrence. A fluffy white cloud appears, a top hat rises from its center, billowing skyward thousands of feet. The first of these oddities is observed while the crew sits quietly on deck during a calm spell, drifting on glassy swells. The intense midday heat has the crew lounging, without cause for concern.

This lone formation continues to expand in all directions, reaching higher all the while. As the cloud matures, it becomes gray on its underside, with a dark anvil shape forming on its leading edge. *Calypso* finds herself directly in the path of the approaching cloud. Its anvil shape grows darker, even more menacing now, as lighting bolts strike the sea from the center of the formation. An intimidating mini-storm has appeared right before their eyes, without another cloud in the sky nor the slightest breath of wind. This mature system bears down on the unprepared boat with her full set of sails flopping, still sitting in dead calm water. When an extreme temperature change occurs, all four hands of the crew hit the main halyard at once. Down comes the mainsail seconds before the anvil strikes a blow against mizzen and jib, broadside. *Calypso* heels hard to the intense gust, skittering across the water. The crew is hanging tight to the gaff and main booms with the mainsail whipping wildly, nearly tearing the gaff boom from their arms.

The gust lasts only seconds. The crews' quick, albeit late reaction, prevented a potentially disastrous situation. Dousing the mainsail ahead of the intense storm force wind was nothing more than a stroke of luck. A freebie.

Enterin' our second week at sea
a gruelin' test of endurance this sail comes to be
Twenty-four sevens at the helm
exhaustion threatens to overwhelm

The blow ends quickly, followed by a cold downpour after which the sun returns; the storm plows off to the west, lightning bolts dance at the base of the low, black cloud. The top hat, still ivory white, reaches skyward evermore.

The crew returns to the flat calm drift, lounging in the sun's warmth, allowing it to wash away the remaining effects of the adrenalin rush. Discussion drifts from rehashing the mini-storm experience to the exhaustion they now suffer.

Yucatan Strait

◆ ver two hundred miles remain, according to calculations which they must trust with no verification other than the results of many more sights on all planets and stars available. The occasional commercial traffic offers clues to the accuracy of their calculated position by virtue of their direction of travel. Trampers carrying Central and South American flags point the way along *Calypso*'s course to the Yucatan Strait.

Without steering aids of any kind, *Calypso* requires a person at the wheel, with a bit of constant pressure, holding her weather helm. This among the other duties in fluky winds, calling for sail adjustments or dropping sail on the approach of hard wind demands constant attention. Needing to work for every mile, the crew disregards the sleep requirement in favor of making the best of the passage. They are not desperate to reach land, however, twenty-four sevens at the helm has them falling asleep on watch and in the worse case scenario, hallucinations.

The recurring visions, even after a three hour extremely deep nap, continue, day after day. Always the same; a lone pole standing off the starboard bow, right on course. They never appear at night, there are stars aplenty to steer by, however, every day they are there, very similar to the ICW guide posts, marking the way. One no longer needs to check the compass. The feel of a consistent ride on the swell, combined with the inevitable pole off the starboard bow, the hallucinations have replaced the redundant magnetic needle at the helm. Admittedly, the navigator never witnessed these markers.

Dodgin' big ships always a fright
passin' Calypso in the dark of night
Addin' to a fear we begin to dread
the Yucatan Strait lay dead ahead

Yucatan Strait. A venturi connecting two giant bodies of water has been a concern since the crew made the decision opting for Mexico as a destination. This imposing stretch of water lies between the western tip of Cuba and Mexico's easternmost point on the Yucatan Peninsula.

The crew has plenty of experience navigating narrow channels connecting two large bodies of water, but never on such a huge hydrodynamic scale. It is plain to see from the charts, currents and sea conditions may well be extreme in this neighborhood. The crew approach the Strait with apprehension, expecting a dramatic crossing. They are not disappointed.

Commercial traffic increases as they are funneled through the passage, requiring constant vigilance from the weary, sleep deprived crew. The watches are no longer a consistent three or four hours as has been the practice. Now, a watch lasts only as long as a person can keep their eyes open.

Fortunately, the winds have picked up and are blowing a steady twenty to twenty five knots out of the northeast. *Calypso* is sporting full sail as she begins her last hundred miles to Mexico.

A hundred miles wide, ten thousand feet deep
fifty foot mountains rollin'' n steep

Calypso sails with a sassy sashay all the way to Cabo Catoche

ollowing another night of straining to interpret ship's lights and taking evasive action in this bottlenecked traffic zone, *Calypso* finds herself in the center of the Strait, wallowing at the bottom of troughs, sails flopping, airless.

Judging the wave tops at twenty or twenty five feet above the masthead, the crew is holding each other tight at the helm, frightened, fatigued, yet marveling at *Calypso's* graceful agility, greeting and ascending the great shoulders of these lumbering giants bearing down on them, one after another.

Nearing the smooth, rolling crest, the sails fill briefly with a light ten knot breeze, then quickly go slack, flopping again, as she slides down the back side of the wave, deep into the trough.

Fully aware they are transiting hurricane alley, the crew understands this is most likely as good a crossing that could ever be expected in this neck of the woods. There is no chop atop these fifty footers. It takes little imagination to visualize these waters in hurricane force winds. The crew is thankful the twenty five knot breeze died off overnight, as conditions would be very different, especially at the crests of these beasts. As evening comes on, the seas subside dramatically to comfortable six footers. The evening sights put *Calypso* just ten miles from an unseen shoreline.

Jib and main are lowered and lashed. The mizzen is left to tend her through the night. The exhausted crew, comfortable they are clear of the shipping lanes with plenty of sea room off the coastline, allow themselves to drift and sleep.

Chapter 5

MEXICO

Summer 1980

"Sailing Directions Enroute"

First sight of land we make course corrections
according to navigation charts 'n Sailin' Directions
"A low lyin' bare sand spit" proclaims the Directions ditty
instead there rises Cancun city!

Sights taken at first light reveal *Calypso* has drifted only a few miles overnight in the general direction of her original course. By this, the crew assumes she has found a counter current running south; *Calypso* has sailed free of the grip of the Yucatan Strait.

Land is still not visible. A snowy egret lands aboard this early morning; an indicator that we will soon be seeing "a low lying sand spit with a few fishermen's huts" as stated in the trusty "Sailing Directions." The sketch associated with the statement is clearly of a desolate beach, a few shacks and low lying treeless hills in the distance.

The navigation box acquired in Rhode Island contained several volumes of the "Sailing Directions Enroute." They are extremely accurate in their artistic pencil sketches of the coastline. Mariel, Cuba had been spotted easily as *Calypso* sailed by. Many of these drawings have been published, updated and re-published since the 1600's. The copy in hand is dated 1976, a mere three years old.

The crew keeps *Calypso* a couple miles offshore, as the chart indicates an extensive reef system running on a north / south line along the coast. They have noted previously from studying western Caribbean charts that this coral reef system is actually the second largest in the world, surpassed only by the Great Barrier Reef of Australia. The reef makes up the shallows lining the western edge of "Hurricane Alley. Spanish galleons, heavily laden with gold and precious gems, dashed to pieces along this coast, are now part and parcel of the system. Gray shapes rising in the distance snaps the crew out of this pleasant reverie, alerting them to a change in the topography. Although still too distant to make out, it is plain to see these ghostly forms slowly taking shape and growing taller on approach are not indicated on the navigation charts or in the "SD."

The navigation chart agrees with the "SD," indicating low lands with a few small structures on the point of the spit. The shapes growing off *Calypso's* starboard bow are foisting immediate doubt on all the calculations made to this point.

Searching the charts, the Merida / Progresso complex is the only city of any size on the Yucatan Peninsula. This would put *Calypso* roughly a hundred fifty miles off course, and on approach, she would find Progresso to port. The city the crew is observing now appears as any large city from a distance, with buildings reaching for the sky over a wide area and commercial aircraft circling above. Most importantly, however, this city rises to starboard.

Reviewing the calculations, the crew determines they are correct, the flaw is simply the outdated "Sailing Directions" and chart. When the city before them is ignored, the remaining topography is identical to the mid-eighteen hundreds artistic conception. Sometime, most likely in the seventies, a full blown resort city had burst on the scene and remained unreported for the 1976 edition.

---

*After recoverin' from the shock
we know Cancun city we'll not dock
"Where to now?" We ask
"At Isla Mujeres our anchor we'll cast!"*

*Just off the coast this tiny island lay
twenty nautical miles away
A bone in her teeth 'n leavin' a frothy trail
the northeast trades fill Calypso's mainsail*

Calypso's bow swings into the wind when the helm is put down to port. The mainsail is set, she's then allowed to fall off to starboard, her sails filling with a freshening breeze out of the northeast. Heeling to the press of wind, jib and mizzen are sheeted tight, the mainsail is sheeted out to spill a fair amount of air as *Calypso* exceeds her hull speed on a sizzling beam reach, directly toward her destination.

Isla Mujeres

Drop anchor back of the bay
next to where fishin' boats stay
After fourteen days 'n five hundred miles
Calypso 'n crew're wearin' broad smiles

Snorklin' 'n fishin's how our days're spent
no worries on how we'll pay the rent
A kilo of tortillas for a few pesos
a few more centavos 'n we're eatin' huevos

Two weeks have passed since leaving Tavernier when *Calypso* drops her mainsail, entering the harbor on the lee side of Isla Mujeres under jib and mizzen. With reduced speed, the crew takes stock on where to drop the pick.

The decision is made when a sixty foot commercial trawler cruises by, throttled up, black smoke pouring from her stack. She drives high up on a sand beach, the bulwarks and guards of what appears to be her sister ship, also parked high on the beach, absorb the shock of the initial strike. A guttural roar from her engine, another blast of black smoke shoves her even higher on the beach. She wags that wide horseshoe stern before settling down, both vessels rocking from the hard, side swiping blow. A short distance from the beach, near the fishermen, *Calypso* finds fifteen feet of water where she splashes her anchor. The crew jump over the side for a refreshing dip before retiring, exhausted. Two days of deep sleep and lounging follow the crossing from Florida. The crew had exceeded their physical limits of sailing *Calypso* long distance.

Fourteen days and nights of constant vigilance has taken a toll on the crew. A four or five day run they now considers reasonable, stopping for rest well before the hallucinations and exhaustion set in.

Mexico is a refreshing change from Florida, altogether new and different. The crew quickly become familiar with the little island, finding excellent diving at the "Garrafon" where a particularly interesting school of fish reside. When one descends about twenty feet, this school, which appear very similar in size and shape to a perch, common in Puget Sound, envelop the diver, staying just clear, never touching, however totally surrounding the visitor in a giant ball.

Sea turtles, a massive school of juvenile barracuda and several very large grouper also reside here. The crew earns occasional pesos taking travelers from the "Pocna," (the local hostel) on day long sailing and snorkeling trips to this unique little dive site.

Southern Scrap

There comes a stormy day
when a fellow sailor sails into the bay
Chock-a-block loaded to the gunnels with crap
a little yellow life boat the "Southern Scrap"

An early evening gale arrives after *Calypso's* first couple weeks at anchor. The crew observes a curiosity blow in from the north. First appearing as a bright yellow dot with an array of color flashing intermittently atop, surrounded by the white claws of churning seas outside the harbor mouth. With impressive sliding down steep blue walls on her approach, she works her way into the smooth, protected waters of the bay.

Dazzled by the bright colors of a tie-dyed, heavily patched mainsail, with matching jib and a mizzen adorned with a huge yin yang symbol, the crew stands, mouths agape, wordless.

This bold entrance is followed up by a loud voice rising above the wind. "Do I hear dinner noises people? I hear dinner noises people!" The lone sailor drops sail, tosses the anchor, then dives in the water, stroking hard for *Calypso*. As the visitor swims, the crew is eyeing this oddity before them. A common steel twenty-six foot lifeboat, rust streaking down its bright yellow hull in many places. She has been converted to sail and ketch rigged with a couple of shaky looking sticks for masts. The mainmast, mangled at the very top, appears to have suffered severe damage. The sails are an artistic combination of tie-dyed sail cloth, patched with a variety of materials provoking the image of a hippy afloat.

A lanky, deeply tanned swimmer clambers aboard introducing himself in a German accent "I heard dinner noises people, do I hear dinner noises?!"

*The Southern Scrap of steel she's built
her patchwork sails a psychedelic quilt
A lively fellow Cosmic Kris
bouncin' aroun' in a never endin' state of bliss*

Tortillas are put on and tacos appear in short order from *Calypso's* galley. An obviously famished sailor dives in. Between mouthfuls, our visitor, Kris, relates stories of his nearly three week crossing of the Gulf, originating in New Orleans. He had

experienced the same combination of infrequent trade winds, calms and localized storm systems, with which the crew was familiar.

When asked about the mangled masthead, a most entertaining tale ensues. The impromptu dinner party descends into fits of uncontrollable laughter as Kris relates a story of the *Southern Scrap's* passing under a bascule bridge en route to the Gulf of Mexico.

The *Southern Scrap*, having no engine, was struggling to make her way under an opened bridge. A tug pushing a loaded barge upstream under full power washes her aside with impunity. Smashing into the sidewall of the bridge, rocking wildly, the mast jams into the workings, tearing off the steel cap at its top. The little boat breaks free, leaving the cap stuck in the giant gear wheel, designed to open and close the bridge. Carried downstream by the current and clear of the bridge, Kris describes the identical scene the crew had witnessed at the Melbourne Causeway. An endless line of cars, smoking, steaming and a bridge master, laying on his horn in the Louisiana heat. Only difference, this bridge would not be operating again any time soon, the *Southern Scrap* has made that a certainty. Recovering from the bridge story, the crew questions the low freeboard of his boat, to which they are treated to the inner workings of this free spirited sailor.

Televisions, radios, mix masters 'n clocks
shoppin' carts, toilet seats, hub caps 'n socks
A boatload of prime American trash
Cosmic Kris's gonna turn into cash

In his preparations, Kris had scoured garbage dumps, Goodwill, Salvation Army and free stores for every imaginable piece of clothing, blankets, kitchen ware, toys and tools his little boat could hold. The crew, being invited over for a look, are greatly amused. The *Southern Scrap* appears as if she had been filled with a front loader full of garbage, packed tight, then the deck put on like a cap to seal it in.

A shopping cart full of a wide variety of small items partially blocks the way below. Another full shopping cart, loaded to the cabin roof comes next, with a third cart peeking out from a bow, stuffed tight. There is a spot on the portside, clear enough for a body to lie down. A can of "Sterno" with a coffee pot makes up the galley. Food stores are simply part and parcel of the garbage. It is a simple matter to dig around for a cracker, can of "Spam" or whatever the desired fare.

Kris, a delightful soul, is not without a plan. He has created a mini-freighter from a ships lifeboat, intending to finance his journey to Central America with the cargo. He will be moving on to Belize where his very pregnant Australian girlfriend will meet him. Their intention is to begin a new life there.

The arrival of the *Southern Scrap*, and particularly, Kris, brings new life to the anchorage. A marked increase of travelers staying at Pocna now frequent the two boats, due largely to the entertaining antics of Cosmic Kris.

A lively social scene materializes in this tropical paradise. The crew settles in for an extended stay. Isla Mujeres has everything these two hedonist sailors had been searching for; the easy life.

Conch Dive

Those Mexican fishermen on the beach
a lesson this sailor they intend to teach
There's a great spot for Conch divin' they know
an' their superior skills they're determined to show

T he crew had been watching and waving to the crews and captains of the fishing vessels as they came and went over the past few weeks, always entertaining, as they slam into the beach and each other on arrival. The early morning hours finds them gunning engines and blowing black smoke, horsing their sterns back and forth in reverse to work their seventy-foot hulls off the sand.

Ultimately, there came a Sunday afternoon when three vessels, on their day off, rafted together on the beach. They wave the crew over to join them for refreshments. Meeting our new friends, with so much in common in the world of fishing, the discussion soon winds around to a trade of resources. The crew will take the fishermen sailing and these locals will show us their favorite conch dive site, after which we could look forward to cevichi, and of course, dinner.

In a matter of minutes *Calypso* has these very able seamen crawling all over her, grabbing lines, pulling anchor, while politely shoving the owners aside, clear of the helm. She has in effect been commandeered by these fellows, who immediately, in a most professional and knowledgeable manner, have her under full sail scooting along at her very best. Another round of beer is served up as she speeds for their secret hot spot.

Calypso comes into the wind abruptly at the mouth of the bay, where rough outside water meets the calm waters protected by a jutting point of shoreline. The anchor is thrown, the line whizzes out then is tied off with the hundred foot mark still in the stack. From this observation, the crew surmises correctly, these will be roughly sixty-foot dives. The antics and excitement of the fishermen, even though they do not understand all what is being said, tells the crew something. This conch spot is very good, and in addition, is designed to embarrass an Alaska fisherman. Fishermen are inherently competitive, and these young fellows are no exception.

They don mask snorkel 'n fins
their confidence displayed in wide grins
Sixty feet deep where Calypso's anchor dropped
into the water my fishermen friends popped

This sailor has a mask
but without fins 'n snorkel
he has a very difficult task
Snorkels 'n fins great advantage they made
but this sailors' secret, he's a diver by trade

Ill prepared for this spontaneous expedition, freediving sixty feet without fins and snorkel, will be a challenge. A heavy bronze belay pin is snatched from the mast and stuffed at the belt. One by one our friends, laughing and chattering on the surface, disappear.

Sitting at the rail, facing inboard, a series of slow deep breaths is taken. A last full breath is held, the blood is now highly oxygenated; a backward roll from the deck to protect the mask from being blown off when striking the water is followed by a straightening of the legs.

Hard, barefoot kicks and several strokes of the arms, added to the momentum of the fall from *Calypso*, sends the body ten feet down, where one can feel the light tug of the belay pin. Motionless, the muscles are relaxed through the descent, conserving oxygen. Visibility improves near the bottom, where the other divers can be seen scrambling about.

Landing in a glory hole of conchs one sees the astonishment

in the eyes of his compatriots and the wide grins behind their snorkeled mouths when the belay pin is tossed toward a diver. Acknowledgments are traded, two conchs are scooped up, saving one arm free to stroke for the surface, then a hard one leg push gets initial momentum off the bottom. A series of arm strokes and hard sweeping kicks has the diver to ten feet. The remaining low oxygen air in the lungs expands markedly, partially dousing the fire burning in the chest.

The conchs are tossed on deck in one motion upon breaching the surface veil. One by one the fishermen explode on the scene, packing arm loads of conchs; splashing around on the surface, catching their breath, excitedly pointing at the diver hanging off the bobstay. A belay pin held high by one individual is waving wildly and returned. They toss their conchs aboard then prepare for a second dive. As they disappear one by one, legs are sprung against the hull, while hanging with one arm from the bobstay. A hard push off followed by two powerful arm strokes and sweeping kicks, allows the diver to descend with every muscle at rest. Again the light tug of the belay pin aids the descent.

Freediving will trace a bell curve as the dives progress. The second dive is always much easier than the first. The body is tuned to the demands after the first dive, and good measure of depth and visibility have been taken, reducing wasteful tensions induced by the stress from the variety of unknowns and variables prior to the first dive.

On bottom a second time, greeted with slaps on the back and hearty waves, no time is wasted. Two more beautiful specimens are scooped up. The belay pin, now a baton, is passed off. A hard push with a leg springs one off the bottom for a quick, painless trip back to the surface.

Two sixty foot dives back to back without flippers and snorkel, the diver is certain he has reached the top of his bell curve. Another attempt now may result in an embarrassing retreat to the surface well before reaching bottom.

With this in mind, he climbs back aboard *Calypso*, collapsing on deck. He is rousted right away by conchs raining down, crashing on deck, as the other divers pop to the surface, tossing their catch before they clamber aboard.

Mexican Fishermen

*Their competition does not end there
now, who could provide the tastiest fare?
Every day we're invited to dinner
on a different boat determined to be the winner!*

*These seventy foot trawlers have freezers below
crammed with the catch from their daily tow
Swordfish 'n snapper come up from the hold
An' every night a new feast would unfold!*

The crew sits back enjoying for a second time the expert handling of their boat by the fishermen following the conch dive. They are whisked back to the trawlers where cold beer is served up, along with freshly made cevichi from a very productive dive.

The vessels will be on the beach for the long weekend, celebrating "Dia de San Pedro." Each of the boats has a Pedro or two aboard, making for plenty of back slapping and jokes. Much has to be explained slowly to the crew, struggling with the little high school Spanish they remember.

Following the appetizers, the fishermen and guests are called in to the galley for the evening meal. Three stuffed red snapper sit, staring at the dinner party from their silver platters. Their eyes wide, the astonished look of a caught fish, still on their faces. It was not just the work of imagination, but the crew is certain, the silly grins and quizzical gaze they wear had been a subtle fabrication during preparation.

Dubbed *"Tres Pedros,"* they honor all the *Pedros* aboard the three vessels. Next to the "Three Petes" is a huge cast iron pot of beans and a stack of hot flour tortillas. The entire display surrounded by platters of fresh fruit with buckets of beer on ice at each setting.

The captains come around to boasting of their cooks and the fine meals they enjoy while out on the fishing grounds. It is not long before this delicious meal, that now looks as though it had been torn and picked to pieces by a flock of vultures, is challenged by the neighboring boats.

To settle the dispute peacefully, the crews will all sit together for dinner again at the remaining two vessels. Judging by the wreckage before them, *Calypso's* crew is looking forward to the next two evenings, being treated to the work of two very competitive chefs.

Late afternoon the following day, a conch horn is sounded. The crew, famished from waiting all day for this moment, waste no time diving over the side.

Swimming toward the trawlers laying cattywompus on the beach, the crew is laughing and joking of the *"Tres Pedros,"* the nickname they bestowed on this group of hearty, fun loving fishermen and their boats. Not an iota of difference from a typical scene in Alaska, for the exception of jumping over the side. Even that may occur on occasion up north, during moments of great exuberance, induced by a very successful fishing effort or alcohol, or most likely, a combination of the two.

Langostinos marinated in cevichi with beer alongside greets the crew when they climb aboard. They quickly learn more of their new friends, mostly, they are all very experienced sailors. All have grown up along the Yucatan Coast, getting their formal maritime education in Merida. This explains their skill in handling *Calypso* under sail. This group is a third of the revolving crews aboard these "Cooperative" owned vessels. The government created this fleet to train young men for a future in the maritime industry to include captains, engineers, cooks and deck hands. The pair are ushered on a tour throughout this immaculately cared for fishing operation. From the wheelhouse of polished hardwood and bronze, to the engine room, as clean and cared for as her galley above. Timbers, frames and planking observed in the engine room, like the anchor gear and winch, are massively overbuilt. The entire vessel, designed to contend with hurricane force winds at sea or on the hook.

The fish hold is next. These fishermen are proud of their catch, grinning broadly when they pull open the heavy door of a standard, stainless-steel walk-in freezer to reveal a wide variety of well cared for seafood. Thousands of pounds of swordfish, grouper, red snapper and dolphin fish (better known to the crew as mahi mahi), cleaned, frozen and stored. The swordfish and marlin hang from hooks, while the smaller fish are sorted and stacked in trays. Several trays carry the largest lobsters the crew has ever seen.

The galley is the final stop in the tour, where the crew is dazzled by a remarkable display before them. *"Tres Pedros"* are portrayed by three mahi mahi. Artfully skewered in a spiral, appearing to chase a school of ballyhoo (deep fried spicy strips), inspired by the fishing story the crew had related of the ballyhoo seining fiasco in Florida. Whole lobsters lay at the base staring at the crew from their warm tortilla pads. Beans, rice, tortillas and ice cold beer round out the feast. The chef, one of the *Pedros*, stands behind his creation to the cheers, salutes and applause of all.

The crew return to *Calypso*, having left the most beautiful, artfully created seafood dinner in a tattered heap of bones and lobster shells; a shambles similar to the red snapper feast the previous evening.

A late morning swim, avoiding food throughout the day, topped by an afternoon swim to the "Three Pete's," the crew are ready for the grand finale. They are helped aboard the high sterns of the trawlers and graciously seated by the captains. The captains, engineers, cooks (chefs!) and deck hands of the vessels are gathered on the back deck, seated around great bowls of cevichi and buckets of iced beer.

The celebration of "Saint Peter" stretches to shore where a parade, winds its way through the village then along the beach, passing under the bows of the *"Tres Pedros."* Following the parade, the crew is called to the galley where they are seated at places of honor before a spectacular presentation; three swordfish heads, with swords crossed at the tips, the centerpiece of the production.

The eyeballs and mouths are tweaked in a comical stare and wry grins. Huge lobsters on their tortilla pads are surrounded by platters of fruit in a most colorful display. Bowls of beans, cevichi, a stack of tortillas and iced beer all within easy reach of each setting. The swords, nearly reaching the ceiling are each adorned with the Mexican flag atop.

The fishermen of the three vessels all squeeze into the galley, and once gathered, fall silent. One of the captains then stands, toasting and wishing safe travels to the crew, followed by a rousing cheer from the crowd. *Calypso's* crew tear up to the warmth, generosity and genuine concern of their friends.

A special effort by the crew of *Calypso* has them on deck at first light. The *"Tres Pedros,"* with main engines fired up, begin wallowing in reverse, squirming their way back off the beach in unison. Once afloat, they steam at full speed past *Calypso* waving and saluting. *Calypso* returns the gestures, saluting, shouting and waving her Mexican flag.

Mexican Customs

◆ver a month has passed since *Calypso* entered Mexico, dropping anchor here in the bay of Isla Mujeres. Life has been so comfortable, it has not occurred to the crew to check with the Mexican Customs authorities. Inquiring ashore, the crew learns they have been anchored right in front of the Customs Office all along.

Embarrassed by their tardiness, nervous as to what reaction they may endure, the crew walk through the doors of the office into an air conditioned room with half a dozen uniformed individuals at their desks.

Cheery *holas* are exchanged, the crew doing their level best to disguise their fear of authority, especially since they may be subject to some discipline.

The crew begin an explanation in two broken languages. They are interrupted by the port captain, pointing to *Calypso*, plainly visible out their front window, "we know you're here" in perfect English. Already jumpy, this stern observation by the port captain does not alleviate their discomfort, rather, the crew becomes increasingly skittish.

Sensing this, the entire office turns to follow the conversation, the room falls silent. With all eyes on them, the port captain says "you have no *mota*," in the form of a suspicious statement.

The crew stiffen, blurting out a *"Si!* No motor! *Solamente velas!"* An empty attempt at mitigation. The other officers begin snickering and exchanging glances, which the crew can not interpret. The port captain presses further, repeating with a furrowed brow "you have no *mota*?"

Still confused in their Spanish, the crew is adamant, repeating, they have no motor! This appears to irritate the officer, while the remaining agents are openly chuckling, now giving their full attention to the conversation.

The port captain turns to his officers, who immediately shush on his cold stare. Turning back to the crew, he repeats again, in a slow, accusing fashion, "you have no *mota*."

At a loss for verbiage, the crew resorts to an animated version of a sailing vessel, with the hands making like a set of sails riding the ocean waves. "No motor. *Nooo macheeena!*"

The port captain responds in kind with his own animated version of the question, saying in a sharp tone, "No!" "*Mota!*" Making motions as though puffing on a spleef; the pair turn pale when terror drains the blood. ("*mota*," a small amount of cannabis).

The officers buckle over trying not to laugh at their bosses theatrics while the crew freezes for an instant before waving and nearly shouting "*no, no no! Solamente velas, no mota!*"

An explosive, bellowing guffaw sends his officers into uncontrollable fits as the port captain loses his composure. The crew now understanding the captain's accusations realize they've been had. They too are also overcome by the contagion of hysterics as they receive this most unusual, entertaining welcome to Mexico, at their expense.

Snowy Egret

Followin' the day of the local fiesta
crew 'n cat're startled from their siesta
A snowy egret flutters in through the hatch
an' for Woody the boatcat an easy catch

On the cabin sole this bird alights
an' Woody's got it in his sights

In an instant that Yankee cat's there
givin' this poor bird a lethal stare

Awakened one early August evening, the crew is startled from their siesta by a commotion in the cabin. Groggily focusing on the disturbance, they find Woody on the cabin sole between them, his nose inches away from a very fragile looking snowy egret.

The late afternoon sun streams through the hatch, shining on this fascinating, spellbinding scene. Woody, rather than pouncing on the intruder, which is his customary action, has stopped short, taking up a classic cat-watch pose, forepaws close together, body at rest. A low, distinct purr fills the cabin. Uncharacteristically, his tail does not twitch.

The egret now pulls one leg up, tucking it away. Its head begins to sway slowly, in a graceful elliptical pattern. Woody continues his stone like watch with a more subdued purr. This delicate, little bird appears unconcerned, standing quietly on one leg with its audience, including the danger posed by a cat, inches away.

With Woody's nose inches away
the bird closes its eyes an' begins to sway
This catbird situation's tense
the crew's watchin' in great suspense

Woody kept cockroaches off the boat
chased away birds wantin' to rest an' float
Now the crew's seein' somethin' strange occurin'
'cause Woody the Yankee cat's a purrin'!?

On one leg, snowy egret's standin' there
the other leg's tucked away somewhere
The little bird's head cocks to one side
the snowy egret stood there an' died

The circular sway of the bird's long neck slows, the head coming to rest on the breast at a very odd, unnatural angle. The eyes close. The crew assumes the egret has fallen asleep when Woody's purr grows louder. He rises slowly, moving forward to the bird. The egret does not respond to his tender neck to neck caress. It does not open its eyes nor put down its leg to steady itself.

Woody backs off, returning to his cat-watch, reducing his purr to a point where it is barely audible. At long last, the crew understands, the snowy egret had come to *Calypso* to die. They feel deeply honored to witness this elegant death.

Of what might have occurred the crew's certain
but somehow, Woody knew this bird was hurtin'
Cause a purrin' cat with no tail twitchin'
for a fight its not itchin'

How Woody was aware
even a guess we would not dare
But somethin' else the crew's not understandin'
how a bird could die an' on one leg still be standin'?!

Yucatan Great Barrier Reef

With hurricane season arrivin' soon
Calypso sets sail under a waxin' moon
Fillin' her sails with a fresh northeast breeze
bowsprit pointin' straight at Belize

An exodus of the sailing vessels anchored in the Bay of Isla Mujeres begins as September looms. The *Southern Scrap* is first to leave the anchorage, about one week ahead of *Calypso*.

Lying in a somewhat protected area between Mexico and Honduras out of the historically predominant paths of hurricanes, the likelihood of encountering one of these fierce storms is lessened dramatically as the land mass falls away considerably.

Calypso sets full sail on a broad reach to the tune of an afternoon twenty knot northeasterly. Ideal conditions for this coastal passage of roughly two hundred fifty miles.

The wind increases to a gusty twenty five knots in the early evening, the mainsail is secured, the crew have an easy time in a boisterous seaway under reefed jib and mizzen. They had expected the northeast trades to settle down on the approach of darkness as has been the pattern the crew had become accustomed to during their time at Isla Mujeres; this night, the trades hold steady.

Puerto Morelos lays off to starboard, the crew opting to drop the pick for the night. A wild night is endured on anchor in the open roadstead. When the wind subsides well before dawn, *Calypso* takes advantage of an early start, getting underway to an easy fifteen knot breeze.

The ruins of Tulum
through jungle growth they're peekin'
Of course Calypso she just continues leakin'
Along this jagged reef we make our way
still pumpin' thirty gallons a day

The wind remains light throughout the morning, picking up in the afternoon. *Calypso* sails the blue water offshore of the reef a safe distance, her evening sight informing the crew they are approaching Tulum. She has made good time south, most likely having caught counter currents during the run. She maintains her compass course which holds her track roughly three miles east of the reef as night falls.

The wind lays down, the surface becomes glassy; the stars, pixie dust on the black rolling hills surrounding the boat. *Calypso* carries full sail into the darkness, holding the compass course on this warm tropical evening and lost in the stars as they sway across the sky. With her gentle roll, an imperceptible change in the swell, or rather, her relation to it, goes unnoticed.

The safe distance east of the reef when darkness fell adds to the shock, when white water explodes just yards directly off her starboard bow. Sheets fly! The helm is put down hard to port. She spins to the southeast, skirting the reef by a narrow margin that seems like inches. The terror lasts just seconds when she bobs to the even swell of deep water, escaping the threat in her signature, nimble fashion.

Twenty degrees are added to the compass course for safe measure. *Calypso* had been tracking steady on her previous course, which was drawn with the final sight of the evening, describing a safe course and distance off the reef. A magnetic disturbance here, the culprit, had drawn her far off course, sending her sailing directly at the reef in the middle of the night.

Wreck of the Southern Scrap

Dawn brings piece of mind to the crew, the reef can be seen breaking a couple miles to the west. The trades having returned with good strength, *Calypso* enjoys the twenty five knot broad reach off her port quarter. She closes with the reef to within a half mile where the crew observes ruins peeking out from the jungle along the coast. Following the reef line, it is apparent the compass is no longer pulling *Calypso* so far off course. The previous night's incident was most definitely an extreme localized disturbance, however, the compass continues to display some added deviation.

Late in the afternoon, a dot of yellow far in the distance catches the eyes of the crew. Possibly the shade of yellow, or the out of place location of the dot, or maybe, the crew simply understands the nature of this coastline, juxtaposed against their image of Kris, bouncing around on his boat. Whatever the clue, the crew knows at once, they are approaching the wreck of the *Southern Scrap*.

For Southern Scrap's well being we have our fears
'cause Cosmic Kris has light years 'tween the ears
Far off in the distance one can just make it out
is the wreck of the Southern Scrap
there's no doubt

Televisions, radios, mix masters 'n clocks,
shopping carts, toilet seats, hub caps 'n socks,

Pots 'n pans, dish drainers 'n bleach,
looks like "Saint Vinnies" crashed on the beach!

Shards of twisted metal
a hank of psychedelic sail it seems
is all that remains of the Southern Scrap
'n Cosmic Kris's sailin' dreams

Approaching the wreck, the crew closes with the reef, hoping for a break where they may pop through and get to the scene. She has been smashed to smithereens on the reef, with much of what she held, and large chunks of her hull washed ashore. A long line of people are carrying items off while others are picking through the wide variety items spread out over about a quarter mile of white sandy beach.

Hopes of finding an opening in the reef as *Calypso* passes the spot where *Southern Scrap* initially struck, fade. When several miles beyond the scene with no way through, the crew is left with great concern for the fate of their friend and lone sailor. His boat, totally destroyed; most likely disaster struck in the middle of the night. *Calypso's* compass continues to show some deviation, not as much as Tulum, however, possibly enough to crash the *Southern Scrap*.

Calypso 'n crew can only sail on
along this rugged coast
An' to Cosmic Kris 'n Southern Scrap
we raise our farewell toast

Spirits are dampened with the haunting vision of *Southern Scrap* spread across the reef and beach . The crew carries this burden, sailing two more days along the reef. With no passage through, they have no way of getting information about their friend.

Risky Passage

Sailing to a subdued northeast breeze with the swell greatly reduced, the crew is eyeing Bahia de la Ascencion. An inviting bay offering excellent protection, with calm waters beyond the reef. From the charts, it is apparent, once inside the barrier, there will be clear sailing among the coral heads deep into the bay.

A break in the reef points the way
from these rollin' blue seas to a quiet bay
Helm hard over sheet'er down tight
gotta' hit that clear spot exactly right

Calypso sails as close to the reef as she dare, the crew searching intently for a hole. The easy seas are not breaking with their usual strong trade winds driven force, leaving many areas clear of breaking water until a larger set moves in, exposing reef too shallow for her to attempt a crossing. The crew spots a likely area where there appears to be numerous small avenues of approach devoid of white water for an extended period of time. They haul Calypso into the wind for a long slow look at the prospective entry points. The main and jib are doused, she lays to under her mizzen for a couple of hours while the crew observes the surf line.

The eyes keep returning to one particular spot, where a possible passage may be attempted. Narrow, but most definitely, the swells do not break much of the time. Only when an extra large set passes under her hull, will a wall of white water appear, closing the opening. Even then, the particular spot in question has a smaller, less violent break. Great patience is exercised here. The crew must choose their moment with precision guesswork. There is no way of knowing the minimum depth she will encounter, the crew only knows, *Calypso's* keel needs just three feet of water to clear the reef.

Another unknown quantity is the distance she must travel across the top of the barrier to reach safe water over clear sand. There is also the possibility of finding even shallower water beyond the initial break line, potentially trapping her atop an inner reef. The charts, marginal as they might be, indicate roughly, good water will be found a short distance beyond the barrier.

The crew settles on the course they will attempt, setting *Calypso's* jib for steerage. This jib and mizzen configuration will allow her to remain agile at the very slow speed the crew intends on approach. In the event the passage must be aborted, she will spin through the eye of the wind to deep water. That is the plan. It is clear, to attempt a downwind gybe would be disastrous.

Calypso moves in, the reef breaking heavily close by to port. Taking the wind on the nose as she approaches the hole, she has clear blue water to starboard. She must simply have enough speed to come through the eye and fall off the wind, should she need to escape. This will only be possible before entering the narrow passage, once committed, there will be no turning back.

The mizzen is sheeted tighter, *Calypso* noses toward the winds' eye slightly, slowing her speed. Her bowsprit is now perpendicular to mid-channel, the crew waits as the set of swells following the "big set" passes under the boat. From their observations, they have chosen the first wave of the third set; when it comes, they make their move.

*Gnarly white water crashin' close by
Calypso makes her perilous try
Three feet of draft is all she carries
but on that reef her bow she buries!*

The mizzen sheet is thrown, the helm put down hard to port. Obediently she swings off the wind to a beam reach, her bowsprit now points straight through the slot. The jib fills sharply with a hard slap, the mizzen is sheeted in, the weather helm assuring positive control. Her stern rises to the following sea, she surges into the gap on the light swell. The wave passes under the hull, the next wave sends her pellmell, crashing into the barrier reef. With their relentless rhythm, the waves roll in, nudging her forward while rolling her awkwardly. The sets are building, becoming increasingly dangerous. Jib and mizzen, tight against the breeze do not produce the power necessary to force *Calypso* forward.

*Of becomin' a shipwreck
the crew has good reason to dread
With visions of Southern Scrap fresh in the head
The wind 'n surge push our little craft
an' we heel Calypso over so she'll carry less draft*

Hastily assessing the situation,the crew opts for raising the mainsail, hoping to reduce draft as well as giving her the full power she requires. Once raised, the mainsail is sheeted tight against the wind, laying her over substantially.

Surge from the building set of seas, now crashing heavily close by, in combination with the increased power from additional canvas has her making progress without steerage.

Careened, grinding her way painfully, inches at a time across the top of the reef, the crew is hanging on to the mast, agonizing, expecting the planking under them to explode when she receives the initial fatal blow of her demolition.

Each swell, being successively larger, no longer breaking either side of *Calypso*, rather, they are breaking all around her, washing the decks, rocking her wildly. One wave of this larger set, lifts *Calypso* high above the reef, spins her, then cruelly drops her broadside to the seas. With a hard roll to seaward the next wave meets the deck head on, slams her, nearly blasting the crew clean off the boat.

*Calm water beckons
destruction threatens
'Cross the barrier reef Calypso crashes her way
into the open arms of Ascencion Bay*

Another wave, less than a hundred yards seaward has *Calypso's* name on it. A formidable crest chews through the gap as it comes barreling toward her. The crew hugs the mizzen mast and each other, bracing for a devastating strike.

She takes the lesser waves, standing in defiance. The crew cannot take their eyes off the monster rolling steadily toward them, and when it comes, hurls *Calypso* thirty yards in a furious display of curling, crashing white water and exposed reef; all its power unleashed, its energy expended in seconds.

The wave passes, leaving her bobbing in a foamy sea. "She's bobbing!" Instantly the crew knows they have been tossed into deep water. When the foam clears, *Calypso* is riding easily over white sand, clear of coral heads. The main and jib are doused and anchor thrown. The crew pumps the water which is a foot or more over the floorboards. When the pump begins sucking air, the floors are ripped up to search for damage; finding none, they return to the deck and take stock.

From their examination of her hull and decks it is apparent, she has come through unscathed. Tears flow freely as the adrenalin wears off. The crew owe a debt of gratitude to *Calypso* for enduring the brutal thrashing to carry them to safety.

Bahia de la Ascension

The terror having passed, the effects of adrenalin leaving the crew giddy with the relief of having survived the fate that had befallen the *Southern Scrap*. They had just had a sampling of how Cosmic Kris was ravaged by breaking seas and the gnashing jaws of the reef.

Comfortable in the knowledge the damage will ultimately be found to be bruises, scrapes and scratches, the crew pulls the pick, sets the jib and begin making their way toward the beach nearby, with an eye on Bahia de la Ascension, still laying several miles to the south. The charts, providing minimal information, will require the crew to sail with a constant lookout for coral heads and smaller reef systems found in patches approaching the Bay proper from *Calypso's* position inside the barrier reef.

Upon entering the bay proper, excellent progress is made in clear water along a white sandy beach, chock-a-block loaded with coconuts. Vigio Chico, a village at the back of the bay is *Calypso's* next destination, where the crew may get news on Kris's well being. They are hopeful there will be information on the wreck a few miles up the coast.

Sailing under jib and mizzen to a steady twenty knots of the trusty northeast trades, *Calypso* makes her way, playing cat and mouse with the numerous obstructions. Her three feet of draft is perfectly suited to this work, winding her way through the shallows leaving a white sandy cloud chased up by the keel, marking her passage.

A surprise awaits Calypso
when she drops anchor at Vigio Chico
A wizened old man in a village of empty huts
an' beaches covered with coconuts!

The anchor is dropped out front of the "village," a disappointing group of half a dozen or so grass huts, appearing from their vantage aboard *Calypso*, to be deserted.

The crew rows ashore in their bright yellow *Rubber Ducky* to explore and find information on the welfare of their friend. There are so many coconuts down, they make the decision to load *Calypso* before leaving the bay. Being professional harvesters, the crew understands a boatload of just about anything is always good for some cash as well as providing trading stock.

Upon entering the village, they find it is deserted. Searching through each of the structures, it appears this is a temporary encampment for coconut harvesters and fishermen. One of these huts contains a truly startling discovery; a lone figure, sitting upright with legs crossed, motionless and stark naked. A wide, nearly toothless grin along with penetrating, bright eyes immediately brings Carlos Castenada's "Don Juan" to mind. Grunts of what sound like subdued laughter is all the crew gets from this very old man. Verbal communication is out of the question, they will learn nothing of Kris here, however they will leave with many questions and conjectures of what they have witnessed.

Setting to work the crew wastes no time
loadin' little Calypso right to the waterline
A boatload of coconuts has the crew giddy
when Calypso sails into Belize City

With the mind numbing numbers of coconuts spread all along the beach, an efficient harvesting operation is set up. *Calypso* is brought close by the beach as is possible, a roughly twenty yard swim. The *Rubber Ducky* is put to work as the tow barge. One crew member aboard receives and stacks coconuts below, keeping the boat on an even keel as the load increases.

The old man is not left out; a coconut is broken open, scooped out and delivered with stale tortillas. Grunts of appreciation, the engaging grin accompanied by sparkling bright eyes, again, set the crew to pondering the possibilities surrounding this curiosity.

Barracuda

The harvest is successful, however, not without incident. While making repeated trips with the heavily laden *Rubber Ducky* from beach to boat, it does not occur to the swimmer, he is towing a giant yellow lure; the violent kicking with bare feet sends signals throughout the bay, attracting unwanted attention.

The coconut harvest is going famously, with the boatload piled on the beach getting smaller with each load ferried out. On one particular trip towing the fully loaded *Rubber Ducky* from the beach a flash of silver catches the eye. Instinctively turning to look back for danger from behind, nothing is seen.

Dropping the eight or ten feet to the bottom to look around, there is a large shape, lurking directly behind the bright yellow raft. Large, but unable to make out due to the distance and silt kicked up.

The shape turns, flashing bright silver again, making its identity clear now. This is a barracuda, a loner, with the girth of a fifty pound king salmon.

No doubt, it is attracted by the bright color of the *Rubber Ducky*. Back and forth in the shallow murk, the shape stalks. Observing the critter, the diver, holding his breath, begins starving for air. Nothing to do but shoot up, take a breath and get right back to the bottom. Splashing around on the surface one is extremely vulnerable to attack.

One breath along with a scream of terror is all there is time for, when the silver flash of silver is seen close by. Back to the bottom, towing with one hand while clawing the sand with the other. Kicking hard serves only to increase the danger, as now, the bare feet become the central attention of this fast moving, unpredictable creature. The barracuda is now focused on bare feet. This animal, with the magnified vision of the face mask, appears every bit as large as the diver, its half open jaw baring wicked rows of sharp teeth and fangs. Lightning quick, it darts at fluttering bare feet.

The move for air, the scream, is repeated charging right back to the bottom for "safety." The beast moving in and out of the tunnel vision of the mask has one on the edge of raw panic.

Another bolt to the surface, a scream and right back to the

bottom. More aggressive moves by the barracuda freezes the diver to the bottom, following every move as well as making direct eye contact. Not thinking clearly under the duress, towing the *Rubber Ducky*, the initial attractor, continues, rather than letting go to distract the animal and escape.

The chase continues in this manner, with screams at the surface followed by a return to the bottom, clawing and kicking toward *Calypso*. On deck, the crew stands helpless. The relative safety under the boat is at long last achieved. The diver grabs the bobstay, moving quickly up to the deck, clear of danger.

The *Rubber Ducky* is unloaded, the anchor pulled with *Calypso* heading for open water, leaving a mound of coconuts on the beach. This harvest is over.

The crew sails out the wide open mouth of Bahia de la Ascencion, embarrassed by the fact they could have entered the Bay just as easily if they had only sailed another night down the coast, rather than attempting to cross the reef through a hole perceived from seaward.

Three days of light winds sailing offshore, *Calypso* passes east of Ambergris Caye where she finally drops the pick in a quiet bay on the western side of Caye Caulker, Belize.

Chapter 6

BELIZE
Summer 1980

Belize Customs

The crew has the anchor up at first light. They had gone ashore the previous afternoon, hoping for information about Kris and the wreck of the *Southern Scrap*, however, the residents are isolated, having heard no news of either Kris or the wreck.

The crew discovers grand sailing behind the barrier reef. The northeast trades have commerce bustling with Belizean sloops working the coast; sleek vessels carrying a tremendous amount of canvas fore and aft. *Calypso's* three foot draft again serves her well in her ability to navigate these waters. Many of the commercial sailing craft observed appear to carry even less draft.

Calypso covers the thirty miles to Belize City in short order, running wing and wing with main and jib, the winds holding steady this day.

The pair tie up to the Belize City dock, making a beeline for the Customs Office. They certainly do not want a repeat of the discomfort they endured in Mexico, even though it was all in good fun, at their expense.

The office is spotless and air conditioned, the occupants impeccably dressed. The crew immediately feeling uncomfortable in their clothes made of discarded cotton sail cloth, still grimy from the coconut harvest.

The customs officer, an imposing black fellow at about six two or better, rises from his desk with no attempt to hide his disdain for the two individuals before him, further adding to their discomfort.

This encounter has an entirely different air about it than their Mexico experience.

Havin' just arrived from 'ol Mexico
Mr. Customs Man sneers "you have coco!"
To which we reply with great sincerity"
We've loaded our boat for free!"

The first query is fired at the crew as an accusation, rather than a question. "You have coco!" His English, wrapped in a thick Caribbean lilt. To which the crew, not understanding nor hiding their excitement over the harvest respond in unison "Yes!" There came an immediate, unexpected response.

A glowering customs officer towering over these two urchins, booms out the question again, "YOU HAVE COCO!" causing the office to fall silent, all eyes turning on the pair.

Again, the crew cannot contain their excitement repeating "YES!" "We have a boatload, MAYBE A TON!" Now the gentleman is furious! Accusing the two of "toying" with him.

Mr. Customs Man appears irritated at our glee
an' becomes very angry with me!
"We have about a ton to be realistic"
an' with that Mr. Customs' man goes ballistic!

This poor sailor can no longer endure
intimidation from Mr. Officer

"Come to Calypso 'n see for yourself"
an' behold!
A load of coconuts top shelf!

The crew, befuddled by this exchange politely ask the officer to join them at the boat and have a look for himself. They could not imagine anything but that they had possibly run afoul of customs by importing Mexican coconuts.

On arrival, the officer is caught off balance, staring blankly at little *Calypso* so heavily laden, the crew could not get below, rather, they had been living on deck to make room for the load.

Calypso's coco comes from palm tree
it's very plain to see
At the root of this hubbub?
Mr. Customs Man's coco
comes from a shrub!

The officer is muttering about "people like you coming to Belize" when one of the crew jumps aboard and begins furiously pumping the boat. Calypso joins in the improvisational performance by spewing gallons and gallons of the Caribbean Sea into the Belize River. The second sailor begins pleading with the officer, inserting complimentary references to the beautiful Belizean sailing fleet. The story went something about our little boat is sinking, desperate for repair and we are so far from home. "How will we ever get to Alaska in this condition, we will be lucky to make it to Honduras yadayadayada." Altogether, a wonderful, nearly tear jerking farce.

"Wooden sailin' vessels in Belize abound
are there any boatyards around?
Poor Calypso's leakin' in a bad way
an' we're pumpin' a hundred gallons a day"

Mr. Customs' man fell back 'n laughed
pointin' at our little vessel "you must be daft!
Sailin' to Alaska in a sinkin' boat?
go see Jones he'll keep you afloat!"

Our Customs officer, softening with the realization he had not just nabbed a couple of criminals with a boatload of cocaine, now breaks out in a wide toothy grin, almost shouting "going to Alaska in that!?"

Pointing, shaking his head, finally unable to contain himself any longer bursts out in uncontrollable belly laughter, along with the crowd which has gathered, a delightful uproar ensues.

Collecting himself after a bit, he begins boasting how Belizean boatyards are very good. He recommends a yard owned by a Mister

Jones, easily recognized as there will be many dogs there. The fellow is now genuinely concerned for our welfare assuring the crew the shipwrights will make our boat safe again. With that, *Calypso* is welcomed to Belize.

Intimidation's set aside now
Calypso 'n crew receive a welcomin' bow
with this nutty issue resolved
The conversation now evolved

"Through that bridge 'n take a couple jogs
the yard's on your portside the one with all the dogs!"
Up Haulover Creek we make our deal with Jones
in his yard full of boats' n their broken bones

Mr. Jones's Boatyard

C*alypso* jogs before a bridge until it opens, the wind pushing her through easily. A stiff onshore breeze blowing upstream has her under jib and mizzen winding her way deep into the city on the slow moving waters of Haulover Creek.

The portside shoreline is favored as the officer had directed. Many boatyards and shanties, tightly packed, crowd the river on both sides. Radio Belize blares Pink Floyd's "Another Brick in the Wall," hitting the crew in stereo from both banks.

Calypso approaches a boatyard, raising a ruckus with a pack of dogs locked in a large cage. They are in a frenzy at her approach, running amuck within their enclosure. Barking, snarling, baring fangs and growling an extremely fierce welcome. This, no doubt, is Jones's Boatyard.

Nosing *Calypso* to the dock, the crew ties up. Mr. Jones, a graying, outgoing fellow is there to greet the crew introducing himself and his lead shipwright, "Poppy," a wiry young fellow of whom Mr. Jones speaks very highly.

The yard is typical and familiar. A conglomeration of boats of every persuasion, in various states of disrepair and neglect. Several are sporting new planking and rebuilt, unpainted topsides. At a glance, all the work is very professional.

A shop with mounds of sawdust piled around a shaded enclosure, with a large, very old bandsaw, is the centerpiece of Jones's Boatyard. There is a full compliment of woodworking power and hand tools, notably, many are vintage and well cared for.

---

*A turnstile haulout with locals lendin' a hand
cranks Calypso from the water onto dry land
Lead shipwright's "Poppy" an' he goes after the rot
has a crew rippin' 'n tearin' on the spot*

Poppy and a helper crawl all over *Calypso's* decks, then go below, tossing coconuts, tearing up floorboards, and generally looking her over, end to end.

When the inspection is completed, Poppy reports his findings to Mr. Jones.

The bulwark rails will be removed due to extensive rot at the frame tops and replaced with toe rails. The covering boards having suffered rot as well, will be replaced. Mahogany will be used for these repairs. The frames are in good condition and once their tops are cutoff at the deck, this will be sufficient. Some refastening of the planking is to be expected and of course, the garboards, at long last, properly corked. That in itself is a great relief to a crew who have pumped so many thousands of gallons of water out of this boat.

Mr. Jones is fine with the crew living aboard while the work progresses. He warns the crew to be on board and remain there after dark, as when night comes, the dogs are let loose, free to roam the entire yard.

The following morning a crew from the nearby watering hole arrive and take their place at an old wooden turnstile. Poppy oversees a crew of younger boys as they pull the cradle down its greased wooden tracks, then position *Calypso* for the haul-out. A wave to the crew at the turnstile has the men bending to the work, *Calypso* makes slow, steady progress into the yard. Once high on dry land she is jacked up and blocked, the trolley is then taken away.

Away with the bulwarks reef out the seams
scrapin' 'n paintin' this boat of our dreams

Two thousand miles has poor Calypso ailin'
but when Poppy's done we're no longer bailin'!

Mom's Cafe

With *Calypso* safely tucked in, the crew make their way to the city center. Coming upon a cafe near the open air market, they discover it is a gathering place for travelers to Belize.

Asking folks for news of their friend and the wreck, proves futile. There is a large bulletin board plastered with notes where they find a possible clue to their search. A note had been left several days earlier for a person by the name of Nadya. Most notably, it was signed by a person, Kris, who would be here each morning at ten o'clock.

They will be at "Mom's Cafe" early the next day, fairly certain Kris will be there. Returning to the yard, well before dark, they find the work has commenced and *Calypso's* bulwark rails are already gone.

As Mr. Jones had said, the dogs were turned loose at dark when the boatyard is secured. The scampering, growling and barking go on throughout the night. The dogs are returned to their kennel as the sun is rising.

Soon the sounds of wood being sanded, an adze chopping away on a timber, chips flying, the smell of coffee heavy in the air; all the signs work in the yard has begun. *Calypso* gets her share of attention, with Poppy and Mr. Jones discussing and agreeing on the course of repairs.

Poppy gets a crew of youngsters working at scraping the hull, while he takes his apprentice in tow. Together, they begin ripping the covering boards off, exposing the framing which indeed, look fine below deck level.

Calypso's crew takes this opportunity, with the dogs safely locked up, and the noise level rising in the yard, as well as on the boat, to head for "Moms" and continue their search for Kris.

"I hear breakfast noises! Do I hear breakfast noises people?!" The familiar cry for food from their friend, alerts the crew to his presence in the cafe. An emotional reunion ensues when Kris spots the crew waving, calling out his name. The crew briefly describes the scene they had come upon. Kris, in his usual comic, light-hearted character, fills in the blanks of what happened.

It is not surprising to hear the *Southern Scrap* had crashed in the middle of the night while sailing to a bogus compass course. Kris had sailed headlong into the reef, striking it with a four foot sea running, dashing her to pieces in short order.

He was able to abandon ship and swim to the beach; when morning came, he woke to the pain of deep coral cuts and jellyfish stings on bare arms and legs. Surveying the scene; a large chunk of yellow hull still being battered atop the reef where it struck, flotsam covering a wide area and pushed up high on the beach as well. Broken, for the moment, he walked away with only the shoes on his feet and the still damp clothing he was wearing when he lost his boat.

He is now here in Belize City, waiting for the arrival of his fiancé, Nadya. She will be arriving from Australia and their plan is to make a home somewhere in Belize where their baby will be born.

The crew returns to Jones's boatyard with a light step to find a fellow waiting for them. He introduces himself as a sail maker, then presses the crew until they cave and order a number one cotton genoa. He had seen *Calypso* sail into town and convinces the crew his genoa will be an excellent addition to her present compliment.

Cayuka

Having tapped their reserve savings in Washington for the repair work, this purchase will further drain what is left. The U.S. dollar is strong in Belize, resulting in the costs of repair and new sail combined, still falls within their budget.

Needing a proper replacement for the *Rinky Dink*, they purchase a "cayuka" for one hundred dollars with the *Rubber Ducky* tossed into the deal. These locally hand hewn boats are the predominant paddling boat in Belize. This new tender will be easy towing for *Calypso*. Not the perfect dinghy, however a great improvement over the *Rubber Ducky*, or so it appears. A remnant of sail cloth from the new genoa, or "genny," is used to make a sail with a low sprit rig; which looked very good, but without a dagger board, it is limited to downwind running. *Calypso* has been in the yard about three weeks, with the work moving apace when the crew are treated to a delightful surprise. The usual sounds wake them as the yard goes into high gear. There is a new sound this morning, that of a fist pounding on the hull and the familiar cry "I hear breakfast noises! Do I hear breakfast noises people?!"

Kris has arrived to introduce a very pregnant Nadya, beg for food and a place to sleep. The crew welcomes their guests aboard, making extra sleeping accommodations on deck. For the next week, the foursome retreat to *Calypso* before dark, making meals, sharing stories and dreams.

Together, they pour over charts, Kris and Nadya are taken by a village to the south, mostly for the name "Placencia;" translated as Pt. Pleasant or "Pleasant Place" from the original naming by the Spanish. With their decision made, the two take their leave, heading by bus for Dangriga. There they will seek water transportation, as road transportation to Placencia is questionable.

Launching

After nearly six weeks in the yard, *Calypso* is now refastened and corked with oakum and cotton in traditional fashion. Particular attention having been paid to the garboard seams, where they flow into the transom. This has been the major source of *Calypso's* elusive leak.

A putty crew is now brought in to seal the corking and prepare

the hull for painting. This crew is made up of a group of boys ranging in age from about five to eight or nine, working under the watchful eyes of Mr. Jones, Poppy and his apprentice.

Hard workers all, their attention to detail literally astonishes *Calypso's* crew. When the time comes for painting the hull, the crew opts for a bright yellow, influenced by the color schemes of many vessels they have seen in the Caribbean. The work completed, *Calypso* is cradled and eased down the ways until she floats free. The crew says their goodbyes to

Mr. Jones, Poppy and all of the helpers. *Calypso* is taken in tow down Haulover Creek as the wind is much too strong to negotiate the bridge opening. Once through and tied up to the city dock for final provisioning, she is at long last, ready to continue her journey.

New Life for Woody

*On what goes through a cat's mind
this sailor would have normally not opined
But when Calypso cut loose from the dock
we suffer a bit of a shock*

Full sail is set while still tied to the dock. The lines come off the cleats, the wind whisking her away as soon as they are loosed. At the instant the spring line is let go, Woody leaps.

With a city full of cats half his size and rats nearly as big as himself, running openly among the pilings and rip-rap, its no wonder this hardy cat jumps ship. The crew makes no attempt to come about, rather, they surmise Woody has it figured out. Eighty degree weather with an abundance of rats and cats to enjoy added to the fact, Woody, the Yankee boatcat, could very well be the largest cat in Belize City.

Sailing Belize

*With Calypso rebuilt 'n no water comin' in
the next leg of this journey can now begin
A great opportunity to give her new sail a try
we let that number one genny fly!*

*The Trade Winds belly that big sail out
an' Calypso now proves she's very stout*

This oversize cotton balloon we've had built
carries Calypso full tilt!

We say goodbye to the city of Belize
Calypso's sails fill with a freshenin' breeze
On the outer cays we spend our days
explorin', snorkelin' 'n anchorin' in small bays

Belize is a small country, less than two hundred miles in length. Sailing the shallow waters with great fishing and diving wherever the anchor is dropped make for a return to the casual life enjoyed at Isla Mujeres.

No longer dealing with the rigors of traveling long distances non-stop, the crew takes the opportunity to make their way slowly in a zig-zag fashion, covering just a few miles a day. Placencia, for a visit with Kris and Nadya is the only planned stop on the chart.

The crew has discovered the new sail to be extremely versatile. Light winds have *Calypso* running wing and wing with mainsail and genny. As the wind increases on the stern, the main is doused in favor of running with jib and genny. Off the wind, the genny combined with the mizzen is a comfortable, strong combination. The observations the sail maker had made prove accurate to the delight of the crew. Sailing the trades in shallow waters proves exhilarating, a sharp look out must be kept for lone coral heads and small reef systems along the way. These systems, dotting the sand provide the crew with their most favored food as well; *langostinos* and conchs are abundant in and around these reefy patches.

Live Boating

Lackadaisical day sailing is not without exciting moments. One such moment occurring during a routine afternoon snorkel hunt is a particularly painful example. When conditions are perfect, especially when in an area of clear sand with a sparse scattering of coral heads and reef patches, a technique known as live boating involves jumping over the side with a towline while the boat is under sail.

With shallow water 'n light winds prevailin'
I'd do a little scoutin' while Pat does the sailin'
Clingin' to the tow rope watchin' coral heads pass by
a purple sail catches the eye

Then another 'n a 'nother 'n a 'nother
an'a 'nother 'n a 'nother an' O' brother!
Now there's a thousand or more
the sails of the Portugese-Man-O-War!

The diver is towed on a long line behind the vessel in about fifteen feet of water, shallow enough to drop to the bottom without letting loose.

When a conch is spotted making its way across the sand, the diver simply drops down, scoops it up and bags it, staying as long as the lungs hold. A conch in the bag, the remaining bottom time is used looking in holes for langostinos, which the diver must be ready to reach in and grab as he passes by.

This particular hunt begins routinely, flopping over the side, tow line in hand. The boat speed reduced to one knot, more or less, under jib and mizzen in a light breeze.

After splashing in, the eyes focus quickly on the sand spotting the telltale groove carved by a traveling conch. Swinging wide, following the trail, the conch is spotted and bagged. Before surfacing from the initial descent, the remaining air is now used to hunt langostinos. Peeling off neatly toward a dark hole where the edge of the reef meets clear sand he spots his prey, however, starving for air, fails to reach the langostinos and bolts for the surface.

Resting, hyperventilating, the first dive always takes more energy than the successive dives until exhaustion begins settling in. Lungs fill to their maximum capacity, then shoot to the bottom under power of the tow.

One glides along, passing by several conchs, in favor of using the bottom time to gather a few *langostinos*. A reef is spotted when it is just a blurry dark shape in the distance. On approach the reef comes into focus, two langostinos can be seen ahead, sitting at the edge of their hole. The diver lays motionless while being towed, they never see it coming, the hand reaches out, scooping the pair into the bag. To reach the surface, the diver angles away from the reef, returning to a course carrying him over bare sand. On surfacing, he is startled by a purple sail, very close to his head. Quickly kicking away, avoiding contact, he looks around for more of the purple devils, who are often found swarmed up by wind and current. A horrifying sight! Purple sails, thousands! A blood curdling scream alerts Pat at the helm, also uses whatever air is in the lungs. Gasping a breath, maybe two, then taking the tow back to the bottom, sustaining multiple lashes from the critters before clearing most of them at eight or ten feet.

Tentacles hangin' down 'n stingin'
this poor sailor starts a singin'
Stop the boat m'dear
an' get me outa' here!

The tow line pulls to starboard, *Calypso* having made a turn presumably toward clear water upwind. The diver hugs the bottom as long as possible, gliding just under the reach of the tentacles, mostly.

Starving for air, a dash through the tentacles is the only way to the surface for a few quick gasps, not wasting oxygen on a scream, even though the flesh is on fire. The strands lash burning skin on the return to the relative safety of the bottom. They are hardly felt now above the pain already inflicted. Another pair of *langostinos* goes into the bag, then a second conch. At least the crew will eat well after this ordeal.

The line goes slack as *Calypso* swings into irons. Hand over hand up the line while kicking hard makes the trip through the tentacles quick. At *Calypso's* side, the catch is tossed on deck then a dash to the bobstay has the severely wounded diver back aboard.

Coconut milk and oil soothes the pain of the stingers. Open wounds caused by banging into coral while avoiding tentacles are cleaned. Some deep lacerations had debris needing plucked out as well.

The trade winds have resumed, arriving with a freshening breeze, building a respectable two foot running sea with a biting little chop. A decision is made to sail the last fifty or so miles to Placencia where the crew hopes they will meet up with Kris and Nadya.

Placencia

Calypso is sailing at hull speed, dead downwind under jib and genny when a major deficiency in the cayuka reveals itself. It is faster than *Calypso*!

A fast moving log with a sharpened pointy end being hurled forward by a wave, passes by the helmsman, stalls, then falls back on the slack towline. When the tow line comes taught it jerks it violently back and the cayuka begins another deadly run at her transom.

Boat and log now begin a game of cat and mouse. *Calypso* swerving first to port, then to starboard with each successive charge of the battering ram. Additional line added to the tow solves the issue for the immediate run to Placencia where the crew will search for an alternative.

Dropping the pick, Placencia presents an idyllic tropical scene. The village is mostly hidden in the jungle and the few visible structures are palapas dotting the beach on stilts.

Kris is clambering down the stairs from a beach front palapa, excitedly shouting an unintelligible welcome. Nadya, appears on the veranda waving the crew ashore.

There are no vehicles, only soft dirt foot paths. Quiet, for the exception of the trade winds rustling the palms. Kris and Nadya have indeed found the perfect environment to start their family. Nadya is looking very pregnant and comfortable in their neatly appointed home above the beach; a fresh breeze off the water is cool and bug free in their lofty abode.

Several days are spent enjoying the company of our friends while making preparations to sail for Honduras. The weather is holding fine however, September is fast approaching. A line from a little ditty describing hurricane timing goes "September remember, October its over" has been on the lips of the crew lately. This refrain having taken root with Cabo Gracias a Dios nearly four hundred miles east.

The crew feels they are in position to make it past this formidable Cape. The Bay Isles of Honduras are one third the way, perfectly located to make final preparations and gain the local knowledge needed to round the Cape.

Along with its most intimidating name, the charts corroborate the dangers, showing a maze of banks, cays and reefs extending hundreds of square miles around the Cape. The reefs and banks extend all the way to Jamaica. If the charts of the Cape are not enough to cause concern, the "Sailing Directions" lays it out in no uncertain terms. The Cape was reported in 1969, and again in1973, to lie about 2 miles E of its charted position.

Clearly, charts must be used as a general guide, rather than a precision replication of the undersea terrain. The charts also continue to show approximate locations of a mind numbing number of wrecks from Cabo Catoche, Mexico to Panama. The crew can only imagine the horrors that must have occurred here during the time of the Spanish galleons to have earned the title "Cabo Gracias a Dios." ("Cape thank the Lord").

Ashore in Placencia, the crew locates a second "Rubber Ducky," to replace the cayuka, which Kris and Nadya are delighted to receive as *Calypso's* departing gift. The Rubber Ducky is handy aboard *Calypso* as it stows below rather than towed; one less thing to worry about during long passages on open water. This being a sketchy time of year for travel by boat, the crew must say their goodbyes. Taking leave of Placencia, they plot a course for Puerto Cortes, Honduras. This is a "Port of Entry," a mere fifty miles distant.

Calypso makes the harbor mouth in ten hours under her new genny and mizzen combination. A respectable passage marred by an opposing current and a sultry dead calm she sailed into on entering the bay. The remaining four miles requires fifteen hours of tedious all night sailing, before tying up at the customs dock.

Honduras is under military rule. The crew receives a stern, cold reception. Uncomfortable in this environment, they waste no time stopping by the market for a few items unavailable in Placencia. The following morning, *Calypso* has the anchor up at first light. The adverse current encountered the previous day prevailing, whisks her out to sea, even though wind is slight to nonexistent.

Chapter 7

HONDURAS

September 1980

Laguna Tinto

Drifting off Puerto Cortes all morning, the afternoon trades pick up and to *Calypso's* delight she has good wind through the night. The following morning the crew is attracted to a neat little cove, tucked behind Punta Sal.

Laguna Tinto, "idyllic tropical paradise" is noted in the log, the impression after only a few hours with the anchor down. Lush jungle bordered by a white sandy beach. A tight little anchorage, a few fishermen mending gear on the beach while monkeys scream unseen in the trees. As has been the case, for the exception of the "dog eat dog" existence in Florida, local people continue to be friendly and generous.

The fishermen paddle out in a cayuka with gifts of fish, plantains, pears, mangoes and *mammies*. Three days of diving and relaxing, sadly, must come to a close, being smack in the middle of hurricane season.

Laguna Tinto may be idyllic, however, it may or may not be good in severe weather. Wind direction is all important, This wonderful anchorage could look much different with a hurricane tracking close by, before making the usual turn to the north with the prevailing currents.

Full sail is set at first light, the crew waving goodbye to their friends who are beginning their day as well. Clearing Punta Sal, the wind is fresh from the north. The mainsail is doused in favor of genny and mizzen. This wonderful combination is perfectly balanced and has *Calypso* zipping along at hull speed.

The Islands of Honduras're soon off our bow
an' navigation becomes very exactin' now
Straight ahead a nest of coral reefs lay
directly in the path to Turtle Bay

Isla Utila

Isla Utila is sighted. The crew fixes *Calypso's* position, taking note of the dangers close by the tiny island. From close observation of the charts, it is clear they will see a breaking reef to port on approach. The southwest side of Utila is a wide area of danger, indicated by both the charts and "Sailing Directions." A long finger of reef is also indicated off the northwest side of the Island. From this information, it is clear, Calypso must pass well south of the Island before turning north into a protective harbor labeled "East Bay" which the fishermen at Laguna Tinto had referred to as "Turtle Bay."

Strong winds push Calypso along
when it becomes clear she's gone very wrong!
Escape to seaward's blocked by a reef
any moment now Calypso'll come to grief

The passage has gone well, the reef is sighted to the northeast, right were it is expected. *Calypso* maintains her course, the crew comfortable they will be clear of the dangers with their anchor down before dark. A shout of terror comes out of nowhere. "Coral heads!"

*Shorten sail to jib 'n mizzen
to deal with this danger which has arisen
Jump to the bowsprit lead line in hand
gotta' keep Calypso over bare patches of sand*

The helm is put down to port, the genny doused, replaced by the jib. A sharp lookout is stationed at the bow, lead line in hand. Utila grows closer, *Calypso* is spilling most of the wind off her sails to keep her speed down. A tedious maneuvering ensues, dodging patches of reef and lone brain corals standing just below the surface. She has sailed directly into the middle of the reef nest, southwest of the Island.

Every trick in the play book is used to work her out of this treacherous situation. Fortunately the outer reef has broken the swell, the waters are calm and visibility is excellent from the bow. Another scream has *Calypso* whipping a turn to windward, the anchor splashes, the jib drops, she swings to the wind; the crew takes stock. *Calypso* has once more avoided crashing headlong into solid reef. From this dead stop, the crew has time to survey the surroundings, The mast is scaled half way for a better look at a trail of white sand appearing to wind its way around to the lee side of a small caye, bordering the much larger island of Utila.

Trapped

*For the bottom keepin' a steady gaze
workin' the boat through this deadly maze
Into the lee of Isla Utila Calypso threads her way
findin' herself trapped in a dead end bay*

The decision to follow the trail, for better or worse, is made. Jib and mizzen are hoisted along with the anchor, *Calypso* swings off the wind to a beam reach on the port side. The wide swath of sandy trail, quickly narrows, minutes later it takes a sharp turn to starboard, forcing her into a hard gybe, then another gybe when the trail turns again back toward the caye. *Calypso* shows off her nimble maneuvers with an obedient grace.

The crew marvels at her ability to thread her way through the labyrinth. After a mind numbing number of quick evasive tacks, she breaks free of the nest, finding a comfortable anchorage in the lee of the caye. The sun sets on *Calypso* with the crew in the water for a refreshing snorkel before retiring.

The following morning the crew intends to make their way around to Isla Utila. According to charts, this small caye, with a few dwellings and cayukas on the beach is connected by mangroves to the main Island.

Calypso's anchorage proves to be double edged. The snorkeling is excellent, there is an abundance of the crews favorite food, *langostinos* as well as relief from strong trade winds, which have been reduced to a comfortable breeze in the lee of the caye.

The downside of the anchorage appears, at present, there is no way out. It is out of the question to sail back the way she's come, the crew spends hours in the water every day. searching for a path through to the main Island. All the suspicious sandy trails, deep enough to carry *Calypso* come to naught. After these few wonderfully comfortable days, finding only dead ends, it is clear, *Calypso* is trapped.

This anchorage is so comfortable, the crew is in no great hurry to resolve the situation. This spot rivals Laguna Tinto, the wonderful screaming of the monkeys being the only missing element. Like Laguna Tinto also, the folks on the beach arrive in a cayuka with gifts of fruit and fish.

Several days're spent snorkelin' about
but alas for Calypso there's no way out
A cayuka from the island now comes into sight
these friendly Islanders're aware of our plight

The conversation, upon meeting our new friends winds around to how the crew had mistakenly found themselves in the middle of the reef and the tricky sailing required to reach the protection of the caye.

The fishermen had assumed the crew was stuck for a way through the reef to East Bay, or as they refer to it, "Turtle Bay." They would be returning to Utila town the next morning and offered a tow, which the crew are delighted to accept.

A tow through the maze 'n shallows we received
an' for this local knowledge we're much relieved
Soon we have our anchor down
right out front of Utila town

ypical of fishermen, first light sees activity on the beach, a cayuka with an outboard engine mounted on the stern is pushed off into the water. A couple fellows hop in, putt out to *Calypso*, toss a tow line and begin motoring slowly toward what appears to be an impassable reef.

The crew of *Calypso* standing on deck can see no way through, there is not even a white sand trail to follow. Their two companions, standing casually in their cayuka, seem unconcerned as they pass over solid reef.

Calypso glides over top of the reef, touching nothing. The crew holds their breath at first, the optics causing the reef to appear less than *Calypso's* three feet of draft. Gradually, with no bumping, they become more comfortable while she is under tow.

As fishermen themselves, they understand the value of local knowledge, having acquired the same awareness of the nuances of areas they work back in the Northwest and Alaska. This skill, or acute awareness of the nature of their surroundings, a necessity of the fishermen's craft, is universal.

Calypso passes over the last of the reef where again there is clear sand below the boat. The cayuka now makes a sharp turn to starboard, toward a

solid green wall of tangled mangrove. The wall appears solid, however a second sharp turn to starboard followed by yet another turn to port reveals a hidden path to clear water a few hundred yards ahead. The crew notes the similarity to "Hole in the Wall" in Alaska, where one may drive right up to the shore before the passage is discerned.

The trail is clear for the mast as well as being of adequate depth. *Calypso's* shallow draft is making this all possible. Soon after passing the last of the mangrove, our friends cut loose the tow and signal the crew to drop the pick.

Calypso finds herself anchored in a wide bay, out front of a small village. Their friends wave goodbye, shouting something nearly unintelligible and cryptic, yet unmistakably about a "bucket of blood."

"Bucket of Blood"

The "Bucket of Blood's" the local hang out
reggae 'n beer's what it's all about
The place gets packed 'n folks start dancin'
From under the Wurlitzer
coconut crabs come a'prancin'!

On their arrival ashore, the crew learns the "Bucket of Blood" is a pub, the local gathering place. Familiar soft dirt paths, cool on bare feet like those in Placencia, lead up a hill into a lush jungle.

Off to the side of this winding path a short distance above the village, the crew comes upon a ramshackle cabin with folks laughing and milling about.

The "Bucket of Blood" is a lively, very funky, beer drinking establishment. The patrons spill out onto the deck and surrounding grounds. The crew melt into this friendly scene.

Reggae music is cranked up when "Bob Marley and the Wailers" come on with their popular song, "Jammin." They are treated to a surprising curiosity when the dance floor fills up with folks rocking hard to the tune.

Several coconut crabs, giants of the crab world, appear from under the Wurlitzer. They join the rocking crowd on the dance floor. Fully aware of what is happening and without any apparent fear, the critters run around among the pounding feet. The crew can only surmise, these crabs love dancing to Bob Marley, since they retreated to their home under the Wurlitzer when the next artist came on.

Three days are spent making preparations for the next leg of the journey, which will take them around Cabo Gracias a Dios. There is information aplenty from the locals on what to expect in rounding the Cape. Isla Guanaja, the easternmost island of these "Bay Isles," will be the departure point for the two hundred mile passage to the Cape. At *Calypso's* three knot average, this is roughly a one hundred hour sail. On deck the pair are going over the charts of this offshore island chain. The crews decision to sail for Roatan, then hop to Guanaja is interrupted by an urgent radio announcement.

Hurricane Hermine

*Over the shortwave radio
comes scary news for Calypso
Destructive wind bearin' down today
an' Isla Utila's standin' right in the way*

Hurricane Hermine is on a rampage, with the Bay Islands directly in her path. Turtle Bay is wide open on its south side, with fetch all the way to the mainland. Surveying the possibilities, it is obvious there are no good places to anchor *Calypso* to prepare her for a force twelve destructive storm.

Calypso is repositioned with an eye to potential wind direction. A spot across the bay is selected where she may gain a bit of protection.

Both anchors are set at approximately a forty five degree angle to the expected wind direction. With so little protection, the crew has agreed to abandon ship and seek safety ashore. *Calypso* must fend for herself. Her survival unlikely, an abrupt, heartbreaking end to the journey.

Encumbered with a sadness conjured up by thoughts of what *Calypso* will be left to endure, the crew begins gathering a few treasured items and necessities. They are already feeling a deep sense of loss for their precious little boat, which has so faithfully looked after their well being all these many miles.

The Islanders have great concern
for Calypso has nowhere to turn
Hurricane Hermine's comin' her way
an' she's anchored in an open roadstead bay

Their melancholy is shattered by the sound of an outboard motor screaming at high RPM. A cayuka is racing toward *Calypso*, the occupants waving and shouting noiselessly over the high pitched whine of their motor.

"You cannot stay here, hurricane coming!" is heard as they draw close, waving their tow line. The crew hops to the anchors, immediately relieved that once again, these good people with their skills will save the day.

Calypso is taken in tow, the cayuka making for the mangrove wall, where once more, no entrance can be made out. A turn is made into a channel which abruptly comes to a dead end, The sleek cayuka cuts the power, gliding silently into thick mangrove without difficulty. *Calypso*, on the other hand, crashes clumsily into the thicket, coming to a dead stop in its clutches.

Our friends tie off their cayuka, then start pulling the tow line, while the crew works on deck hauling *Calypso* hand over hand, into the mangrove.

*Again local knowledge plays a major role
an' from another cayuka Calypso welcomes a tow
Deep into the mangrove swamp she's tucked away
safe from the monster approachin' Turtle Bay*

*Lashed Calypso to the mangroves
from every direction
The villagers said
"this'll give you the best protection!"
With limbs 'n roots we toiled 'n wrestled
now in the arms of Utila we're nestled*

Calypso's heavy anchor is wrapped with a life preserver for flotation then towed out with adequate rode by hand. The flotation is removed, the anchor drops and the diver chases it to the bottom. The water so murky, he must keep a hand on the line to find the anchor. Once there it is worked into the heavy tangle of roots and mud. Back on the surface the folks are yelling for the diver to get out of the water "very dangerous man eaters in there!" Preparations for the hurricane takes precedence over crocodiles, real or imagined. A second anchor is prepared and set, before exiting the water.

Every available line is put to use, lashing *Calypso* from all points on deck to the gnarly tangle surrounding her. The villagers arrive with more boats; several runabouts and cayukas. The fleet is lashed until all are secured, when they take their leave, wishing the crew well.

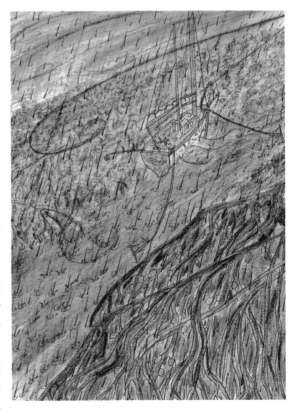

Calypso will now ride out the hurricane in the traditional way of the Islanders. They are prepared, albeit an edgy fright niggles at the back of the minds of the pair in their new-found, unfamiliar surroundings.

Having witnessed the birth and growth to maturity of mini-storms in the Gulf of Mexico, particularly to the "anvil" or leading edge at the base of the newborn storm, images are conjured of what must be bearing down on them. With darkness, comes the wind. A rustling of the mangroves along with an equally slight rocking of the hull is the first indication a change is in the atmosphere. The crew braces for that first powerful sledge hammer strike at any moment.

Calypso 'n crew're left alone
the world grows dark twisted limbs groan
The wind pipes up to hurricane force
Calypso bucks like a rodeo horse

There is a momentary halt to the rocking. *Calypso* is felt to be listing slightly to port, followed by the sensation of being hurled through the air to starboard. The vines of the thicket, recoil, springlike, tossing her violently back to port. *Calypso* is now more soccer ball than boat.

Unlike the Gulf storms, the passing of the anvil is not followed by a lessening of the wind's intensity. Even in the protection of the mangrove it is clear, the wind is continuing to gain strength, whistle screaming at an ever higher pitch through the vines. *Calypso* takes the cushioned pummeling in stride. The crew, not so much.

Throughout the night Hermine vents her wrath
bent on destroyin' everythin' in her path
Torrents of rain poundin' down
will anythin' be left of Utila town?

The buffeting continues, the wind maintains its intensity with higher violent gusts laying *Calypso* on her beam ends at anything but rhythmic intervals. The combined flexibility of lines and vines give her the freedom to be tossed and tumbled about in her nest.

Now comes the rain. Those who have experienced hurricane rain will know, the amount of water coming out of the sky defies adequate description.

Furious pounding at the decks and cabin top by the deluge is so loud, combined with the high pitched howl of wind, has the crew hollering to carry on a conversation, even though they are only three feet apart.

Calypso and crew are tortured in this fashion throughout the night. Before dawn can shine a light on the world, the wind dies off considerably.

A twenty knot breeze now rustles *Calypso's* nest. At full daylight, blue sky with white clouds scudding by can be seen through the leaves of the canopy.

The crew gets down to the business of preparing

for the return of the storm. The assumption being, they are in the eye and will soon suffer another beating at Hermine's back wall. Lines are double checked along with an examination for damage which turns up just a few minor scratches on *Calypso's* new yellow paint job.

The mornin' dawn's quiet when villagers return
all 're safe we're relieved to learn
Mud in the streets 'n store signs down
Utila's certainly one hardy little town

About the time the crew begins discussing what length of time is involved before the return of wind and rain, the whine of outboard motors can be heard above the breeze. Cayukas arrive from town with news that the hurricane has passed. The eye of the storm had tracked north of the Bay Islands, and is now heading for the Belize and the Yucatan.

The vessels are wrestled free from the grasp of the mangrove, *Calypso* included, and given a tow back to town. A valuable lesson has been learned should *Calypso* need to seek similar shelter in the future.

Ashore in town, the crew can see the damage is minimal. Slogging through a foot of mud it is apparent, the structures stood the test quite well. A few shutters and signs, tweaked by the hurricane are the only visible effects, aside from the mud.

Folks in the village go about the business of cleaning up and making small repairs. The sun will do the lions share of the work, drying out the town and repairing the muddy paths, returning them to the soft soothing condition enjoyed before Hermine. The crew allows several more days to pass, giving time for the seas to settle down while a more favorable weather pattern develops.

Passage to Roatan

*With the passin' of Hermine
hard wind 'n rain have ceased
Calypso says goodbye to Utila
an' sails fair winds east
current 'n breeze workin' in her favor
conditions sailors really savor*

"September remember" continues to roll off the tongue, the crew having repeated it throughout the storm and the days following. This mid-September arrival of Hermine has the crew more determined than ever to make for Cabo Gracias a Dios and the turn for Panama before another storm moves through.

After one last evening socializing and saying their goodbyes at the "Bucket of Blood," the crew has their anchor up at first light. Sailing slowly out of Turtle Bay to pick up an easy fifteen knot morning breeze on passing the easternmost point of Isla Utila.

A comfortable four foot swell along with clear weather replaces the violence of Hermine. Roatan, at thirty miles distant on a beam reach, can be made in ten hours, even less with the prevailing favorable conditions.

*Within an hour
weather turns sour*

Ten foot seas breakin' heavy
Calypso shortens sail her course held steady

Steadily increasing wind speed and rising seas do not deter the crew. The wind veers from north to northeast by east which has *Calypso* dousing the mainsail. The genny follows in favor of the jib. Jib and mizzen are sheeted tight; *Calypso* settles in to a hard driving beat against a short, choppy seaway. Determination has set in to make Roatan.

Into the seas crashin' 'n tumblin' all day
to Roatan Island just twenty miles away
A halyard gets loose 'n starts a whippin'
then lets go high in the riggin'

Calypso, still feeling light as a feather from her six week haulout in Belize, crashes happily along. The crew, reacting to the increasing wind and sea conditions, had been wise to shorten sail. Her reduced speed adds a modicum of comfort in the rough seas. Tumbling at hull speed under jib and mizzen the crew is settled in on course for Roatan. The wind is strong yet fickle. It attempts veer to a due east vector, before backing again to the northeast. Should an easterly develop, *Calypso* will be forced to begin tacking into the teeth of wind and sea to make Roatan. If this develops, the crew may anticipate a very long night ahead.

The wind has been teasing *Calypso* in this fashion for several hours, the seas are steep and have built to an occasional set running six or eight feet, trough to crest.

Jib and mizzen are sheeted tighter when the wind veers

eastward, then allowed to slacken a bit as the breeze backs toward the northeast. In this fashion, *Calypso* is able to maintain a good course to Roatan.

The timing could not be better for "Murphy" to step into the picture. A loud snap heard above wind and sea, followed by the helm being buried under the mizzen sail. The mizzen halyard has parted, chafed through at the masthead sheave. "Murphy's Law!" The peculiarity of the "Law"- it only takes effect at the most inopportune moments.

On losing the mizzen, *Calypso* takes it upon herself to run with the wind, falling off in a clumsy gybe, while the crew wrestles their way out from under the sail. She is brought under control, steadied up, then allowed to run free under reefed jib.

Goin' aloft with a fresh halyard
Calypso's gallopin' like a horse for the barnyard
Climbin' the mizzen in a wild sea
swingin' in the riggin' like a chimpanzee!

The wind is pushing up toward gale force and the rough seas complicate the operation substantially. Going aloft is never easy; doing so while sailing in gnarly waves with a stiff breeze whipping at the sailor simply adds danger to an already difficult task.

Conditions demand action be taken immediately to remedy the situation. The only alternative without the mizzen is to return downwind to Isla Utila. With Roatan in view, this is unacceptable.

The mizzen is easily scaled in calm weather, as the diameter is so small. The arms and legs wrap around tightly, providing a good grip. There are stays, port and starboard to haul on, allowing the legs to shinny up the pole.

The mizzen mast whipping in a seaway and buffeted by wind is a horse of another color. A tedious white knuckle climb ensues. Powerful gusts of wind tear at the body while the mast itself threatens to flick the climber into the sea, or break in half when *Calypso* snap rolls on the steep Caribbean waves.

On reaching the masthead, a marlinespike is used to lever out the remains of the parted halyard. A fresh line, having been carried up with the climb, is ready at the waist, run through the sheave, then carried back to the deck.

Back on deck lines squared away
losin' our light it's the end of the day
Reef strewn Roatan now in sight
blowin' forty five 'n turnin' to night

A hasty knot, a bowline, is thrown into the line, attaching the fresh halyard to the sail head. The mizzen is reefed, set and sheeted in. *Calypso* immediately stands to weather in response. Roatan lays off her port bow, the mizzen and jib are sheeted out to spill much of the wind, as *Calypso* endures this gusty gale force nor'easter.

Roatan, like Utila, has extensive reef systems off the Island on approach. As evening comes on, the crew makes a decision to sail upwind as high as possible while maintaining good speed, then heave-to for the night. The plan is prudent. Wait for daylight with plenty of sea room for drifting downwind under a reefed mizzen, jogging back upwind as needed. For the exception of the return of that familiar old seafarer's nemesis, heaving-to would have been routine.

After sailing upwind in the darkness for a couple of hours, the crew prepares to heave-to for some rest. The jib is lowered, the helm put down but there is nothing there. The wheel spins free, rudder control is lost. Murphy strikes again.

*With this treacherous scene so near
now to our horror we cannot steer!
The helm's just spinnin' free
Calypso's rudderless in a heavy sea*

*Caught in the throes of a full gale's fury
gotta make repairs in a hurry
Wind 'n sea're ragin'
Calypso's steerin' gears' they ain't engagin'*

Murphy has teamed up with a "Tommyknocker," one of those gremlins living in the bilges that occasionally created havoc with the engine. Ridding *Calypso* of her "Blue Jacket Twin" did not include losing the treachery of her tormentor. The steering gear is in shambles. This is the handywork one can expect when "Tommy" is busy down below.

Intermittent flashes of white in the darkness catch the eye. A breaking reef is much closer than the crew had anticipated when they chose to heave-to. *Calypso's* drift appears to be carrying her right down on the outer reaches of the system.

*Hove to as darkness envelops
a grave situation now develops*

Less than a mile to a reef
where Calypso'll surely come to grief

There is no time to study charts, for that matter, no need as well. It is irrelevant at this moment whether the charts are in error, or the crew has miscalculated.

Deep water is hard to port, from where the swells materialize out of the darkness. The crests are pearly white teeth, snapping at *Calypso's* hull as the relentless train shoves her, wave by wave, ever closer to the grinder.

Grabbin' bailin' wire 'n twine
this is the moment mariners shine
Tearin' into the problem at hand
for this could be Calypso's last stand

Adrenalin pulses through the crew generating immediate action. The access hatch is flipped open to reveal the problem. The toolbox is brought out, a roll of bailing wire, an essential, is right on top, as well as the needlenose pliers. Tuna cord is used, lashing a bracket back in place, from where it has torn away from the transom. The bailing wire serves to hold the steering gear back in position to mesh with the quadrant gear at the top of the rudder post.

The jib is set. *Calypso*, drifting dangerously close to the breaking reef, claws her way to windward. The crew under great stress, must make a critical decision: Continue to sail back up wind several hours and heave-to, or run downwind, returning to Utila.

A good repair makes her safe
Calypso's no longer a rudderless waif
Jib 'n mizzen sheeted tight
helm in hand she's back in the fight

Drop the mizzen 'n come about
this sail to Roatan's a rout
A reef in the jib, weather on her stern
Calypso rides easy after the turn

Exhaustion tilts the argument in favor of running with the wind back to Isla Utila. The intensity of wind and sea, Murphy and the Tommyknocker, wearing on the crew. The jib is set with a reef, the mizzen doused, *Calypso* swings downwind on her track back to the west.

Stress is greatly reduced on both boat and crew. The wind still hovers near gale force, but the downwind run eases the tension, allowing the crew to set up a watch, where one person might get a little rest down below. There remains a concern for the hastily jury-rigged quadrant, but it will have to do. Twine, wire, along with a variety of tools are kept close by the helm, ready for use in a jiffy.

Gradually the wind eases, backing to the north well before first light. At fifteen knots the angry chop *Calypso* has been contending with on six to eight foot seas, disappears, replaced by a comfortable four foot ruffled lump.

Approaching Utila, the light on the east end of the Island lends comfort to the crew. The mizzen replaces the jib, *Calypso* heaves to, waiting for daylight before making a final approach.

Standin' off Utila at the break of day
Roatan Island's thirty miles away
Over twenty four hours since we started
Calypso's just a mile from where she departed!

With the abrupt change in conditions, and daylight still a ways off, there is a sea change within the crew as well. *Calypso's* bowsprit, dipping to gentle swells, greet each unseen wave this pre-dawn morning. A peaceful ambiance; there is coffee on, beans and eggs, smothered in habanero sauce, ready for their tortillas. The aromas overtake the senses, the food fills the bellies, soothing the crew.

Our boat's proven she's very stout
"we'll make Roatan without a doubt!"
Up with the genny, mizzen 'n main
spirits're soarin' 'n feelin' a touch insane!

First rays of light begin streaking across the sky, the crew rested, satiated, discover a fresh resolve within themselves. This morning's light airs and comfortable low swell, with Isla Utila in plain view, has them reassessing their immediate plan.

Plans are always subject to unexpected change and this dawn is no exception. As much as they love Isla Utila, especially with the friends they have made there, the idea of *Calypso* having lost ground on her track does not sit well. Roatan remains a simple day sail away.

With all that has occurred over the last twenty four hours, the crew is undaunted. *Calypso's* mainsail and genny are set, she falls out of irons obediently, swinging her bowsprit back to the east. The sun rises, the wind backs to the northeast, signaled by a surprisingly strong gust initially, then settling in to a steady twenty knot breeze. A light chop adorns each wave. Her sails full, she hops up to hull speed, igniting a giddy excitement, backed by a renewed determination to round Cabo Gracias a Dios. Before noon the wind increases to a steady breeze of twenty-five knots with occasional higher gusts. *Calypso* is brought into irons, the main and genny lowered, replaced by the jib.

Roatan can be held just off the port bow with mizzen and jib sheeted tight. Pointing as high as possible, *Calypso* labors through rough water until the sun begins setting off her stern.

Calypso drives hard against the breeze
boundin' along in choppy seas
Just before nightfall the wind becomes fickle
Calypso finds herself in another pickle

Breakers form a line to seaward, knocking the swell down. The wind too eases as afternoon wears on. There are still a couple hours of daylight remaining, to work her way into the harbor roughly four miles distant. Making a steady two or three knots, the crew calculates they will have the anchor down just about dark.

The charts and "Sailing Directions" describe a large reef system on the approach to Coxen Hole, our intended anchorage. The mainmast is scaled partway up for the best view of the obstructions that lay between *Calypso* and the point of land she must round to enter the bay.

Tension builds as the wind has become so light, jib and mizzen are having difficulty staying full, the resulting slower speed has darkness descending well before she will reach her anchorage.

Gnarly white teeth abound
there's danger all around
By jagged corals Calypso's surrounded
an' in grave danger of bein' grounded!

This fickle post hurricane wind continues to veer further east, forcing *Calypso* off her nearly direct course to Roatan. The formation of an anvil cloud commands the undivided attention of the crew. The jib is doused and a reef taken in the mizzen.

Calypso takes the blow from the southeasterly quarter, laying her on her beam ends, while stand up waves are created by the northeast swell slamming the reef beneath her. Her decks receive a good salt water wash down when heavy seas breech the toerails. The cell passes quickly, leaving *Calypso* with a few knots of wind out of the southeast. The waves generated also expose dangers previously unseen, nearly surrounding her. The mainmast is scaled again as darkness descends, for one last observation of the way in.

Sailin's now extremely tricky
this situation's very sticky

Under jib 'n mizzen through this maze we're tackin'
lead line 'n a star keep Calypso safely trackin'

Reefs are shaken out of jib and mizzen, the jib is set and the leadline put to work at the bow. A star is chosen, on the course to round the southwest point of the Island to make harbor.

White flashes in the dark, along with depths shouted out, has *Calypso* zig-zagging in a general direction toward the unidentified star rising above her. The crew relies on *Calypso's* shallow draft to carry them through. The squall has unsettled seas crashing on shallows, lighting them up and giving *Calypso* just the information she needs to make safe passage into Coxen Hole.

Into Coxen Hole, Calypso winds her way
splash of the anchor signals end of the day
Restin' in an anchorage so hard fought
the peace 'n quiet Calypso had sought

Roatan

The crew do not venture very far into the unfamiliar harbor before dropping the pick. Weary from enduring two days of very little sleep, along with many hours of stress, punctuated by moments of adrenalin coursing through the arteries.

Leftover beans and tortillas are heated and wolfed down. The crew then retires, dropping into deep states of sleep until morning when *Calypso* is rolling uncomfortably in the wakes of passing boats. The rocking stirs the crew into action to move to a quieter anchorage.

Graveyard Anchorage

Havin' dropped anchor durin' the night
Calypso's crew wakes to another fright!
The local boneyard's across the beach, off our stern
an' in the morn' when we pull the pick
the wicked truth we learn

Groggily pulling the pick, eyeing the bay for quiet water, the crew does not fail to notice they had dropped anchor over a dark blotch rather than white sand. The indication, that even though they are anchored in a comfortable twenty feet of water, they are not in clear sand, as is their custom. Arriving in the dark did not afford the crew the luxury of picking out the best spot.

A favorable wispy breeze is available at first light to move *Calypso* deeper into the Bay. The anchor is pulled and the rode flaked out on deck. Before the anchor breaks free of the ground, a moment is taken for a brief glance around to see what will be in the path of *Calypso's* drift.

A precarious spot to say the least with an onshore breeze. Straight down wind and dangerously close to shore where the reef lies very near the surface. On shore, the crew does not fail to notice crosses and headstones all askew, some peeking out from the lush overgrowth in an unkempt, ancient looking graveyard. A bit distracted by the immediacy of the situation, the mizzen is raised, the jib readied as well, to be set when the anchor comes aboard, giving her the ability to sail off the lee shore.

The hands gripping the line as it comes aboard are the first to notice something is not right. The eyes are focused away, attention given to the drift and readiness to hoist the jib. The mind is preoccupied with making a plan of action to sail clear of the reef, which is coming ever closer. With the anchor having released its grip on the bottom, the speed of *Calypso's* drift is increasing.

The left hand holds the line, the right hand reaches out, robotically, the result of having pulled miles of anchor line on this journey.

The routine is shocked into full stop when a thin strand of line falls into the right hand. The crew freezes at the sight before them. The anchor dangles by one thin thread of rode.

The left hand grabs undamaged line beyond the nearly severed spot. Chain and anchor are whipped aboard. The jib is raised and with a shove on the mizzen boom into the wind, *Calypso* pivots, the jib fills and is sheeted tight.

Our little boat responds, obediently sailing off to starboard, clearing the danger by a hairs-breadth in her typical nail biting fashion. Anchorage in clear water is taken near an islet within the bay. The crew being lured to the location by the twanging sounds of a banjo, drifting across the water from the veranda of a grass shack, just off the beach in the shade.

Durin' the night while logs we're sawin'
On our anchor line the coral reef was gnawin'
The rode held together by a single thread
nearly lost Calypso where Islanders bury their dead!
In Roatan we choose to rest
exhausted from this most recent test
forty eight hours for a thirty mile run
relaxin' now under a tropical sun

Roatan provides the crew with the opportunity to travel by ferry to La Ceiba, do banking and provisioning for the next leg of the journey, which at this moment in time remains undecided. Cabo Gracias a Dios is two hundred fifty miles east; miles the crew has cultivated a respect for.

They understand more than ever the dangers which lie ahead. Hurricane season is not over. The charts and "Sailing Directions" are not providing any comfort, as the way ahead has very little to offer in the way of protective harbors.

The crew, now armed with the knowledge of hurricane survival feel they are well prepared for another event, however, the intention is to minimize the necessity of doing so.

The Big Picture

Reassessin' our current position
time has come for a strategic decision
Headwinds 'n dangers lay ahead like a beast
Cabo Gracias a Dios lies two hundred fifty miles east

Pouring over the charts, the answer to the Cabo Gracias dilemma is spread out before them, however, it takes days, rather than minutes to come to the obvious decision. Isla Guanaja, roughly fifty miles east is the final harbor of refuge. Once Calypso puts this tiny island behind her, hundreds of miles of uncharted waters lay ahead. Not that the area is entirely uncharted, however the accuracy must be questioned. An inaccurate chart, will eventually cause the crew great stress, if not disaster.

In light of situation with which we're dealin'
we find Isla Mujeres, very appealin'
Three hundred miles north by northwest
this is the tack that'll serve us best

G rowing weary of the focus on Cabo Gracias, with the chart's mind boggling display of potentially disastrous misinformation, the alternative looms large. Simply standing back, looking at the big picture (a large chart of the entire Western Caribbean) with a bit of imagination, the practical approach jumps out at the crew. When they visualize the northeast trade winds sweeping across the chart, then add Calypso to this mental image, the way forward is clear; one tack, roughly three hundred miles north to Isla Mujeres followed by a second tack south past the Cape. A challenging course of action, however, the alternative of pressing ahead on the present track, is a terrifying prospect.

The way to Panama's 'round the Cape
an' from its treachery Calypso must escape
From Isla Mujeres we'll make our tack
at Cabo Gracias we'll have another crack!

S ix Hundred miles to make the two hundred fifty mile straight line passage to Cabo Gracias a Dios. The hurricane threat having diminished in mid-October also plays a role in the decision; the prospect of open water sailing appeals to the crew. Much of the exhaustion they suffer results from the stress of sailing near this reef strewn coastline.

Calypso is no exception; she has sailed straight in to the barrier reef at Tulum, physically climbed over the reef in southern Mexico, nearly rammed and stove by her cayuka log in Belize, dodged disaster at every turn in the Bay Isles of Honduras and scratched her new paint job in a mangrove swamp during a hurricane. *Calypso's* bowsprit bobs in anticipation of sailing open seas to the tune of the northeast trades.

The arrival of a steady twenty five knot northeaster replacing the unsettled conditions following Hermine, has the crew going about the business of making preparations for the sail back to Isla Mujeres.

Northeast trades settled 'n steady
Calypso's shipshape 'n ready
Cast off lines 'n wave goodbye
let the jib 'n mizzen fly!

Chapter 8

ISLA MUJERES

September

Caribbean Sea

---

*Wind's twenty five knots 'n gustin'
through gnarly blue seas Calypso's bustin'
On a close reach sheets hauled tight
Honduras disappears in the fadin' light*

The last of the palm trees drop off the horizon as *Calypso* goes barreling into the evening. A rolling seaway out of the northeast, the choppy tops slapping *Calypso's* starboard bow. Vega, Altair and friends appear, offering themselves for navigation.

Anxieties harbored in preparation dissipate as the crew settles in to the evening on a rhythmically heaving sea under this sparkling canopy. A firm hand on the weather helm feels each wave as it passes under the hull.

---

*Three days we sail this fresh breeze
playfully boundin' through Caribbean seas
Approachin' Cozumel on the third night
we suffer yet another fright!*

Exhilarating open water sailing, *Calypso* on a beam reach is enter- ing her third night. The sky had become overcast in the late afternoon, resulting in the loss of the evening sights. The crew must dead reckon toward Cozumel, which should be appearing within the next few hours. The wind veers east about ten degrees, the sheets are slackened some, *Calypso* falls off a few degrees, so as not to drive quite so hard into steep waves.

A light pops up in the distance, then disappears when *Calypso* drops into the trough, reappearing again when she nears the next crest. Cozumel Island, right where it is expected. *Cozumel Light*

To a light ahead Calypso makes her way
"Cozumel Island" charts 'n compass say
Slack the sheets 'n put the wind abeam
all's well it certainly does seem

After two hours beating toward the light, *Calypso* is allowed to fall further off the wind, now she sails on a beam reach to skirt the island's western shore. *Cozumel's* light affords the crew a sense of security, a watchful guardian at the island's southernmost point. The light moves abeam as *Calypso* passes the end of the unseen island. At the helm, a question arises. When will *Calypso* be far enough up Co-zumel's western shore before the light disappears from sight?

Without warnin' comes an unwelcome surprise
when gnashin' jaws of ocean arise
Calypso's sailin' straight into the teeth
of the great Yucatan Barrier Reef!

Put down the helm let the jib 'n main go slack
come about sharply on the port tack
Our compass appears to be in error
an' thus the source of this new terror

As *Calypso* sails, there is an uneasy feeling, the light is remaining visible for an unusually long time. This is passed off as a lack of trees as well as its placement on the point. She is driving hard on a beam reach, dead on course, when white water explodes in the black seas just yards ahead, blocking her path.

Cursing the world, the helm is put down, jib and mainsheets let fly, the mizzen hauled tight. Tossed wildly by standing seas, *Calypso* pivots awkwardly, hard to starboard, passing through the eye of the wind. Jib and main are hauled back in a fury to prevent her from sailing into crashing white water on the new tack. The bow is steadied up on the port tack, aiming for pitch black, clear of white flashes to port and starboard.

Calypso's bowsprit bobs to an even swell, clear of the standing seas against the reef. The terror subsides the instant the swells begin marching in order. She is no longer negotiating the sloshing of standing waves that result from the steady Caribbean wave train that's thrown into confusion against the reef. The light, now off her stern, puzzles the crew.

A Magnetic Disturbance is very strong
causin' our trusty compass to go way wrong
Calypso nearly meets her doom
in front of the ruins of Tulum!

T he answer jumps off the chart in "3D." A black arrow is pointing to a location at the edge of the reef, off Tulum. Another arrow with an ominous black "X" penciled in to the south, points to the wreck of the *Southern Scrap*. A note below both arrows: "Severe deviation," says it all.

Calypso has fallen victim to her own observation on the southbound passage from Isla Mujeres to Belize. A rough calculation of the light's position tells the crew they had nearly crashed into the reef, just south of their previous incident.

Near disaster resulted from inattention to the magnetic disturbance detail. The lack of sights during the day had the crew relying solely on the compass, which guided them straight into the barrier reef.

This ancient reef is strewn with bones
an' remains of galleons' ballast stones
Of these dangers Calypso sails clear
the poundin' reef she can no longer hear

Only eighty miles left for this trek
so lucky not to be just another wreck
A northerly current, an easterly breeze
these last miles're covered with ease

Relax & Regroup

A drenalin leaves the crew shaking, hot coffee is comforting, though unnecessary to keep them awake for the remainder of the night. Their oversight of the magnetic disturbance serves to strengthen the resolve to pay ever closer attention to their navigation practices.

Over the centuries, this barrier reef has destroyed countless vessels of every description, possibly even entire Spanish Armadas carrying treasure back to the homeland.

Located on the edge of "Hurricane Alley," Tulum is perfectly situated for disastrous events. Hurricanes and ships are forced into the relatively narrow channel of the Yucatan Straits by the land masses of Mexico and Cuba. The hurricanes feeding and growing more powerful over the warm Caribbean Sea were not forecast in the fifteen hundreds. Galleons are visualized lumbering along a lee shore then taken by surprise and hurled against the wall to their demise.

Could the magnetic disturbance be cannons? A diver's thoughts are consumed with the possibilities. Is there an entire fleet, maybe even multiple fleets of ships carrying enough iron to swing the compass in such a radical fashion? For the remainder of the sail to Isla Mujeres, visions of gold, silver and precious gems dance in the mind

---

At Isla Mujeres Calypso hauls tourists for cheap
with snorklers 'n sunbathers she earns her keep
Makin' a few pesos 'n divin' for fun
easy livin' under a tropical sun

Calypso finds her way in the dark to the spot she had anchored months before, out front of the port captain's office. An exhausted crew fall into deep sleep, secure in the decision to have returned to Mexico, more specifically, Isla

Mujeres. This little Island provides the crew with an oasis to rest and recuperate for another assault on Cabo Gracias a Dios. Rebuffed by the treacherous path along the northern coast of Honduras, the crew remains undeterred; rather, they redouble their efforts in making preparations for the roughly one thousand mile passage to Panama.

Early the following morning, The crew checks in with the port captain to enter Mexico in a more timely fashion than their initial visit. A hearty welcome from the entire office is a delight, with much animated joking about the *"no mota"* tease on their previous encounter.

Yucatan Treasure

Golden George comes on the scene
to find the "Atocha" is his dream
Long blonde hair, jewels 'n gold
George's lookin' big 'n bold

Searchin' for galleons more than just a pleasure
his catamaran's loaded with Spanish treasure
Bein' a diver the temptation's strong
an' half hopin' he'd take me along

A plan is devised to send Pat back to Port Townsend to check in with family as well as procure items difficult to find in Mexico. Dennis will stay with the boat, resuming the hedonistic lifestyle so easily maintained on this wonderful island. Left to his own devices, and no fishermen parked on the beach to frolic with, he turns to the tourists to provide entertainment and a few pesos. The afternoons find Calypso drifting off the Garrafon with a boatload of young folks from the "Pocna," diving and cavorting until evening.

One particular morning, waking to the splashing of a swimmer followed by the sounds of a person boarding *Calypso*, a young lad, maybe twelve or so, sporting long locks of flaming red hair, appears at the hatch. He is from a neighboring catamaran and had been watching *Calypso* sail off to the Garrafon with the young people and wished to join the fun.

Together we swim back over to the catamaran where the boy introduces me to his father, "George." Tall, muscular, long blond hair curling down over his shoulders and gold. Lots of gold. Bracelets, earing, chains around the neck along with a number of rings on the fingers of both hands, some with precious stones embedded. George flaunts the impression of a modern day swashbuckler.

A diaphragm air compressor on deck gives rise to the conversation which revolves around diving. Not so much the diaphragm design, which is oil-less, delivering clean air without the danger of oil leaking into the system. This is not considered a commercial grade compressor, however they work well as a light weight recreational unit.

The point of interest for this diver is a curiosity; commercial grade dive hose has been replaced by everyday garden hose for the air supply. The regulator, a divers most treasured and cared for piece of equipment has been replaced by a snorkel.

The garden hose is plugged into the top of the snorkel which has a slit in the bottom to exhaust excess air. Disbelief at first, which amuses George, saying "I would never dive with anything else." An air of disdain is sensed toward traditional dive regulators. The absolute simplicity of the design sinks in as one imagines using this outfit.

Like a free-flowing regulator, one which is malfunctioning underwater, this "system" works on exactly the same principle. One can still breath from an out-of-control regulator, simply by taking what ever air is needed out of the stream that is blowing by, the tongue working as the valve controlling the amount of air being taken in while keeping the splash water out.

With the system before him, it is plain to see regulator maintenance and repair are a non-issue. Replacement parts or commercial grade dive hose would be difficult to obtain in Mexico. Garden hose and snorkels are widely available, eliminating equipment issues.

A tour of the vessel reveals the results of George's efforts. Dropping down the companionway one passes several small cannons. A large brightly colored squawking parrot leaves its perch, landing on the boy's shoulder.

The vessel's main salon has been converted to a museum of artifacts, retrieved from the wrecks of ancient Spanish Galleons. All have been meticulously cleaned, labeled and displayed throughout the vessel. Large urns, chains, tools, and small pottery are everywhere, the scene taking one back hundreds of years.

Surrounded by the booty, the fire of a diver's desire for a treasure hunt is exposed and immediately spotted by George; he wastes no time extinguishing it, making clear he is a loner..

George explained his mission is to find the *Nuestra Senora de Atocha*[3] which went to the bottom of the sea during a hurricane in the early sixteen hundreds.

The flame is persistent however, witnessed by the letter that is already being crafted in the diver's head as he swims back to *Calypso*. No time is wasted, an urgent message is sent straight away to Port Townsend, requesting the air compressor, hose and regulator along with any other gear available to be shipped to Mexico.

Divers have their secrets, George is no exception. He was evasive during our chat whenever the subject of diving locations

---

[3] The "Atocha" sank in 1622. Discovered July 20, 1985 by Mel Fisher off the Florida Keys.

was broached. Likewise, no mention of the magnetic disturbance off Tulum was proffered either.

Could it be that *Calypso* has happened upon the wreck of the Atocha? George did mention the ship went down with a fleet of vessels, which coincides with the theory in the minds of the crew after their second encounter with the reef.

George had doused the flame, however, the embers continue to burn. Back aboard *Calypso* the chart is laid out, the two courses from north and south nearly intersect, coming within a couple miles or a little more; the locations being inexact, from the lack of sights on the trip north from Roatan. They are close enough with dead reckoning however, to fuel the embers right back to a burning desire.

On Pat's return it's time to regroup
Doug comes aboard, now we're a troupe!
Calypso returns to the Caribbean Sea
with her happy go lucky crew of three!

Doug

In Port Townsend, Pat had coaxed Doug from his life and meditations in Port Townsend's "Zendo" with the lure of sunken treasure and sailing adventures. A welcome surprise when they arrive at Isla Mujeres, unannounced, loaded with dive gear. Doug is an easy going, good humored addition to the crew. He also was a dive harvester in the shellfish and kelp fleet.

Doug can be relied on for a steady hand at the helm and trusted to stay cool when a demanding situation arises. Commercial diving is solid training for remaining calm in sticky situations.

After several days cavorting around Isla Mujeres, the crew grows bored with the activities, diving for treasure becomes a distant fantasy while visions of Cabo Gracias a Dios loom large

This journey to Panama offers real adventure. Doug in particular is fresh and ready for sailing; just the spark the crew needs to regain the momentum lost, having back tracked three hundred fifty miles.

Gathering one evening for a chat after dinner, they find themselves in accord. *Calypso* will sail for Panama via Cabo Gracias, leaving Isla Mujeres in the morning at first light.

Puerto Morelos

Settin' off on a glorious broad reach
takin' turns at the helm three hours each
Lookin' at the chart it does appear
Panama's 'bout a thousand miles from here

L eaving Isla Mujeres, the morning light airs are the perfect opportunity for Doug to get his hands on the helm and lines. With the afternoon breeze picking up and settling in at a steady twenty five knots, *Calypso* puts the thirty miles to Puerto Morelos behind her, sailing on a sizzling broad reach under mizzen and genny. By the time the crew are anchoring off the pier, Doug is tuned in.

Puerto Morelos offers an opportunity to shop for items not available on Isla Mujeres. Pat and Doug set off in the *Rubber Ducky* while Dennis remains aboard. The afternoon trades are stiff with *Calypso* vulnerable, riding the hook on a lee shore.

Soon after the shore party departs, the skies darken with gray cumulonimbus clouds, wave heights increase, the wind gusts build a nasty chop. *Calypso* bucks wildly, jerking on the rode, her bow swings off to port, downwind, dragging her anchor. The bow is hauled violently back to starboard when the anchor bites into sand. Before it has a chance to set and hold, the anchor is ripped from the bottom, again she goes sailing off under bare poles. *Calypso* is dragging fast, directly toward the cement pier, in danger now of being chewed to pieces. There is no time to pull the pick and set sail, rather, the spare anchor is wrapped in a life preserver, taken over the side, then swum out until the rode comes taught. This second anchor goes to the bottom in the direction of the gale. The *Rubber Ducky* arrives, the shore party having seen the weather turn are acutely aware of her precarious open roadstead anchorage. They had cut their shopping short to assist in the protection of *Calypso*. With all hands on deck, it is a simple matter to raise sail and get anchors up simultaneously, tacking clear of the pier.

The squall passes quickly, the northeast trades settle back in. *Calypso* takes a bearing on the southern end of Cozumel Island less than thirty miles to the southeast. Four hundred fifty miles beyond Cozumel, lies Cabo Gracias a Dios.

Chapter 9

CABO GRACIAS A DIOS

December 1980

Hove to

---

*For two days, sailin's a thrill
until dark clouds the skies they fill
White caps slappin' 'n splashin' the hull
announcin' sailin' won't be dull*

The crew settles in for three hour watches at the helm. A pleasure to have an extra hand aboard after the experience of taking turns steering for two weeks from Florida to Mexico. That passage had deteriorated to watches only lasting as long as a person could keep their eyes open, at times, just a matter of fifteen or twenty minutes.

Day three, nearing two hundred miles under the keel, the wind backs due north. This northerly backing is preceded by a fierce squall, forcing the crew to shorten sail.

The cold northerly sets in as evening approaches. With plenty of sea room, the crew chooses to heave to for the night, getting a good rest after a comforting meal of bean burritos. Dinner is especially delicious with all the trimmings fresh from Puerto Morelos.

The intensity of the wind havin' risen
Calypso heaves to under reefed mizzen
In Calypso's ability, we have no doubt
nuthin' to do but ride this one out

Early morning the following day sees the northerly die off rather quickly, *Calypso* piles sail back on, only to watch the fickle airs veer to the southeast and pump up, forcing a chop against the swell out of the north.

Rather than bucking into the fresh wind, main and jib are doused, the mizzen reefed; *Calypso* rides easy, hove-to again. The skies cloud over, preventing afternoon and evening sights.

Another night passes. Another day of gray skies finds *Calypso* drifting in a rough seaway, with another day of dead reckoning. A third day of monotonous rolling and heaving wears on the crew as *Calypso* drifts to leeward, entering her third night.

Tossed and tumbled by a rough Caribbean sea for so many hours with no navigation, the crew wake on day four to light winds and calming seas.

Celestial Navigation Lesson

Once the storm abates star sights're taken
on course to the Cape there's no mistaken'
A hundred more miles or so
round Cabo Gracias a Dios we'll go

T he lack of navigation has the trio pursuing a lively discussion, the topic being "where are we?!" This results in a show of arms, each pointing in a different direction. To be fair, all did point to the southerly quadrant, ranging from south southwest, due south and south southeast. The morning sight is taken and plotted, not showing enough new information in the minds of Doug and Dennis. Pat however, has faith in her assessment, reaffirming her choice is correct.

The doubters steer all day, each on their chosen course, while the navigator remains steadfast. When one attempts to change the navigator's mind, there is no satisfaction for either of the two intuitive helmsmen, arguing their case. The evening sight serves to cement the navigator's assessment. She adjusts slightly eastward and holds firm, stating Cabo Gracias a Dios is south by southeast of *Calypso's* present position.

On Pat's navigational skills we rely
when she appears at the hatch she's not shy
She's bundled the Sun Moon 'n Arcturus
with father time in order to assure us

C alypso is set on the southeasterly course, prescribed by the nav- igator. Genny and jib are set wing and wing, the wind having eased substantially, backing from the northeast to due north.

There is a new twist to the routine today. Just before noon the navigator cranks up WWV on the shortwave radio, bonging time. The first noon sight is taken in months, The winter sun presenting itself at a more easily measured angle.

After a long absence below, the navigator pops her head out the hatch, making an astounding proclamation.

"We'll see palm trees in one hour" is her claim
The doubters checkin' watches make it a game
She has our position down exactly
an' announces it so matter-of-factly

Her two companions, guffawing, are incredulous; looking around at the rolling blue seas, no sign of land in any direction. The navigator, however, is unwavering, confident in her calculations following the noon sight.

As the sixty minute mark nears
our navigator may be incorrect it appears
An' when that sixty minute mark has passed
nuthin' but empty blue ocean so vast

The doubters are looking with a skeptical eye at the navigator, then all around the boat, finally they look at their watches, double checking with WWV. There is no land anywhere in sight as the one hour mark passes.

Just thirty seconds more pass by
somethin' on the horizon catches the eye
There's palm trees straight off our bowsprit!
Our navigator has just nailed it!

The skeptics can almost hear the ping of palm trees as they pop up on the horizon, so startled by their appearance. The navigator, on the other hand, sits quietly, amused by their astonishment.

Before dark, as *Calypso* closes with the coast of Honduras, and Cabo Gracias, the water turns muddy, the mainsail and jib are lowered, the mizzen is set for the night, heaving-to, well offshore. Around the evening meal, navigation is a big topic. At this time, our navigator reveals a very surprising tidbit on her accomplishment.

She had not simply found *Calypso's* position, she had taken the calculations one very perceptive step further. Our navigator had the forethought to consider the low coastline, lined with palm trees. Estimating the tallest trees at one hundred feet, combined with the eight feet of height the sextant is above the water when held to the eye on deck, she had determined the distance *Calypso* would be offshore when the tree tops would appear over the curvature of the earth!

Sleep comes easily to the crew this night, the breeze having died off with the onset of darkness. *Calypso* is drifting on a glassy Caribbean Sea under her blanket of stars, the crew now secure in their deeper understanding of the accuracy of celestial navigation.

First light, the crew is up, the shortwave bonging time, sights are taken, along with a hearty breakfast of "huevos y frijoles con habanero," wrapped in a flour tortilla, a favorite since *Calypso* had arrived in Mexico.

Light on their feet on deck, a communal excitement is coursing through the crew. One can not avoid the eyes darting to the palm trees as they appear and disappear with the rise and fall of the boat.

Raising all canvas in hopes of catching some of the wispy morning airs, a course is charted well off shore, taking *Calypso* through the clearest passages around the Cape.

The water here is muddy, the Caribbean blue has given way to a milky coffee color from the many river drainages on the Honduran mainland. The lead line is busy, unable to dead reckon by avoiding dark patches in clear water, indicating a submerged reef; daggers to a wooden boat. *Calypso* is worked gingerly into an anchorage near a small caye off Cabo Gracias. A repeat of the tedious sail follows the next morning. Early afternoon the trade winds return and blue water reappears for a blistering sail to Man-O-War Caye, on the Miskito Coast, Nicaragua.

New Year 1981

At Man-o-War Caye a New Year's toast
Calypso stands off the Nicaraguan Coast
On Great Corn a quiet bay beckons
our next anchorage the crew reckons

Excellent anchorage is found at Man-o-War Caye where the first week of the New Year is savored, a well deserved rest for three weary sailors at this remote Caribbean oasis. Once rejuvenated the desire to resume the rhythm of the journey is strong. The crew sets sail as wind conditions shape up nicely.

Genny 'flyin' in a twenty five knot breeze
surfin' down these blue mountain seas
Strong northeast trades broad reach sailin's grand
two hundred more miles we'll drop anchor in sand

Chapter 10

NICARAGUA

January 1981

Great Corn Island (Isla de Mais)

The trades now veerin' to a close reach
Calypso claws her way toward Brig Bay Beach
Tedious tackin' full sail flyin'
then the wind, it just starts dyin'

Wind's quit. Calypso's driftin' outa the bay
then lo! There's a Cuban gunboat comin' our way
Wonderful hospitality they immediately show
tossin' a line an' givin' Calypso a tow

C alypso works to windward on her early morning arrival off the north end of Great Corn Island. The winds becoming fickle overnight, now only a wispy five knots at best. The crew working to catch every breath of the elusive airs, sail into a glassy calm where the catspaws vanish from the surface.

Failing to make the mouth of the bay, *Calypso* drifts with the current, retracing her approach to the island. Working to make harbor for several hours unsuccessfully does not go unnoticed by the islanders.

A Cuban warship moored in the bay launches a small gunboat which speeds to the aid of the becalmed sailors. A line is gratefully received, the crew of the vessel laughing and chattering as they tow *Calypso* into the bay.

The Cuban crew's all smokin' cigars
'n wearin' shorts
A mustachioed Commandant
receives our passports
"Welcome to Corn Island" is his decree
then commences to give us the third degree!

Passing the warship, a repeat of the scene off Havana; it's crew lines the rails in their skivvies, the excited waving and shouting follows Calypso all the way to the wharf. An equally animated crowd awaits Calypso's arrival. Eager hands reach out as lines are tossed over to the dock. She is hauled in and tied up. The crew hops off the boat into the crowd, receiving a very warm welcome.

Sandinista Commandant

The folks make way for a uniformed gentleman strolling down the dock toward them. An imposing, mustached fellow introduces himself as a Colonel and Commandant of the Corn Islands, in excellent English.

The crew hands over their passports. A tense moment, the crowd having quieted, we are unsure of the procedure, as military governments can be unpredictable. The Commandant, shuffling through the passports, appears more interested in the vessel than the documents in his hand. Without raising his eyes from the documents, the usual questions arise: "What is your destination?"

"Panama. Our final destination is Alaska." This answer raises his eyes from the passports accompanied by murmurs from the folks who have gathered on the dock.

"Goin' to Alaska in that little boat?!"
then makes like he's shiverin' 'n puttin' on a coat!
Folks roar with laughter as the Commandant teased
it's obvious with Calypso's arrival he's very pleased

Scrunching his face, the officer turns to the crew, pointing down at *Calypso*. The scowl disappears, replaced by a wide grin, half hidden under that bushy black mustache. "Going to Alaska in that?! " Pointing down at *Calypso*, drawing a roar of laughter from crowd and crew alike. He then proceeds to mime donning an Eskimo parka while shivering against the cold, then falls back, joining all in a fit of belly busting laughter. The stock answer of the crew has worked its magic again.

Of this island he's extremely proud
an' as he speaks there gathers a crowd
When the Commandant ends his welcomin' speech
a wonderful soccer game erupts on the beach!

Beach Soccer

T he tensions of arrival evaporate and a soccer ball appears. Bounced and knocked about above the heads of the folks on the wharf, it goes sailing off to the beach. The gathered horde, *Calypso's* crew included, race in exuberant pursuit, caught up in a collective state of backslapping hilarity.

Corn Islanders, Cubans and two American sailors engage in a rough and tumble game of soccer on the wide expanse of beach. A no holds barred game leaves the contestants battered and bruised, bonding the participants, exhibited by the arms over shoulders as they stumble off their makeshift soccer field. All are still laughing and cavorting, although subdued by exhaustion.

With the game havin' played itself out
the Commandant takes the crew out 'n about
This military gentleman now our guide
we're shown the source of his great pride

G reeted once again by the Commandant, he is now insistent we join him for a tour of the Island. The crew gladly accepts the invitation, hopping into his old, well maintained nineteen forties U.S. Army Jeep.

Passing by a tidy little airport, the Commandant explains the U.S. had built it when they occupied the Islands in the early nineteen hundreds. It was returned to Nicaraguan control just ten years earlier. The original treaty was signed in nineteen fourteen which included the lease of the Islands to the U.S. It served as a naval base and airstrip for the protection of the proposed canal which would connect the Atlantic and Pacific

Oceans. Over the years, after the abandonment of the proposal in favor of Panama, a hotel sprung up, financed by an American entrepreneur.

For this reason, the Commandant explains, the Islanders are very appreciative; Americans are well liked here for these developments, thus the welcome the crew had received is heartfelt.

---

*For Nicaragua these're tumultuous times
Somozas' regime overthrown for its many crimes
The Sandinista Liberation Front now looms large
of this fledgling government they're now in charge*

*Over the Corn Islands the Commandant presided
pointin' out the mansion where Somoza had resided
An' during those war torn days
he'd personally set Somoza's home ablaze*

As he drives, the Commandant talks of various highlights of the recent struggle and eventual overthrow of the dictator. Winding along the shore, lush jungle crowds the road then opens to a wide clearing with an expansive view across open water to the west. Near the top of the hillside is a house, burned out completely; the cement walls still standing. Black claws of smoke stains reach out, gripping the structure from window and door openings.

The Commandant waves up at the scene, his eyes alight, "That was Somozas' house. I burned it." Our tour guide swells with pride. The crew is silent, staring up at the structure. One can visualize the dictator standing on his veranda, looking toward the mainland, and the Country he ruled.

A Teacher for the Island

*Pat's a teacher the Commandant discovers
an' his idea he soon uncovers
A house 'n food'll be provided
so the Island' ll have a teacher if she so decided*

Continuing on around the Island, the crew is quizzed on topics ranging from fishing in Alaska to "do you live in an igloo?" Our jolly guide is having great fun teasing the crew, while learning quite a bit about them. He takes particular interest in Pat's university education, especially with the fact she is a certified teacher by profession.

Arriving at the end of the airstrip, having come full circle, the Island's sole hotel can be seen; a tiny, ivory white structure under a red roof, surrounded by shading palms and well manicured grounds. The tour comes to an end at the marketplace where the Colonel takes his leave. The crew loads up on fresh fruits and vegetables, while meeting new friends with every step along the way. Several restful days pass when a message is received to report to the Commandant's office. The jeep had been sent to collect the crew, a kind gesture of respect, as the Commandant's office is located within sight of the wharf where *Calypso* is docked.

Following a quick, friendly greeting, the Commandant gets right to the point of why the crew has been called to his office. Without hesitation he launches into a long winded request, tinged with his personal excitement. Great Corn Island has a school, but they are struggling, as they are without an educated teacher on the Island.

Any uneasiness the crew may have had on being called to the Commandant's office vanishes. As he lays out his proposal, his eyes brighten with anticipation that his offer will be accepted.

The crew are welcomed to join the community with Pat becoming the Island's schoolteacher. A house and food will be provided in lieu of cash money as payment for her employment.

This most generous offer stuns the crew. The opportunity which has opened before them is irresistible, Pat accepts the offer to the great delight of the Commandant, who jumps away from his desk to shake hands with a renewed welcome to the "Islas de Mais".

A collective excitement has the crew lightheaded, walking on air back to their little boat. Plans for the immediate future whirl in their heads, as from all appearances, *Calypso's* journey ends here.

On the surface a fortuitous event
until our new found friends begin to vent
The Islanders express their great frustration
our food 'n shelter's inadequate compensation

Conversation during the evening meal revolves around the day's big event. Plans are made, hashed over, scrapped and made again. The teaching opportunity, an undeniably wonderful stroke of luck could not be passed by easily. Opportunities for diving for treasure while settling in to an easily maintained hedonistic lifestyle round out the list of positives. There is no apparent downside to taking advantage of this fork in the road.

As on any island, or small town for that matter, news travels like wildfire. Great Corn Island is certainly no exception. Mid-afternoon the following day finds the crew at the marketplace surrounded by folks overtaken by a joyful excitement; their Island is to have an American schoolteacher. A crowd of folks gather around the crew at the marketplace, eager for details. Questions are coming rapid fire, when one young fellow's query results in a crowd dampening hush. "How much will you be paid?" All eyes turn to the crew, awaiting the answer.

When folks hear
no cash their teacher will be earning
The crew witness an anger deeply burning
"We're not communists you see,
Cubans're here takin' our jobs 'n workin' for free!"

Open Wounds

The unseen downside. The crew is unprepared; struck silent at first, off balance, then stammer through an explanation involving the house and food to be provided. In their minds this being extremely generous compensation, however the eyes staring at them are telling a different story. A tense atmosphere evolves as though a dark raincloud has cast its shadow, signaling the advance of a windstorm.

"Two years in the bush for nothing, I'm ready to go back into the jungle." A closer look at the young individual reveals the weary eyes of civil war, disappointment, and anger refueled.

Of the open wounds of war the crew's now aware
an' it certainly gives them a darn good scare

The people're ready to do battle
the crew decides, "We better skedaddle!"

" Collaborator." The word pops up in conversation aboard *Calypso*, the crew sharing their thoughts at the evening meal.

Ten years earlier this sailor found himself caught up in civil war in Vietnam. He has no illusions of how the madness could turn against the crew, even though they had been so well received. Neighbor against neighbor is a hideous situation.

Should the embers of a civil war so recent burst into flame, the potential to find themselves caught between opposing forces is real. Even more frightening, is the thought of becoming a focal point in the conflict; a target. Seeing their situation as untenable, a possible flash point, it is determined *Calypso* must sail for Panama without delay.

Early next morning, the Commandant accepts our apologies along with the explanation that the crew has decided they must press on for Panama and Alaska. Handing over passports, he makes no attempt to convince the teacher to remain. He displays no indication he knows the truth behind the crew's decision, for the exception of his lack of surprise. Graciously he shakes their hands, wishing them a safe journey. The crew is left with the impression the Commandant knows this Island and its inhabitants sentiments very well, possibly through his own personal grapevine.

On their return to *Calypso*, they find a group of folks waiting, a young boy on a donkey among them. Once again, word has quickly spread around the Island, this time it is word of *Calypso's* imminent departure.

Generosity

*We inform our friends it's time to go
an' extreme generosity they now show
"Follow the boy on the donkey" they said
an' through lush jungle Calypso's crew is led*

Folks gathered around the crew express their disappointment at the decision to sail on, however they understood the story they were told; the crew's yearning for home had weighed heavily on them, resulting in a change of heart. They could not however, cover their own discouragement at the turn of events, making it clear to all, this decision has not been taken lightly.

The people now implore the crew "follow the boy on the donkey." The young fellow turns, beaming, gives his patient companion a couple gentle pats on his whithers and off they go at a donkey walk.

The crew follows along, a gaggle of children in tow, frolicking to and fro, screaming and giggling. The donkey veers off the road onto a foot path ascending a hill where half way up, the path dives into the jungle. Under the shade of the canopy, the eyes adjust to lower light, revealing a pathway, soft underfoot, lined with fruit trees. Oranges, mangoes, bananas, limes and mammies surround the procession.

The path winds out of the jungle to a clearing on the hillside where a small neighborhood is located. Passing by one of the tiny homes, a woman with several children are standing by their vegetable garden, waving our guide over. A net bag of fruits and vegetables is produced and secured to the donkey. The crew expresses their delight and appreciation for the gifts, the boy pats the donkey and the caravan is underway again. Further on, another modest home, another small family and another bag of fruits and vegetables. This scene is repeated along the way until the donkey is fully loaded.

Farewell

The donkey's loaded right up to his ears
so much food brings the crew to tears
For Panama Calypso now sets her sails
fruits 'n vegetables lashed to the rails!

L eaving the neighborhood, the path circles back down the hill, winding its way again through the lush jungle undergrowth. In the coolness under the canopy the crew is sharing a communal sense; they had stumbled into paradise, so unfortunately marred by war.

Full sail is set, the generosity and well wishes the crew receive has them casting lines with a heavy heart. Light morning airs in the bay has *Calypso* ghosting away from the dock, crowded with the band of well wishers. All are waving and calling out, the donkey stands among them, his head hanging low with a sorrowful stare from those big brown eyes.

Pearly white clouds racin' up high
Calypsos' locomotive in a light blue sky
Ridin' a wave train with a chop on top
The Isthmus of Panama Calypso's next stop

Calypso picks up the trades as she passes the southern point of Great Corn Island. Twenty five knots out of the east northeast has her under genny and mizzen. Sizzling along at hull speed, the motion of her fantail stern so much like the tail feathers of a seabird as she lifts high over each steep Caribbean wave, negotiating the crests, one by one. Clear, hazard free sailing with excellent wind has the crew in high spirits. Less than three hundred miles to Colon; with present conditions holding will have Calypso at the Panama Canal in three days.

*A sliver of land sixty miles wide
a great ocean hidin' on the other side
Three hundred miles south
there's a path cut straight
to where adventure lies in wait*

Chapter 11

PANAMA

January-March 1981

Colon Yacht Club

---

*The Colon Yacht Club welcomes the invasion
of vessels 'n travelers of every persuasion
Two continents 'n two oceans intersect here
the crew ties up an' enjoy a cold beer*

Chaos best describes the approach to Colon. Traffic is about equal to or greater than that encountered at the "Battery" in New York City. Vessels move in all directions, most at a high rate of speed, and of a size that restricts their maneuverability. Hair raising for a sailboat without auxiliary  power, dependent now on the captains to respect the rules of the road involving vessels under sail. Thankfully, the traffic is commercial, the professionals allowing *Calypso* a clear path to a berth at the Colon Yacht Club; an American enclave, as the Panama Canal is under American control.

A beehive of activity on the dock
crews makin' preparations 'round the clock
World cruisers from afar
cuttin' deals in the Yacht Club bar

C alypso is dwarfed by powerful world cruising yachts surrounding her. The crew, walking down the dock, their necks
craning, eyes squinting to see the tops of the sixty and eighty foot
masts. Their decks are clean, fitted out with an abundance of
winches and polished hardware. Without exception, they are constructed of steel, fiberglass or cement. Hired crews attending to
details make ready to transit the Canal or having just arrived from
the Pacific side, preparing their vessels to depart for points east.

A humbling walk
to the yacht club bar
where the crew finds
the place packed
with owners and sail-
ors swilling beer and
hard liquor, boast-
ing loudly of their
boats and exploits. A
feature of the yacht
club proving to be ex-
tremely useful to the

crew, beyond the cold beers and mixing with folks, is the bulletin
board, plastered with small pieces of paper. Notices of all things
maritime from people looking to crew or ride free on a sailing vessel, to a mind boggling number of parts, pieces and many whole
boats for sale.

Self-Steering Windvane

*Trade off the air compressor
for a wind vane we name Hector
Doug refashions Hector makin' it ready
assurin' Calypso's course will hold steady*

Making themselves comfortable, the crew settles in, exploring a colorful, lively Colon for its bakeries, fresh foods and sundries. Several days are spent enjoying the scene at the yacht club, learning the ropes of transiting the canal and pouring over the bulletin board. The latter, producing the first vital piece of equipment needed to continue the journey. Vessels in the forty to fifty foot range invariably are outfitted with some form of steering gear. A concept with which the crew are only vaguely familiar. We are more knowledgeable of sheet to tiller steering, a technique handed down over many years of small boat steerage. *Calypso* is fitted with a traditional spoked wheel, which does not lend itself to the method, except with the possibility of some complicated, makeshift system the crew has never attempted to master.

Twenty-four hour wheel watches with hands-on steering in the Gulf of Mexico had made clear to the crew their limitations in that regard. A majority of the vessels headed to the United States are sailing to the Marquesas Islands, the jump-off point for Hawaii. The crew, still unsure of their route forward, are quite aware of the long distance passages, regardless the route chosen, which will require sailing around the clock.

As it happens, one of the scraps of paper on the board is offering an "RVG," state of the art, windvane for sale. The ad mentions it is too small for his boat. The crew contacts the owner, finding him aboard a roughly fifty foot vessel. The wind vane, dismantled and laying on the dock is very obviously much too large for our little boat. Before the crew can walk away, Doug, who had been examining the contraption very closely pipes up "I can make that thing fit *Calypso*."

Knowing Doug's abilities with such things, the crew has no doubt he could accomplish the task. Not having the cash to buy the item outright, the crew resorts to bartering, and a mutual agreement is made easily, benefiting both parties. The air compressor, hose, volume tank and regulator are traded straight across for the windvane.

Doug dives into the job, cutting the thing to pieces and reassembling the vane to one third its original size. He then finds a shop where mounts are fashioned and welded together. In short order he is bolting a perfectly redesigned windvane to *Calypso's* transom. Only one mystery remains: will it work?

The Way Forward

The crew waste no time with sea trials, rather, having discussed ad infinitum the immediate plans for the future, and there being strong disagreements on the way forward, a vote is taken.

Dennis is convinced the whole idea of heading to the Strait of Juan de Fuca via the Pacific Ocean in little *Calypso*, is madness. His solution is simple. Load the boat onto a freighter and either travel aboard with her, or find their own way back to the Northwest. Pat, with the opposing argument that since we do not have the financial resources to afford the shipping costs, we must continue on. Doug, now an integral part of *Calypso's* crew is given a vote in the matter, which is settled in short order, *Calypso* will transit the Panama Canal and sail for points north.

Yacht Club Life

A fascinating scene here at the yacht club and its surrounding docks. An American enclave where world travelers congregate, having arrived from every corner of the earth, in all manner of sailing vessels.

There is a couple in their seventies who have been sailing around the world continuously for thirty years. Their current vessel a spacious thirty-six foot cruising catamaran. Another vessel, a sixty footer, is single handed from England by a fellow who's legs had been amputated. His vessel fitted out to a tee, accommodating his needs.

The only other wooden sailing vessel, for the exception of heavy schooners laying at anchor, is a forty foot Stone Horse. This design extends the cabin top athwartships, eliminating the side decks, thus creating a voluminous interior for the main cabin.

The individual aboard starts up a conversation warning the crew of roaming the streets of Colon, especially after dark. He maintains hoodlums and miscreants are out in force, looking for victims. He begins relating a personal experience he had recently at the city bus station.

He had been to the bank and gone shopping a short bus ride from the yacht club. On his return trip, after disembarking at the crowded central station, he is approached by a man wielding a knife close to his face and demanding money.

Scared and obedient, he pulls out his wallet which the assailant rips from his hand, then turns, running away. Unfortunately, he only runs a few yards before stopping and returning to repeat the attack. This time he holds the knife to his victims belly, yelling, "drop your pants!"

Terrified, he obeys, the attacker cuts the money belt from his waist. He disappears into the crowd, leaving him standing with his pants around his ankles. How could he possibly have known it was a bad day to go out into the oppressive heat of Colon without underwear?

Super Hydra

At the end of the dock there's a mutiny
the crew has their cap'n under great scrutiny
Super Hydra's taken over by the crew
an' Doug jumps into the middle of that stew

As captain's bodyguard Doug's now hired
by this capn' who'd just been fired
An' while this's all goin' down
Calypso's lookin' for a tow outa' town

Then, there is the *Super Hydra*. A full on mutiny in progress, with the captain locking himself in his cabin, fearing for his life. This sixty footer out of Germany, carries a "crew" of paying customers. Dissatisfied with conditions, venting their anger, the "crew" had terrified the owner/captain/entrepreneur.

Doug is kind enough to sleep aboard a couple nights to help keep the peace while the mutiny plays out. Eventually additional individuals are drawn into the fray, the crew being threatened with arrest. The story ends somewhere in the gray areas of Panama. The paying customers found their own way home, while the *Super Hydra* sailed back into the Caribbean, where rumor has it she was anchored, stripped and sunk.

La Cucaracha

Our Swedish neighbors have a mutiny
of a different sort
an' their journey they're nearly ready to abort
A gazillion cockroaches've taken command
so bold they look ya in the eye 'n take a stand!

C ockroaches. The romance of sailing juxtaposed with another of the harsh realities that may befall seafarers of any stripe. Cockroaches. Insects of the ages. Here for millions of years and in all likelihood will feast on the remains of the human race when it is gone.

Having read accounts of the bugs taking over ships to the point crews are deserting, this mariner's malady appears a distant, even comical, threat. Certainly not an issue to be overly concerned with; until a sleek fiberglass yacht out of Sweden, is met on arrival at the Colon Yacht Club.

On cabin walls tables 'n floors, insects scurry
runnin' aroun' in a great big hurry
An' when ya catch 'em eatin' yer lunch
whack 'em good 'n they go crunch!

From outward appearances all seems fine, with the boat that is. The four souls aboard are another matter altogether. Friendly faces greet the crew of *Calypso*, who receive their lines, making them fast to the dock. As final adjustments are made, *Calypso's* crew senses something is amiss. Maybe an unexpected shift from their cheery arrival to a noticeable tightened set of their jaws. As though a dark storm cloud is filling these bright blue afternoon skies; the sailors steeling themselves for that which lies ahead.

The two couples, albeit in a somewhat hesitant manner, invite the crew aboard for a cold beer. On going below a seat is taken at the compact, yet comfortable galley table. Even before conversation can begin, our friends turn red with embarrassment, their necks go board stiff. All this, in the reaction to the arrival of a cockroach running across the table.

No move is made to kill or capture the critter, rather, our friends have taken on a kind of stony stare, clearly avoiding eye contact with the insect. That bothersome stiffness in the neck, now throbs with increased blood pressure.

Dead silence befalls the group. The tickle of a bug running across the top of a bare foot, diverts the eyes to the cabin sole, which has come alive. Cockroaches by the thousands had come out as soon as the movement of the crew had settled at the table.

Even worse, looking back up and around, the plastic walls of the interior are now alive and crawling as well. White walls, now dark reddish brown, solid insects in constant motion, the yacht transformed into a prehistoric cave. A Hellish scene right out of some terrifying "end of the world" blockbuster playing out before their eyes.

Calypso's crew are stunned; witness to a cockroach event, right there at the yacht club dock. The silence is broken with a query concerning the infestation which is met with a curt "We don't talk about them," effectively shutting down further conversation. The crew sits, for a short, polite spell, then quickly, beers in hand, take their leave. The shuffling of people on the exit sends the insects into a frenzy running across bare thighs franticly searching for dark places to hide. The crew have an entirely new perspective on the very few cockroaches *Calypso* currently has aboard.

Pat shoulders the mission to rid our boat of every bug. In

short order, by word of mouth around the dock, she discovers the solution; a mixture of boric acid and sweetened condensed milk is effective in ridding *Calypso* of her small but persistent infestation. The concoction draws the bugs in, the little dabs spread about the boat in strategic places are carried off rather quickly to the nest. The remainder, dries, yet continues to work on the next generation. The little piles are refreshed often; after a couple weeks, *Calypso's* cockroaches are eliminated, never to be seen again.

"Sea Horse"

A boat outa Norway catches Doug's eye
price is right 'n he makes a great buy
Holdin' now the reins of his "Sea Horse"
together they'll chart a brand new course

"Boat for sale." The bulletin board produces a second life altering scrap of paper. Just as the board had connected *Calypso* with a wind vane which will allow her to travel the ocean shorthanded, this day a scrap of paper is pinned there carrying a message with the power to change a young man's life.

The back story in this case concerns the tragic death of a lone sailor out of Norway in an automobile accident here in Colon. The boat left stranded and for sale by the parents of the young fellow.

Sea Horse is a sweet twenty six foot sloop with fine lines, fitted out for ocean travel, complete with a diesel engine, awaits a new owner in her slip at the Colon Yacht club. Doug's acquisition sets him on a fresh course, making his own preparations. Initially, by attacking some structural issues suffered while *Sea Horse* waited, sitting untended in Panama's ultra humid climate.

Additionally he begins talking more seriously about a lady back in Port Townsend. He had mentioned her several times on our passage from Isla Mujeres. Soon to be left alone, he invites her to join him in Colon. The *Sea Horse* will serve them well, it is plain to see.

Transit Preparations

*Food' n necessities stored
a hundred twenty gallons of water aboard
Only one thing Calypso's missin'
the putt putt putt of her ' ol engine*

The crew has been preparing diligently for transit of the Canal. The weeks here at the Yacht Club have been filled with intrigue; an unusually high number of nefarious individuals involved in webs of secret dealings frequent the bar and docks.

Now, deep in the fabric of the community, the crew steers clear of the pitfalls of becoming involved with the abundant opportunities for criminal endeavors, adhering to the old admonition: "Piracy begins ashore."

Colon. A fascinating international marine intersection which has a continuous stream of traffic of every persuasion one encounters on the sea lanes, forced to stop, gather paperwork then wait their turn to make passage. There are enough

scams and payoffs involved in procuring the paperwork for transiting the canal to give the crew a clear indication of how things work in Panama. "Take this taxi" and "go to this office" are heard repeatedly as the crew chases around the city of Colon; rats caught in a bureaucratic maze designed to take cash at every turn. All small time pilfering by cabbies and government officials working in concert. Nothing so dangerous as the stories told, true or not, of grand theft, sunken yachts and murder.

"Intrepid"

For a vessel with power
the docks we scour
A fishin' vessel transitin' the Canal
the "Intrepid's" happy to be Calypso's new pal
This connection's really terrific
'cause Calypso's gettin' a tow
all the way to the Pacific!

The Canal has a strict set of rules; beyond having the proper number of line handlers aboard and lines of required length at the ready, the vessels are required to make a minimum of eight knots to reach the Pacific elevator within the alloted time given to transit Lake Gatun. Underpowered vessels must make special arrangements, whereas *Calypso*, without power, has no recourse but to secure a tow.

The bulletin board is quick to produce an answer to the crew's query: "Motorless twenty-six foot sailboat needs tow to Pacific side." The captain of the fishing vessel *Intrepid* hunts down the crew at the yacht club bar where, over a couple beers, a curious example of "it's a small world" reveals itself. *Intrepid* is bound for Cordova, Alaska from the east coast to participate in the "Herring Roe on Kelp" fishery, which will occur in April.

The captain and crew are new to the fishery and full of questions as to its nature. *Calypso's* crew is forthcoming with loads of valuable tips and local knowledge from their years of experience, for which these fishermen are greatly appreciative. *Intrepid* is laying at anchor, scheduled to transit in two days time. What are the chances of this meeting? This vessel geared up with diving fishermen, bound for an obscure fishery thousands of miles from their home; the same town and fishery where the crew of *Calypso* began their journey.

Excitement ripples through *Intrepid's* crew. The stories of the icy cold, clear water diving, with glaciers calving house size icebergs into Prince William Sound. Sea lions, massive herring schools combined with visions of pockets full of cash paints a picture that has them about ready to crash the gates of the Panama Canal.

So it is done. *Calypso* will soon be transiting the Canal on *Intrepid's* towline, after which she'll make her turn north, for home.

Final preparations are hurried along. A red box is procured to replace the *Rubber Ducky* which had disappeared mysteriously in the Corn Islands. Dubbed the *Red Box* dinghy, this new acquisition is a totally inadequate attempt to build a serviceable dinghy from a single four by eight sheet of plywood. One person with a few groceries overloads this comical little craft, constantly in danger of swamping, as the smallest of wavelets lap over its sides.

These weeks have passed quickly. Doug is settled in to his *Sea Horse*, making repairs and formulating plans for the future. His friend Nancy will be joining him very soon. These spontaneous events appear to suit Doug to a tee. The crew is comfortable they are leaving their friend at a fork in the road. He has charted a fresh, adventurous course.

Hugs and well wishes are exchanged, jib and mizzen hoisted, lines tossed. *Calypso* pays off quietly from her slip. Jib sheet is hauled tight, the mizzen left slack, she swings to starboard as the crew waves their goodbyes, shouting last words until out of earshot.

The helm is put down and the sheets fly at *Intrepid's* stern, *Calypso* goes into irons, the tow line is tossed down and made off to the bits. Jib and mizzen lowered and stowed, the crew then climb aboard their host.

"The Big Ditch"

Whirlpools 'n upwellins' as the locks fill
slimy green walls give the crew a chill
Steel gates closin' screech 'n moan
Calypso's lines take the strain 'n groan

Calypso is pulled along side, as she will be side tied through the Gatun locks, then dropped back on the towline once the vessels are released into lake Gatun. Intrepid pulls her anchor, moving into position behind an oil tanker which has pumped off her load to pass through the Canal. She will then put the oil back aboard on the Pacific side.

The tanker is showing about fifteen feet of bottom paint to her waterline, with nearly half her two giant propellers exposed above the surface. The hull itself fits snuggly into the chamber, with just over a foot of clearance either side. *Intrepid* is squeezed in with very little room left behind her stern for the closing of the gates.

The transition from hot tropic sun to the lock has the crew shaking off a chill. This first chamber is shaded, cool and dank, with slimy cement walls rising thirty feet or more.

At the top of this cavern, individuals are scurrying, making *Intrepid*, lines off and moving "mules" (electric locomotives) into place to tow the ship forward. None of this activity can be seen from *Intrepid's* deck, only the occasional person looking over the side from above to check the vessels and lines.

Lines are winched taut, to the extreme. Steel doors begin to close slowly, the vessels are trapped in a darkening, damp, cold cavern with a screeching, ear piercing complaint. Whirlpools created by the closing doors tug at *Intrepid's* stern, her restraints holding her firmly in place. The whirlpools work on *Calypso* as well while she is held firmly against the heavily cushioned hull of her escort.

Locked in an elevator where water rages
Calypso rises eighty five feet in three stages
Rafted snug to her escort it's very soon
when Calypso enters Lake Gatun

A final thud signals step one is complete. The doors are shut. Now huge upwellings begin tugging at the vessels from underneath, pushing up in all directions. *Intrepid's* lines are kept taut, she strains them, but is held securely in position, *Calypso*, side tied, is another matter.

From *Intrepid's* deck the crew is helpless to improve her

restraints. She is tied bow, stern and sprung in both directions from amidships.

She has become an angry child in the throes of a temper tantrum at her mother's side. Lines are screaming as she tugs violently, trying in vain to tear her self away. Lashing out in such a fashion that if sufficient fenders had not been deployed, she would have beat herself to shards of kindling in short order.

Thankfully, this chamber is filling fast, the vessels rising at surprising rate. Reaching the top, the force of the upwelling subsides. All goes quiet, whirlpools return as the gates are opening and water is exchanged, equalizing.

Black smoke pours from the tanker's stacks when her engines rumble to life. The huge twin screws begin churning, the propulsion sending *Calypso* into another conniption fit. The force of water and half exposed propellers, coupled with a redoubled roar of engines and volumes of black smoke, gets the wall of steel that is dwarfing *Intrepid* and *Calypso* moving into the next lock.

Intrepid tucks herself in behind the big ship as before, the gates are closed, the scene is repeated. First the whirlpools, then the upwellings combined with *Calypso's* theatrics until the chamber is filled and a second repetition begins at the final lock. When completed, the trio will be eighty-five feet above the Atlantic side.

Cross the lake the two boats race
Intrepid's towin' Calypso at a furious pace
At Pedro Miguel Calypso's on a hillside
a great ocean awaits at the end of this ride

On completion of the filling of the third lock and opening of the final gates, The ship leaves the lock ahead of *Intrepid*. *Calypso* is dropped back on her towline, which has been made off directly to her forward bits; rather than fashioning a bridle, in the assumption this will be a casual tow across a quiet lake. Wrong.

The Intrepid's skipper "firewalls" his engine to get her up to speed in the effort to make his appointment for the Pacific locks. Intrepid is making ten or eleven knots, dragging *Calypso* by the nose at more than twice her hull speed. *Calypso* follows obediently, albeit sloughing around to port and starboard like the town drunk.

A few hours running finds the vessels entering the historic "Culebra Cut." The construction of this channel is a story, in and of itself. Man against mud, an epic battle waged over many years, and when completed, had forged an eight mile passage across the Continental Divide.

The tanker had out paced *Intrepid* and her charge enough to have entered and exited Pedro Miguel Locks; leaving the two vessels, on their arrival, waiting for the chamber to fill and the gates to open. They will then begin their descent to the Pacific Ocean.

Calypso is brought alongside for passage through the lock, the crew hopping aboard to make lines fast. Extra precautions this time for the violent thrashings she will endure.

Satisfied they had done their best, the crew takes pause, standing at the bow of their little boat, gazing out to sea. The wide expanse of the Pacific Ocean before them, the thousands of miles gone by. All thoughts evaporate, overwhelmed by this moment of calm. There is communion. There is peace. Pacifica.

Of the journey ahead the crew's thoughts're mixed
of the wide expanse before them
they stand transfixed
This bundle of wood 'n nails
driven by wind 'n sails
out in the Pacific Ocean with big ships 'n whales

Part II

Chapter 12

PACIFIC OCEAN

March 1981

Mira Flores Locks

T he spell is broken with the opening of the gates, whirlpools rock the crew back to life. They hop back aboard *Intrepid*, a puff of smoke from her stacks poops out, the props churn up the water at her stern, pushing the side-tied duo into Pedro Miguel Locks.

A repetition in reverse begins at this single lock, lowering the vessels thirty feet along slimy walls into the now familiar damp, chilly cavern as the chamber empties. The gates open to Mira Flores Lake where *Calypso* is dropped back for the short tow to the final set of locks, a two stage system which will carry the vessels to sea level.

Calypso endures the tow into the waiting arms of Mira Flores Locks. No time is wasted as the doors begin closing behind them the moment the two vessels are secure. The water flushes to the second stage level where the forward doors open, water is equalized

between the two chambers and the vessels move into the final lock, the doors close behind them; the water drops. All goes quiet when sea level is reached; massive steel walls open before them, releasing the two boats into Panama Bay, gateway to the Pacific Ocean. *Calypso's* towline is tossed off when she drops her pick at Balboa Harbor in Panama City.

The two crews say their goodbyes at this point as the *Intrepid* is wasting no time in heading north. Typical in the world of fishing, where much of the time "fishing" is actually spent running hard, to and from fishing grounds. *Intrepid's* "run" to the grounds in this case is nothing short of extreme; ten thousand miles, give or take.

Panama City

Final preparations for the voyage ahead
makin' sure unwanted critters're dead
Soakin' banana stalks over the side
eliminatin' tarantulas without insecticide

One final trip into the city, the crew makes a beeline for the market in order to put on a load of fresh fruits and vegetables which will ripen on board. Dozens of eggs top off the fully loaded *Red Box* dingy. So much so, the crew must swim the box of supplies out to their waiting boat. *Calypso* is bobbing to a light chop at anchor, mimicking the crews anticipation, a prancing pony in her corral, moments before being released to the freedom of the open range.

Staples of rice, beans, flour, cooking oil, coffee, tea and spices along with one hundred twenty gallons of fresh water had been put aboard in Colon. Having no water tanks, the water is stored in six gallon plastic vegetable oil containers. These are carried on the center floorboards from what used to be the engine compartment all the way to the bow.

The cabin sole, as a place to put one's feet is effectively eliminated, forcing the crew to crawl on hands and knees throughout the interior. Having lived without standing headroom for all these months, the water is hardly an inconvenience, considering the security it represents.

Assuming the worst, stalks of bananas and net bags of fruit are hung over the side for the evening, another tidbit learned around the docks in Colon. The thought of tarantulas loose in the cabin is unacceptable and, of course, the catastrophic outbreak of cockroaches on the Swedish yacht is still fresh in the minds of the crew.

The journey to this point has seen multiple styles of stoves aboard *Calypso*. The crew has settled on an alcohol primed, pump pressurized, kerosene burner. This critical item has served them well, accordingly, a five gallon jug of kerosene and a substantial amount of alcohol in one litre plastic bottles  for priming had been put aboard in Colon. Relief from a restless night comes with the first hint of daylight. After a hearty breakfast of "*frijoles y juevos*" smothered in habanero sauce then rolled into a freshly made flour tortilla, the soaking fruit is brought aboard and checked thoroughly for bugs of any description, then hung in the rigging. Some are stored below in hopes of slowing the ripening process.

When the crew is satisfied preparations are complete, the anchor is hauled aboard and stowed, the main and genny are set wing and wing to light offshore morning wisps of wind. Eyes at the helm keep a sharp lookout for the "catspaws" where the wisps reach down to the surface of the water.

Gliding silently out of the anchorage, the crew stands in the cockpit before the immense span of the "Bridge of the Americas" another engineering marvel, connecting two continents.

Smuggler's Cove

One last problem needs solvin'
for finances're fast dissolvin'
At the yacht club a nefarious scheme
had been planned
Now the remedy to our financial woes
is close at hand

Calypso sails into a secret bight
just before the cover of night
A cayuka paddles out from shore
to see what offer we have in store

B eyond the bridge, *Calypso* enters the open expanse of Panama Bay. Light winds provide the first opportunity for toying with the windvane. Although the breeze is light to nonexistent, the vane appears to respond to each little puff. Evaluating its overall capabilities will have to wait for more challenging conditions. *Calypso* sails and drifts to an anchorage, a discreet spot discovered during conversations at the yacht club bar, dropping the pick shortly before nightfall.

This last stop prior to entering the Pacific Ocean is popular among cruisers. The crew has hardly settled when approached by a large cayuka, the paddlers, a half dozen locals grinning, waving greetings as they approach. The scene is slightly intimidating, but the "vibes" are good.

The welcoming committee makes room for the crew as they come alongside, encouraging them to take a seat. Dennis, accepts without hesitation jumping in; Pat, taken aback, opts to remain aboard, showing concern for the general security of *Calypso*.

Taking the *Red Box* dingy in tow for a return vehicle, the villagers paddle back to the beach. The cayuka along with the *Red Box* are hauled ashore. Children run out from their hiding places laughing and screaming, make straight for the *Red Box*.

The paddlers, all quiet for the exception of the fellow who appears to be in charge leading the procession up the beach to a shaded trail. After a very short distance, the trail opens to a much wider foot path through the center of a small village. There are no motor vehicles or their tracks, reminding one of Placencia, Belize; the wind in the palms above, the lapping of waves at the shoreline, the only sounds.

"Welcome to our village" is accompanied by a warm smile and arm outstretched toward two neat rows of modest stucco homes with perfectly maintained palapas atop. The first impression of this tiny village strikes one as a very orderly, tight knit community who take great pride in their homes and surroundings.

This is further evidenced upon entering the home of the individual who had taken it upon himself to act as personal guide.

The care and well maintained look of the village extends into this modest one room abode.

A picture of impeccable, humble simplicity. The floors are hard-packed dirt, cool and comfortable under bare feet; so clean one would not hesitate to invoke the "five-second rule" here.

Colorful woven seating pads on the floor surround a low table, hewn from the cross section of a giant log. My companion welcomes the group to take seats, then opening the top of a large wooden bowl on the table, displays a very familiar commodity. "Panama Red." Songs have been written about these beautiful red haired flowers.

A "spleef" is rolled, then another and another in quick succession and passed around the group as they're completed. My guide is studying me closely, his dark eyes boring deep. With a friendly little elbow jab accompanied by a mischievous wry grin, he remarks, "your boat is quite small." This sends the entire room into a fit of uncontrollable, contagious laughter; the comic relief is the perfect segue to the true nature of *Calypso's* visit, which is quite obviously already known to the villagers.

A hundred dollars is the end of our cash
an' for this we hope to acquire a small stash
The locals want a forty horse outboard
an' for that they'll put a whole ton aboard!

The laughter subsides when questions are posed; "how much do you want?" From another individual "do you have an outboard motor for trade?" These queries are followed up with an explanation that a forty horse outboard is a perfect trading item. The village is in need of two fresh motors. They would be very happy to make a trade, straight across; two motors for two tons of fresh product.

A fascinating insight into the relative values of commodities. No doubt, the huge price disparities contribute to the manicured look of this village. This is a very lucrative enterprise which benefits all who reside here.

One hundred dollars in bills along with spare change in the pockets which had been ferreted away during the Colon stop for this very moment elicits a murmuring chuckle from the group when sorted out on the table. Desperate to make the best deal possible, and having seen the children go for the *Red Box* dinghy, it in effect is placed on the table as well. The group, exchanging glances and grins, agree to something, sending one individual out of the room.

*A hundred dollars 'n the Red Box dinghy's
our best offer
It's all we have for trade an' in the coffer
The children're all over the dinghy with delight
while the elders take pity on our plight*

onversation returns to questions concerning *Calypso*, Alaska and the general nature of the journey. Being coastal folks, they are not unfamiliar with the immensity of the Pacific Ocean and its many moods. Impressed with *Calypso's* journey to this point as well as showing genuine concern for the well being of the crew, the group begins offering helpful details of the prevailing currents and wind conditions which may be expected traveling northward off the Panama and Costa Rican coast. "Local knowledge" is a most respected navigation aid to those entering unfamiliar waters; this sailor leans on every word.

The young fellow who had been sent off on an errand returns, dropping a full size sugar sack on the table to the nods of approval from his mates.

A sugar sack stuffed full of product
the fellow produces
Ten thousand dollars back home
this sailor deduces
Calypso sails outa Panama Bay
wearin' big smiles 'n packin' her load 'o hay!

Never having been in the presence of such a large quantity, the mind jumps to rough calculations of weight and the going rate up north, coming to a quick conclusion; this is about ten grand or more in Washington. Double that in Alaska. The hundred dollars on the table represents the price of one quarter ounce in Alaska.

The deal is struck without hesitation to hand shakes and back slapping, along with the heartfelt well wishes from these friendly folks.

We take our leave as a group back to the cayuka, where there are a half dozen kids laughing and rocking in the *Red Box*, still sitting where it had been towed up on the beach, above the high water line.

Taxied out to *Calypso*, the cayuka bumps alongside, the sugar sack is tossed aboard. Pat's head appears at the hatch, eyes widen, her mouth drops open at the sight of the sack on deck. Again the well wishes come from the cayuka as they pull away.

Last tidbits of navigation hints are repeated in shouts with arms pointing north. The crew of *Calypso* standing on deck, returning gestures and shouts until the distance becomes too great.

Homeward Bound

Leavin' Punta Mala the mornin' sky is hazy
under Calypso's keel the swell long, low 'n lazy
Land disappears standin' far offshore
how many moons before she'll touch terra firma once more?

T rue to the nature of local knowledge, this glassy calm morning sees *Calypso* drifting under full sail to the northwest in Panama Bay. A second day is spent with these light airs. The onset of evening brings a pleasant offshore breeze which allows *Calypso* to run wing and wing with the windvane engaged; she holds course through the night.

This encourages the crew, however, there is still some skepticism as to how the vane will perform in a seaway with a gusty twenty-five or thirty knots on a variety of tacks. Running with the wind being the most critical due to the increased danger of a broach. Sideways in a seaway can prove instantaneous disaster.

A Course is Plotted

◆ ffshore winds die off before dawn, sights are taken, even though Punta Mala is plainly visible off to starboard a comfortable two miles. A serious decision must be made at this juncture: to sail up the coast, close by, where landings may be made in Costa Rica or other ports if necessary? Another option, for the exception of traveling to the Marquesas, is a circled dot on the chart which is a randomly selected point between Hawaii and San Francisco, smack in the middle of the Pacific Ocean.

Vessels encountered at the Yacht Club headed to the mainland of the U.S. are following the tried and true route taking them to the Marquesas Islands, their "jumping off" point to Hawaii. This route takes advantage of prevailing winds and currents. Additionally, it avoids bucking the prevailing northeast trade winds back to the U.S. west coast.

Hawaii is not in consideration as a stop, nor are other intermediate ports. The issue is simple. Every stop now will involve Customs, which present potential problems the crew intends to avoid at all cost.

So it is settled. Two lines are drawn; the first line is from the boat's present position two hundred miles due west where at this approximate location, *Calypso* will alter course.

This first line is drawn to clear *Calypso* from all shipping routes, known or presumed. Traffic on routes to and from the Canal is extreme; commercial vessels travel up the coast as well as follow great circle routes to Asia. The crew is anxious to move well clear as quickly as possible.

The second line represents an adjustment on the compass of fifteen points to the north, running more than seven hundred miles at two hundred eighty five degrees. A somewhat random point determined from knowledge of currents imparted by our Panamanian friends. This point is at the very top of the chart, over a thousand miles west of the southern coast of Mexico, positioned for a run to the circled dot on the next chart. No further lines are drawn, as this second intermediate point near the top of this chart is a combination of guesswork and wishful thinking.

A glassy drift takes *Calypso* to sundown, when the offshore breeze of the previous evening returns. Beginning as a light easterly, *Calypso* is treated to a freshening breeze off her stern. Genny and main are set flying wing and wing. This combination handles a surprising amount of wind, running well balanced in a seaway such as that which has built this night.

Hector

A fresh Pacific breeze sweeps Calypso on her way
she makes a hundred miles the very first day
An' on that first night we learn
'bout this contraption hangin' off her stern

Named for Homer's legendary prince 'n fighter
Hector makes our workload lighter
Steerin' Calypso without food or sleep
regardless the seaway choppy or steep

---

ollowing seas running four to six feet with a light chop provide the first real opportunity to observe the windvane at work. *Calypso* is steadied on course, the weather helm held by securing the wheel in place with a line from the spokes to a cleat. A simple flick of a lever engages the vane. With few moving parts, the unit goes to work instantly, transferring its wind direction information to the rudder section of the unit. The rudder receives the information via a movable tab on its aft edge. In effect, the windvane rudder has a miniature wind powered rudder of its own.

With the boat's rudder tied off holding the weather helm, in other words, doing the heavy work of steering *Calypso*, the job of the more nuanced helmsmanship belongs to the windvane.

Hands now free, the two sailors may go about their routines and daily life in a leisurely fashion. No need to watch a compass, the attitude of *Calypso* riding the waves tells the crew they are steady on course. The hands are not only free, the eyes are free as well to focus on the world beyond the boat. The windvane steers *Calypso* with precision. The vane's rudder dimensions had not been altered during the refit. *Calypso's* main rudder is smaller than the vane rudder, as the vane was built for a much larger vessel. This overkill appears to have a very positive steering effect.

The nature of small boats in following seas, while making for easy, comfortable running, also requires the greatest accuracy at the helm, much more so than sailing off the wind, quartering the waves. Inattention in following seas may result in a gybe, broach or both at once with potential for devastating consequences.

The accuracy of the windvane's ability to keep *Calypso* "stern to" in this following wind and sea bodes well for all other points of sail. At the conclusion of a twenty four hour run, *Calypso* has made one hundred six miles straight offshore. She has done this on her own with the aid of her new addition, dubbed "Hector."

As evening approaches, bringing to a close this first full day offshore, the wind *Calypso* had been enjoying all morning and afternoon dies off. Sights are taken as stars appear after sundown; a glassy calm settles in, the sea flattens, gently rocking the crew into a deep, restful sleep.

Daily Routines Evolve

An abundance of fruit hangin' in the rig
skipjack for dinner caught on a jig
All the comforts we're afforded
includin' that sack of produce we've hoarded!

Pancake flat seas persist through the night, complimenting the exhaustion of the crew. Panama has taken a toll, a spell of windless drifting will be pleasant. The crew can use some slack time to put *Calypso* in a semblance of order. As much fresh food as possible is carried on deck and hung from the stays in such a fashion there will be no interference with sailing when the wind comes up.

Early morning, there are flying fish popping out of the waves, chased into the air as they are being attacked from below. One unfortunate fish offers itself to the crew, making a hard, near fatal landing on deck. A hook and hand line are brought out, the winged visitor is sent back with a tiny pebble of lead squeezed onto the leader.

The wounded fish, swimming lethargically, sinks away from view, the line is left slack as it plays out. Within seconds of the bait disappearing from sight, the line is whizzing through the hands. A slight jerk hooks the fish.

Hand over hand twenty feet of line is brought in; a flash of silver near the surface races past the hull, a hard pull straight up has a football sized skipjack tuna flying over the heads of the crew, landing with a smack on deck, the tail now a blur beating the cabin top, ineffectively, as its plump torso lays motionless. This fish will provide protein to the crew for a couple days, as well as bait for the next fishing effort.

Bumper Crop

Now the afore mentioned sack must be protected
from pryin' eyes 'n remain undetected
A simple plan's devised
usin' a bumper which's oversized

The sugar sack crowds the tiny cabin with its inert bulk. It has found a temporary home at the base of the mainmast, blocking the way forward, which is unacceptable. This "elephant in the room" must be given serious thought as to its handling and stowage. A healthy quantity is separated and made easily accessible. The remainder is destined to be squirreled away in a discreet fashion, somewhere in the boat, but how?

The crew ponders the question, finally settling on a solution. Somewhere along the ICW, a very large oblong bumper had been retrieved as it floated in their path. It had been tossed into the bow to be brought out whenever *Calypso* had occasion to tie up to a dock.

The bumper we pack super tight
an' glue the seam back exactly right
"We'll hang it over the side at our next port
then go to customs an' report!"

A razor is used to carefully slice open this oversize bumper along its seam. Before transferring the very loosely packed product from the sugar sack the stalks are removed. The flowers are then stuffed into the bumper using as much pressure as possible to pack it tight; pressed ever tighter to the tunes of "Comin' into Los Angeles" and "Thunder Road" until all the product squeezes in. The seam is then glued very carefully back in place. Once the glue has dried, the seam is dirtied to conceal the tampering. The cache is now tossed back into the bow where it appears as an innocent element of common equipment found on every boat.

Brilliant, this little piratical bootleg seems appropriate. Sailing out of Panama with contraband cargo, the way ahead, fraught with danger coupled with visions of an instant fortune on arrival up north. Classic.

Mr. Nimbus

A breathless ocean afternoon heat's oppressive
Billowin' clouds're impressive
The signs cannot be misunderstood
Mr. Nimbus's in the neighborhood!

After two days adrift, land is sighted. Having been following *Calypso's* progress celestially, this is no surprise. Also no surprise is the direction and speed of drift coinciding once more with knowledge gained from our Panamanian friends.

Calypso has floated on calm, airless seas back to the coast. She now stands thirty miles north of Punta Mala. This is unfortunate, only in that she has reentered the commercial traffic lanes; the upside being, she is drifting in the general direction of home.

Afternoon skies, filled with billowing white clouds bring on a noticeable rise in humidity. *Calypso* is nearly motionless, the crew observes the familiar "top hat" of the cumulonimbus growing high at an alarming rate. The lower reaches of the structure are turning dark.

Tremendous energy accumulates before our eyes
risin' thousands of feet into blue skies
The suspense is particularly frightenin'
'cause there's no thunder 'n lightnin'

They are relieved however, when there is no "brim." No anvil is forming at the base as witnessed in the Caribbean. Also absent is the cool breeze which precedes the powerful knockout punch of the leading edge. Lessons had been learned and taken seriously. The crew makes ready, which is accomplished with a few extra lashings on deck, as all the sails are already stowed. The sunshade which is stretched across the cockpit over the mizzen is wrapped around the boom and lashed in place. All there is left to do, is wait.

The bottom of the formation continues to grow dark. Very dark. Still, no anvil takes shape. This certainly is a curiosity. Neighboring cloud formations are taking on similar attributes with their top hats along with the telltale graying at the base. The suspense is building; something is about to happen. Why are there no anvils forming, no lightening bolts? For the moment, caught in the wonderment, answers to their questions are not forthcoming.

Waterspout

From a black knob a tornadic vortex extends
to the ocean's surface the funnel descends
In the face of this danger Calypso stands proud
while a top hat's suckin' ocean into a cloud

A terrifying answer to all our questions first shows itself as a black knob pooching out the center of the bottom of the top hat. A small twister springs from the bulge, dropping down a few hundred feet before quickly retreating back into the knob.

This begins a series of pulsations reaching out for the ocean with its tendril. Each attempt brings the funnel closer to the surface, the knob swells, growing larger, more powerful with every pulse, now threatening to send the appendage to the surface less than a mile from *Calypso* and her hapless crew, standing silent on deck. Less than a mile off to starboard, a tramp steamer, its crew lining the rails slows to a crawl, presumably preparing to render assistance when disaster strikes.

Two thousand feet tall this menacin' twister now we discover it has a sister!
Cumulonimbus produc-es a storm where tornadic funnels spawn 'n swarm

The moment the funnel achieves its goal, the touch down sends a chill down the spines of the crew who are hanging on to each other, including the mizzen mast in their embrace. The ship continues steaming ahead slowly; altering course slightly toward

Calypso. The appendage is now firmly attached to the ocean, angrily chewing a ditch directly toward the little boat, with only several hundred yards separating the two.

Water spouts diggin' trenches in the sea
a harrowin' situation has come to be
Absolutely nothin' can be done
Calypso just sits frozen in the sun

This atmospheric event which has unfolded, ends as a movie played in reverse. The funnel which has descended, threatening to overrun *Calypso* with its gyrating black snorkel, takes on a shade of gray, first appearing as a light mist in the midsection of the tube. With this development the base of the funnel drawing ocean into the cloud disappears, its connection to the cloud having been severed.

The remainder of the twister, hundreds of feet above the ocean is again pulsating, in reverse, until the appendage retreats into the knob, which in turn, melts into the cloud. In the distance, surrounding *Calypso*, the sister twisters also recede into their clouds. Puffs of black smoke and a low bellowing, the sound of the ships foghorn, bids *Calypso* farewell.

As quickly as Mr. Nimbus appeared
the funnels dissipate 'n disappeared!
These threatenin' twisters havin' receded
Calypso drifts on unimpeded

Chapter 13

DOLDRUMS

April 1981

Northwest Drift

A strong Northwesterly current prevails
still no wind for Calypso's sails
Driftin' along at a comfortable pace
nearly oblivious to the human race

Calypso is alone once again on the ocean, providing shade and protection for small fish gathering under her hull. One wonders where this variety of colorful visitors have arrived from, how they survive the predators surrounding them? How they manage to find Calypso? One hazards a guess the vibrations created by the hull slapping the surface as she drifts emanate signals which travel great distances. Fish may detect these signals via their lateral line.

A fisherman may offer a more simplified explanation of this curiosity; they are simply "in the soup," where *Calypso* is a floating lure, providing a moderately safe haven.

This airless drift, after about a week, shows no sign the pattern will change any time soon. The afternoon heat is oppressive; midday activities cease in the extreme equatorial humidity. Routines develop around the drift, which the crew now refers to, correctly, as "The Doldrums."

Certainly, this *is* a designated oceanic area known as the Doldrums, occurring between the northeast and southeast trade winds; complete with the associated tornadic storm witnessed the day before.

Each morning begins with the navigation duties of taking sights and making calculations, resulting in a fresh line of position. This first week at sea has *Calypso* averaging almost two knots over a twenty four hour period. This information pleases the crew, as *Calypso's* average speed to date, with all the vagaries of wind and sea, including the Intracoastal has been a consistent three knots.

Thirty to forty nautical miles in twenty-four hours is now *Calypso's* new average. Conditions being so pleasant, the crew is quite content. They want for nothing; surrounded on deck with their load of fruit, down below the eggs, rice, beans, flour, and water all in abundance.

The short wave radio's an exception
to the outside world it's Calypso's connection
Voice of America brings "Mornin' Edition"
"All Things Considered" our evenin' tradition

◆nce the sight is taken and the time is verified, the "Zenith Trans-Oceanic" radio is then switched to "Voice of America" which provides the crew with news via their daily broadcast of National Public Radio's "Morning Edition." This shortwave radio is *Calypso's* sole piece of electronic equipment. A vital component, providing Greenwich Mean Time on demand; the essential element in determining one's longitude.

The turmoil in Ireland tops this morning's report, as it has the last several days concerning a hunger strike which had begun about two weeks earlier. A few more headlines satisfies the crew's curiosity of the goings on around the planet.

Aboard Calypso pleasant routines evolve
aroun' navigation 'n fishin' the days revolve
Stars 'n planets captured at first light
breakfast caught on the mornin' bite

True to the customary routines aboard *Calypso*, the radio is shut down until required for the next sight, or NPR's "All Things Considered" broadcast. Breakfast follows, always a whimsical affair gravitating one day toward fresh made flour tortillas, beans and eggs to another day where fish and fruit are desired. A second pot of fresh Panamanian coffee often accompanies the morning meal.

A hook is baited with a flying fish then hurled off the stern. The bait is taken instantaneously on splashing into the water. A slight tug on the line sets the hook, then the fish, still unseen, dives deep. The line is paying out through the hands at a terrific speed when a tight grip is applied, pulling the fish up short. There is a brief struggle as the fish plays itself out. A small mahi mahi is pulled up on deck, perfect for several meals.

The northerly set to the current persists, Panama's coast has given way to that of Costa Rica. On occasion this stream displays itself as a swiftly flowing river, gurgling loudly with pronounced rips and a standing chop of about a foot at the surface. *Calypso*, still without wind is carried along in any number of lackadaisical attitudes as she drifts north.

Freighter!

The reverie is interrupted one particular afternoon. *Calypso* has drifted out of sight of land, when a freighter is spotted on the horizon. These giant steel walls move at great speed across the ocean. From the moment they appear in the distance to their arrival at one's position, their speed never fails to astonish this sailor.

This ship is on a course well clear of *Calypso*, the eyes drawn to it repeatedly, as for the exception of the approaching vessel, the seas are barren. Lounging under their shade in this idyllic, hedonistic fashion, the crew are undisturbed yet acutely aware of its presence as it continues to loom larger with each passing minute.

A change in its course does not go undetected. Always wary when sharing the ocean with a vessel of this size, speed and limited maneuverability; the change in course, toward *Calypso*, has the crew on deck, on alert, staring intently.

The ship appears to be on a collision course, unaware of our presence. The crew of *Calypso* is dependent on the professionalism of their fellow mariners which, at this moment, is their sole hope of survival.

When the ship is

almost upon them, sailors can be seen lining the rails atop the steel walls, instantly dousing the fears of the crew. As the ship passes, without throttling back, she is about twenty yards off *Calypso's* starboard beam.

The sailors are waving, the captain appears at the wheelhouse, high above the deck, joining his crew in their greeting; their shouts muted by the deep rumble of heavy machinery combined with loudly whooshing water. *Calypso's* crew return the greeting wholeheartedly in their relief.

It is very possible the ships captain had attempted hailing *Calypso* on the VHF radio. Becoming concerned with her silence, he had altered course to investigate. Alert seafarers are comfort to the crew. They are thankful for all the professionals plying the inland waterways and wide open seas. For the exception of the errant helmsman in Cuba, who received a severe tongue lashing from his captain for his mistake, the crew has encountered this sort of professionalism consistently throughout the journey to date.

Fishing

A variety of fishin' tools're made
canvas over the mizzen boom for shade

*Schools of fish gathern' under the boat
we're discoverin' an idyllic life afloat*

Two weeks drift into three, the course is steady. The two knot average on this glassy, windless surface is still maintained. Gradually, *Calypso* drifts further west, far enough offshore, she appears to have left the traffic lanes, as no vessels have been sighted in the last several days.

The mizzen boom serves as a beam carrying a shade tarpaulin protecting the cockpit from a relentless tropical sun. This is where the crew spends the bulk of their time, watching the ocean, reading and generally lounging, as activities in the Doldrums are reduced to the most basic daily requirements. The menagerie below the surface, in the shade of *Calypso*, has grown substantially, providing meals whenever desired. Juvenile tuna have become very abundant, as well as being one of the tastiest fish under the boat. A tool for catching these miniature tuna is fashioned from a ten foot bamboo pole with a series of half a dozen treble hooks lashed one above the other six or eight inches apart.

The pole is slowly lowered down alongside the hull and held steady for a minute or less. When a good number of fish can be seem gathered around the pole, a quick jerk inevitably hooks one or two pan sized tuna.

---

*A hundred miles off the Guatemalan coast
caught a nice mackerel for a dinner roast
However that roast never came to be
flipped off the hook 'n back to the sea*

Fatlip

*The followin' mornin' a curious sight
a Mackerel looks like it'd been in a fight
The fish caught the day before
has a fat lip an' it sure looks sore*

The morning ritual of looking over the stern is a habit which evolves from sailing in light airs to discern if any headway is taking place. Forward progress will show in the form of telltale miniature whirlpools, spinning off Hector and the after-run of *Calypso's* hull.

However, there is still not a breath against the sail, Hector is simply bobbing up and down, kersplashing in harmony with the kerflopping of *Calypso's* hull. This kersplashing and kerflopping has gone on so long now in the background, the crew has nearly lost awareness of its incessant, monotonous plunging.

A white spot catches the eye causing one to look much closer into the water. A curious, rather unsightly bulbous clump is attached to a fish. About a foot long, torpedo shaped; it is hanging idle, next to Hector.

The image of yesterday's fish flying through the air on a hook, then lost, causes one to look even closer. There is no doubt, the white spot is a wound, the upper lip having been ripped open. This is the mackerel lost off the hook yesterday. Pan fried mackerel is now on the menu. A fillet of flying fish is put on a hook then dropped right in front of the fish's nose. The bait does not get so much as a look. The mackerel is not biting. Not surprising, maybe it will be hungry later, and it will be a dinner mackerel.

Ocean Observation

With so many days now on the drift, one tries hard to focus on the light swell, in the not surprising futile attempt to discover swells originating in the northeast trades. Each day some time is devoted in the pursuit of this endeavor. Trade wind generated swells are persistent, their proximity of less than a thousand miles should produce detectable swells to the trained eye, right here in the Doldrums.

One of the early skills a fisherman working the ocean in a small boat will undoubtedly learn, is to ascertain when an ocean swell signals the approach of a large, dangerous storm. Weather conditions may deceive, where the swell, as its size increases, is a bullhorn blaring a warning to the fleet.

A rapidly increasing height and bulk to the waves sends fishing boats scattering for shelter, the radio abuzz with weather chatter; this all happens under clear skies, revealing no hint of the tempest beyond the horizon.

While fishing salmon, one would sit quietly when presented with calm ocean conditions and slow fishing, looking for, as well as feeling for, elusive waves to pass under the boat. One observes swells from different quadrants crossing through each other. The nature and origin of ocean swells is an endless source of wonder for mariners of every stripe, right along to the occasional visitor or individual witnessing the ocean for the first time.

Each set, identified as they move through each other may contain clues to one's whereabouts or conditions at sea near and far. The ancient navigators of the South Seas developed techniques which they passed down through the generations. These methods are worthy of study by the modern mariner.[4] The goal being increased awareness of the origination of ocean swells which

---

4   See "We the Navigators" David Lewis 1972

may have traveled a thousand miles or more, down to wave action signaling the vessels approach on an unseen island.

Combined with observations of celestial bodies, bird migrations, behavior of whales and other mammals, even the subtleties of phosphorescence, enabled the Islanders to guide their catamarans across great distances making Inter-Island trade possible, many of which are separated by hundreds, if not thousands, of miles of open sea.

These skills, so alien to western practices, are responsible for the habitation of the Hawaiian Islands a thousand of years prior to Captain Cook's discovery in the relatively recent seventeen hundreds. Early Pacific Ocean seafarers accomplished this without compass, sextant, or employing a grid drawn on a globe, then flattened on paper followed by complicated mathematical computations.

Rocking on this undulating world, the mind drifts into this inquiring state. Several hours pass before becoming exhausted with the concentration. One has the impression the swell generated by the the northeast trades would have an extreme wave length, the crests possibly passing by a day or even days apart. If one were to discover this series of swells, or singular waves, whatever form they take, a door will be unlocked to an entirely fresh approach to ocean navigation.

Calypso has now drifted over four hundred miles. It must be noted, this drift has her right on course to home, roughly five thousand miles of open ocean; two long tacks northward.

As the heat of the day diminishes, the crew prepares for dinner and the routine star sights which follow the evening meal. No attempt is made to lure the mackerel at *Calypso's* stern. The bamboo hooker brings a small tuna aboard in short order which is filleted. The scraps are then dropped in front of our friend with that painful looking fat lip, still idling next to Hector.

From the immediate reaction, gobbling the scraps without

hesitation, it is quite obvious this fish has learned the difference between food and bait. A fascinating diversion begins here.

The little mackerel is dubbed "Fat Lip" with a vow to not make a meal of *Calypso's* companion. Once Fat Lip has had its fill, a delicious combination of tuna strips, spiced plantains lightly fried with a fresh coconut milk finish is prepared; standard fare here in the Doldrums.

Following the evening meal, the crew relaxes, watching for the first opportunities to begin a series of star sights while the horizon is clearly visible. Regulus, clear, bright and bold, is singled out, providing the first sight of the evening. Betelguese, Capella and Polaris are next to fall into the sextant's sights, offering additional accurate elevations which will combine with Regulus, resulting in four lines of position crossing *Calypso's* track. These lines intersect within close proximity of one another, pinpointing her position.

Calypsos' drift is angling westward, on track to pass midway between the mainland and Clipperton Island. This position, when finalized on the plotting chart is then transferred to the small, weathered "Hammond Atlas," which has been a book of reference since leaving Rhode Island. The slow progress is beginning to wear a hole in the North Pacific Ocean page.

Another week of drifting in this lackadaisical fashion, an additional hundred fifty miles pass under the keel. Now four weeks into this idyllic routine, this particular day wears on as the day before and all the previous days since the drift began. The afternoon heat has the crew lounging under the mizzen boom shade when, without warning, *Calypso* is laid on her beam ends.

Chapter 14

GULF OF TEHUANTEPEC

April 1981

Doldrums Demise

*From the Bay of Campeche
this norther comes a screamin'
Funneled through a mountain pass
this fabled wind's a demon
Taken by surprise at its ferocious arrival
this sea of tranquility now a struggle for survival*

"Dry south-
easter!"
Those dreaded words
hollered across VHF
channel 16, blood cur-
dling on the fishing
grounds in Alaska,
instantly flash vivid-
ly in the mind's eye.
Calypso is skitter-
ing across an ocean
blown flat by an eighty

or ninety knot gust. The hammer blow lasting only seconds, then settles down to a steady fifty or sixty knots, the seas build quickly, cresting with a nasty chop atop.

The sunshade, the sole piece of canvas aloft, suffering from sun rot is shredded, most of which goes by the boards. The crew jump to the mizzen mast, wind tearing at them, in an effort to get a reef in the sail before setting it. *Calypso* is wallowing in the trough, confounding the struggle.

Six hundred miles thirty days adrift
a weather change comes very swift
Initial gust hits like a boat wrecker
Calypso just drifted into a Tehuantepecer!

Wind's rippin' at Calypso with a tiger's claw
perfect timin' for Murphy's Law
Tryin' to reef the mizzen as the wind howls
at the masthead the halyard fouls!

The Colon Yacht club had provided a steady exchange of stories, rumors and solid information. Cobbled together from the combined experiences of sailors passing through this area, most of whom had been traveling south to Panama, the crew is well aware of their geographical location along with the possibility of one of these events occurring, even though they are over fifty miles offshore.

Conventional wisdom has the preferred passage routed close by the beach, which shelters vessels from higher winds and big seas, to some degree. The effects of a "norther" funneling down from the

Gulf of Mexico into the Gulf of Tehuantepec through a venturi are reaching far offshore, to hand *Calypso* this severe pummeling.

Reef points are tied off, *Calypso's* heaving making a difficult chore of it. The halyard is whipped off its cleat, a fierce tug is met with solid resistance, the sail does not budge. MURPHY! The complaint heard above the wind, reinforced with an extended round of livid profanity.

To solve this problem there's no doubt
gotta go aloft 'n straighten this mess out
Gustin' sixty seventy knots an' more
this proves to be a most difficult chore

The halyard sheave is centered in a slot at the masthead. The line has jumped out of its groove, lodging securely between the outside of the sheave and inside of the mast. This had occurred off the coast of Honduras when the worn halyard had parted under the strain.

Assuming all that will be needed is to pop the line free, rather than replacing it as before, the nearly instant reaction, with the additional aid of the jammed halyard, has the mast scaled, halfway. The extreme tossing in the trough forces a stop to grip with arms, legs, hands and bare feet. Hugging tight to keep from being thrown into the ocean with the snap roll, the cheek is pressed hard against the mast, adding a head grip to the effort. Surviving the snap roll to the lull moment, another effort has a couple more feet gained, however still out of reach of the masthead when another steep roll signals the next savage snap. Another white knuckle grip, with arms and legs spliced into the halyard, the bear hug withstands the Tehuantepecer's vicious attempt to flick the climber into the sea.

The mizzen mast's not very tall
an' its diameter quite small
Gettin' to the top's in vain
'cause this little mast can't take the strain

Winds howlin' at storm force
Calypso's buckin' like a wild horse
At the top, the mast starts whippin'
it's come down to white knuckles grippin'

Hanging forty five degrees to the world, progress halts, the masthead is just out of reach. Another lull, another effort followed by another hug through the next toss. The strain on the small mast is considerable, the possibility it may snap is real.

This excruciating climb ends when a firm grip is had on the halyard next to the sheave. Every effort is made at the first lull to relieve the jammed line. *Calypso* is dropped rudely into the trough in a deep downwind roll to port, a near knockdown under bare poles. The next sea slaps her upright with such violence, arms and legs are ripped free of their desperate entanglement.

Floppin' aroun' top o' the mast
hands let go! They can't hold fast!
Flyin' through the air arms 'n legs flailin'
all splayed out an' silently wailin'

With the boat's extreme motion
damn near flew off into the ocean!
Calypso's thrashin' so wildly
the landin' was rough to put it mildly

Adrenalin has falling from the masthead a slow motion illusion, floating above the bright yellow cabin top, far below. Arms, legs, fingers and toes extended, mouth wide open, devoid of sound; a flying squirrel stealing itself for a hard landing. The pain of the crash not felt, only the sensation of relief one is not treading water in the ocean, comforted further with a cheek pressed hard against a cool, wet cabin top.

Back on deck the solution's revised
a plan to drop the mizzen mast's devised
In calm conditions this task's easy
but at seventy knots it's way too breezy

Calypso's patience with the ineptitudes of her crew is nothing short of remarkable. The agile little craft taunts an angry ocean, hopping about, she is a jack rabbit on a desert; try as they might, the seas cannot catch her. Her crew is shaken by their failure, a momentary reaction overcome quickly as waves continue to toss and pound while the wind tears and shreds. Somehow, other than an occasional light splash, the seas never breach the rails. The one time *Calypso* has had heavy seas breaking on deck she was hard aground on the Yucatan Barrier Reef.

When all four stays we detach
there ensues a terrific wrestlin' match
A struggle with wind, sail 'n a big wooden stick
tossed by the ocean proves no simple trick

In wind 'n sea Calypso thrashes
onto the deck the mizzen mast crashes
The crew scrambles to make the mast ready
to step again so Calypso'll ride steady

Seizing on an alternative solution, the crew hops to the four deadeyes tensioning the mizzen. These are slackened when the bracket bolting the mast to the back of the cabin is removed. The mizzen is eased down toward the deck in her tangle of rigging with great effort, as *Calypso's* quick moves have the mast swinging wildly out to starboard. With the mast at the perpendicular, the next deep roll followed by a severe thrust to port, all control is lost. The mizzen swings from its extreme extension seaward slamming into the mainmast stays *Calypso* shudders right to her keel with the blow. Were it not for the generous lengths of lines at the deadeyes, the mizzen mast would have gone by the boards.

The marlinspike makes quick work of the jammed line, prying it free from where it had become lodged. The fix is quick, lines and stays are put back in an orderly fashion as much as possible, leaving ample slack at the deadeyes to allow the mast to reach the full upright position, unhindered by shortened stays. Preparations for re-stepping complete, no time is wasted in the attempt to raise the mast.

*Timin' the lift with the boat's roll's a must
usin' the wind for extra thrust
Up she goes but way too fast!
Back to the deck crashes
the mizzen mast*

Exhaustion is a factor after repeated failures, the crew pauses to collect themselves and gather strength. Storm force gusts, steep seas and snap rolls continue to wear on them. This momentary respite gives rise to a fresh approach to the problem.

The mast is swung 180 degrees, which allows it to lay across the transom, parallel to the keel. The topping lift is unshackled from the main boom and taken to the downed mizzen, where a couple loose wraps are are wound three fourths the way up. A short length of twine secures the topping lift wraps in place. The twine is very light in order to break it away when the mast is upright and bolted to the rear of the cabin. This breaking of the twine will allow for retrieval of the topping lift. The mast is now shoved far enough aft where the foot will drop off the cabintop into its "step" on the cockpit sole. The mizzen is now in position for the lift into its bracket at the back of the cabin.

*Ragin' conditions make for a most difficult chore
'cause that mast falls several times more
With perseverance there's success at last
when finally we step the mizzen mast*

T he crew readies themselves, patiently watching the seas. They fall into the rhythm of the roll of the boat when several jumbo waves pass under her hull. Their crests slap her sides hard. There follows that fortuitous pause of motion prior to the heave of the next wave. The crew's already lifting and hauling on the topping lift when the sea pushes. Now in concert with the inertia, they stand the mast up perfectly straight, its base buries in the step. The bracket is instantly attached, clamping the mast to the back of the cabin, the four deadeyes are drawn tight which secure the mast in position. She is now ready to carry sail.

A fierce tug at the topping lift breaks the twine, the topping lift is retrieved, then shackled back in its place on the main boom. The mizzen sheets are cleated off port and starboard; the sail is set amidships with a double reef. *Calypso* swings abruptly to weather. She rides easy, now taking the seas and chop bow on.

The crew goes about tidying the deck, which after a month adrift, was not prepared for the onslaught of big weather. Loose fishing gear is tangled with the deck bucket. There are galley items, clothes, remnants of the cockpit shade, dried fish and tools scattered about in a most un-seamanshiplike manner. All the trappings of life aboard our seagoing shangri-la are scooped up unceremoniously and dumped down the forward hatch.

---

*Squared away the deck and retired below
nuthin to do but ride out the blow
Two more days Calypso's tossed and tumbled
a weary crew sits quietly humbled*

Chapter 15

NORTHEAST TRADEWINDS

April - May 1981

Clues from Afar

Wind drops to fifteen knots on day three
a hundred twenty miles farther out to sea
Raise the mains'l 'n sheet er tight
let the genny fly 'n set the course right

Blue Pacific swells big 'n bold
a comfortin' gurgle as the breeze takes hold
Tirelessly seekin' the winds' vector
at the helm stands a vigilant Hector

Late afternoon on day three of the blow the chop begins to disappear from the wave tops, the seas calm, running six to eight feet out of the east northeast. The reef is shaken out of the mizzen, the main and genny are set, the wind now just fifteen knots.

With the horror stories told at the Colon Yacht Club having now been verified by firsthand experience as well as *Calypso's* tenacity in her response to this fabled tempest, the crew's faith in their little boat and her capabilities has taken a quantum leap.

Waking from the first restful night following the heavy weather the crew takes note, an even six foot swell has set up out of the northeast. The wind has backed considerably north overnight while the fifteen knots from the previous day holds.

From this observation, the disparity between the height and nature of the seaway and the light breeze have the crew pouring over the North Pacific Ocean chart of prevailing winds and currents.

The wave lengths are long, the seas smooth; one imagines a stone dropped in a pool. The outer, furthest reaching rings have long wave lengths. The deduction from all available information taken together with *Calypso's* present position, northwest of the Gulf of Tehuantepec, this seaway has been set up by a distant, unseen force off the starboard bow. It is within the realm of possibilities, this pleasant breeze is the wind line at the extremities of the northeast trades. *Calypso* has entered the outer rings of the stone in a pool on an oceanic scale.

They are comfortable with their assessment, confident even, steady winds are in the offing. Not exactly rising to the level of the South Pacific Islander's powers of observation, however, a clear demonstration of their technique at the rudimentary level, they are certain. Fifteen knots on the long Pacific seaway with not a whitecap in sight; a marked, pleasant difference from the steep Caribbean and Atlantic seas with their shorter wavelengths. This, the reward for patience in sitting out the blow, allowing their seaworthy little craft to handle wind and wave in her own way.

Hitchhiker

---

*With Calypso underway
time for breakfast 'n the catch o' the day*

Lookin' over the stern a surprisin' sight
There's that mackerel looks' like it'd been in a fight!

First order of business following the pre-dawn navigation is catching a fresh fish for breakfast. A chunk of dried tuna is used to bait the hook. A quick glance around the boat for a likely quarry reveals an oddity. There is a fish, less than a foot underwater at *Calypso's* stern.

"Fatlip!" There is no doubt. The telltale white scar on the little mackerel is plainly visible. The wound has healed, leaving a carbuncle on the upper lip. Still holding tight at its station in the eddy next to Hector this little fish had stuck with *Calypso* through the Tehuantepecer.

A tasty fillet's dangled
next to that nose so mangled
But this fish never gives it a look
an' will not touch the baited hook

A tiny tuna swoops in an' gets caught
to this mackerel it matters not
I guess 'ol Fatlip don't hold a grudge
from Calypso's stern he does not budge

The bait is dropped as a greeting from above, the assumption being Fatlip will not bother with the lure, which proves correct. A small fish shoots out from under the boat, taking the hook. One jerk and a flip has the little tuna flopping on deck. Pan size for two, plus scraps for Fatlip.

Our little hitchhiker takes the morsels with lightning speed when they hit the water. Whatever he misses or lets pass, other fish swoop in, mostly these interesting little tuna. This mackerel swam through heavy seas for three days, hanging tight to the protection of the hull. *Calypso's* back eddy provides the perfect home, as the eddy goes wherever *Calypso* goes. This fish has acquired a mobile home with sushi prepared by a personal chef.

The Final Frontier

NPR tells us "Scan the night sky
for a hundred tons of metal hurtlin' by
The Space Shuttle Columbia's up there
in that vast expanse somewhere"

Calypso's position, 12.5 degrees North Latitude by 99.5 degrees West Longitude, April 12th is noted on the chart, roughly two hundred miles west of the Mexican coast. She had drifted six hundred miles in thirty days since leaving Panama, gaining about five degrees in latitude. Hector is engaged, "All things Considered" is replaced by "WWV" and its bonging of Greenwich Mean Time (GMT). Evening sights are taken, after which the crew turns their eyes skyward. The news headline has the crew light on their feet, with great expectations on the approach of this particular night.

Darkness reveals a gazillion stars, constellations, the Milky Way, even satellites and sputniks are sorted out, however the Space Shuttle (*Columbia's* voyage), in progress somewhere high above *Calypso* is not observed.

Columbia. Appropriately named after the first American sailing ship to circumnavigate the globe. This is the maiden voyage of a crew carrying space ship, the pair begin waxing philosophic as they lay searching the night sky. There is a connection sensed, a kinship with those explorers racing through the stars at over seventeen thousand miles an hour. *Calypso* and *Columbia* cavort on the edges of the unknown. Their respective crews, fragile, lost in wonderment, helpless but for the evolution of knowledge that has designed and built such vehicles as wind powered pocket cruisers and rocket powered space ships. The crew raise their evening tea in a toast, clinking their cups to Mr. A. A. Bernard of Woburn Mass. and to the many thousands of dedicated individuals who built and launched the state of the art flying machine above them.

Over a million miles they travel in two days
so much like Calypso in so many ways
In space 'n sea one hears the Sirens' call
Astronauts an' Argonauts adventurers all

April 14th, 1981 a navigation point is placed on the chart. A significant mini-milestone in that *Calypso* is crossing the one hundred degree west meridian, roughly five hundred miles east of Clipperton Island. *Columbia* returns to earth safely, a magnificent milestone for humankind.

Bucking the Trades

The breeze freshens quickly after sunrise
Doldrums are far astern we surmise
Shorten sail as the wind demands
to the north by northwest, Calypso stands

White caps appear as the wind freshens. The seas build, now running eight to twelve feet. The intermittent sparks of white across the expanse of undulating blue have graduated to a respectable, steady chop. Every wave sports a snow white toupee. An abundance of caution has the mainsail stowed. The jib replaces the genny, the helm is eased five degrees to port however, *Calypso* continues to buck hard upwind into the trades. The helm is eased another five degrees to accommodate the comfort of the crew as well as reduce strain on the boat as she drives to windward.

Under jib 'n mizzen Calypso charges ahead
in the crew there's no fear or dread
For challenges ahead eager anticipation
for this moment in time wondrous exhilaration

A train of choppy swells outa' the northeast
ten or twelve feet high at the very least
Slack the sheets, let'er fall off slightly
take these seas a little more lightly

Spirits are high aboard as if the journey has begun anew. In effect, it has. *Calypso* is discovering an ocean with a completely new character. The water is a much deeper blue. The color blue adopted in the 1700's by the British navy, commonly known as "Navy Blue."

The Gulf of Tehuantepec appears to have been a transition zone. The change as stark as crossing a desert to come upon a land of low, rolling green hills; a new world. The wave train generated by the trades is strong, a sense of timelessness pervades. These seas have remained steady many thousands of years, interrupted intermittently by hurricanes and calms, inevitably to return this present state of equilibrium.

Through this choppy seascape Calypso's slidin'
at her side flyin' fish're glidin'
High above the mast Man-o-War're soarin'
on this glorious trade winds mornin'

A speck of wood on this ocean so vast
a lone Albatross circles the mast
Beatin' to windward the order of the day
a chorus of critters usher Calypso on her way

Sea birds soar high while others swoop tight circles around *Calypso*. Her immediate surroundings are a beehive of activity. The whirring buzz of flying fish, flashes of silver in the water, albatross sweep low over the waves, a lone frigate bird (man-o-war) makes wide circles high above the scene. A curious visitor from the deep surfaces then disappears before being identified. "What was that?" or "Did you see that?" are now the two most common phrases aboard *Calypso*. An ocean caravan moving along apace, growing larger as it attracts newcomers.

Life under the boat has increased markedly as well. A notably more aggressive Fatlip keeps busy, defending his sweet spot at Hectors' side. The back eddy pulls him along, he appears to only use his tail as a steadying sail, much the same as *Calypso's* mizzen. As the boat picks up speed, surfing down ten footers, Fatlip's tail flutters just a bit to keep up until the back-eddy takes hold; he is right there, stuck like glue.

At the surface shearwaters 'n skuas're skimmin'
In the swells swordfish 'n tuna're finnin'
Calypso's world a livin' collage
On this great ocean with her entourage

Blue Footed Booby Boo Boo

A blue footed booby bird lands on deck
Calypso's crew says "what the heck!"
Thinkin' this poor bird's needin' a rest
never occurred it's lookin' for a nest

One new arrival, a blue footed booby has been circling close by since just after sunrise. This bird with its bright blue feet delights the crew when it lands on the bowsprit. Bird landings have always been treated as special events aboard *Calypso* since leaving Rhode Island. This bird is no exception, being the largest bird on board to date.

The snowy egret event back in Isla Mujeres will be tough to beat as landings go. This bird, although there is no intrigue, has a ton of character, a social creature with a comic, yet feisty, personality. The extra large, webbed blue feet of course are a clownish touch to this most entertaining seabird.

A friendly sort big as a turkey
has no interest in tuna fish jerky
An' this Booby's not a lonesome bird
'cause here comes a second an' a third!

Bits of sun jerked tuna are tossed onto the foredeck, a welcoming gesture to *Calypsos'* visitor. The big bird shows no interest, appearing quite content to perch on the bowsprit, preening.

A second booby circles low, spying on the bowsprit booby. Making another sweep around the boat, this next bird lands, taking the spot right next to the first at

the end of the bowsprit. The two birds greet each other as though they are mates.

With this second landing, a glance skyward reveals several more boobies circling, eyeing the pair on the bowsprit. This day is shaping up to be a fascinating avian event combined with the dramatic introduction to trade winds sailing the crew are currently enjoying.

Calypso breaks trail in the seaway as she beats to the northwest. Our passengers ride the bowsprit like old salts, swaying in concert with the rolling and bucking of their hard charging steed. When the wind pipes up, the crew makes the decision to drop the main and jib, content to beat to windward under genny and mizzen.

They create a commotion on the foredeck, dropping and stowing main and jib. For the exception of some light fluttering, this work does not disturb our visitors. The pair simply cock their heads, eyeing the sailors, nodding their approval as the work progresses.

Dropping the jib and hanking on the genny to the forestay is another matter. This procedure crashes the birds' comfort zone. The boobies had put up with the bustling about on deck, however, the human gets too close when working at the bowsprit, dragging the genny in place, attaching it to the forestay.

The pair fly off, circling *Calypso* until the genny is set. They return immediately to the bowsprit when the crew finishes their business up forward. A glance skyward reveals several boobies in a glide directly for *Calypso*. When the crew has returned to the cockpit, the landings resume in earnest.

All day long boobies're circlin' 'n landin'
on both rails 'n out the bowsprit their standin'
At the top 'o the mast an' on the gaff boom
for another bird there's just no more room

Mid-afternoon has birds landing, flying off only to return, forcing their way back onto the rail with much squabbling. They compete for position, the bowsprit tip being the most favored, fought over post. The masthead is seeing frequent arguments as well.

The rails carry roughly twenty five birds apiece. The boobies respect the cockpit area and surrounding sea rails, occupying the toe rails from the rear of the cabin, forward. An additional five or six more ride the bowsprit along with one perched high above at the masthead.

The masthead is seeing many altercations for its lone, commanding position while the cabin top, sidedecks and foredeck remain clear, possibly their flat surfaces are not desirable for a steadying grip.

As *Calypso's* list of interesting wildlife encounters grows, the snowy egret event must now make room for this newest oddity. What a sight *Calypso* must present, sailing happily along covered in her full contingent of flapping, squabbling, circling blue footed boobies.

Calypso sails into the evening, the wind drops to an easy fifteen knot breeze well before sunset. The crew sets the mainsail in response to the reduction in wind strength; going forward on the sidedeck causes no more than a light fluttering. The moment the halyards are cleated off, boobies are landing aloft on the gaff boom. Fighting for the masthead position intensifies. The crew carries on with the evening routines, creating a tasty meal of mahi mahi tacos followed by preparations for the star sights after sundown.

The sun sets, sights are taken and worked out while *Calypso's* birds, seventy or eighty strong, settle in for the night. The crew, now accepted members of the flock, join them in a restful night, sailing easily along on smooth seas.

The birds along the rails stand as statues, swaying as one with *Calypso's* motion. Two battles, one at the mast head the other at the bowsprit rage on until dark, when all arguments cease.

For several days Calypso carries her flock
like a mid-ocean floatin' rock
Buckets of salt water are required
when in guano we are mired

A new day begins, morning sights are taken, dinner scraps are tossed over to Fatlip. The sun rises on a noxious scene on deck which must be dealt with before the crew will be able to enjoy a breakfast of their own.

Going forward with a bucket, the birds along the rail are not bothered by the human rudely brushing buy. It certainly does not dislodge them from their perch. The chore of flushing the decks goes quickly as the sun has not yet dried the mess.

The birds fuss, flutter and squawk a bit through the wash down, especially when they are doused with full buckets tossed directly on them, as one cannot help but have a little fun with the chore. Full buckets fail to discourage the birds enough to move them from the rail.

Our guests have become family by the end of this second day. The deck washings are repeated often as the birds all face outboard, their rear ends hang over side decks. Our gaff rig riders are raining down from above onto the cabin top, occasionally splattering the cockpit where the crew reside.

Calypso's initiation to the trade winds continues as the afternoon breeze freshens. The mainsail is replaced by the genny which has her breaking a hard trail northward. The smooth seas of the morning are replaced by this rolling, white capped churn which accompanies the trades when they pump up. *Calypso* has the flock swaying and bouncing as one. The squabbling nearly eliminated, our friends seem focused on hanging on, holding their spot.

With a bamboo pole they're chased away at dark
not allowin' another bird to park
When mornin' comes no more scrapin' 'n scoopin'
'cause blue footed booby birds ain't a poopin'!

Calypso's seaborne circus grows larger with each passing day. The birds continue to increase in number, so many now the onset of evening sees fierce battles. Calypso fills up fast, leaving the majority to fly off for the night. At the conclusion of a week long visit, the novelty of having our guests aboard is wearing thin. The deck washing chore has become just that, a chore. Together with a genuine health concern, becoming ill so far out to sea, the crew decides it's time for the flock to take its leave.

The initial attempt to shoo the birds off is laughable. The effort stirs them up, reducing the numbers on the boat, however empty spots are quickly taken. The air is filled with birds, many of which are gliding in for a landing. Some crash brazenly into the flock at the rails, knocking birds off in the melee they unleash.

The flock is fighting amongst itself, while, at the same time they are dodging wide sweeps of a bamboo pole. This tool is efficient at moving birds without the necessity of getting physical with each individual. A noisy, chaotic flapfest ensues. A circus clown chasing birds around the boat, slipping, sliding, cussing, falling and rolling around in the guano. Great fun, but the effort bears no fruit; come evening the clown is played out on deck surrounded by boobies settling in, equally tired of the game.

The sun retires below the horizon, evening sights are taken, calculations are worked out while decks are getting a complete washdown. The first skirmish has produced a mess topside exponentially heavier than the norm. There is guano everywhere, the mizzen and genny are not spared.

The crew are concerned for their workhorse. The cotton genny is already suffering the effects of sun rot from time at sea. The sails are brought in for a thorough scrub.

A hearty bean burrito follows the routine, always a good meal to sleep on. All is well with the crew, their flock is resting peacefully; the wind holds steady at twenty five knots, the seas still running twelve feet. *Calypso* continues to break trail charging doggedly to the northwest.

Sleep eludes the crew this night, the worries of sickness on their minds. Something must be done, the crew feeling real urgency now. They are well aware of the boobies habits, most importantly, they settle at night; they have not been observed circling the boat in the dark. Armed with this tidbit of knowledge and the bamboo pole, the sleeping birds are assaulted in the dead of night. The "Grim Reaper" jumps into the flock, wide swings of the scythe batter the birds, creating pandemonium on deck. Birds are flying away when bare feet slip on a gooey deck. This is the Grim Reaper's undoing. He is the clown again, rolling around buck naked, cursing and sliding with the roll of the boat. Scrambling to his feet, running, falling, yelling and batting boobies. Ultimately there is success, every bird is gone, save one.

Down below, the last booby clings to the bookshelf, web feet with claws have a firm grip. In its beak it has Joshua Slocum firmly by the binders.

This bird gets a full body hug when ripped clear of the bookshelf, one hand pulls Joshua free.

The bird is thrown out the hatch where it heads for the pole position at the bowsprit.

The clown is in hot pursuit, falling, cursing and swinging the bamboo pole, finally chasing the bowsprit booby from its perch. This last effort completes the exercise, all the boobies have flown off into the night. The clown, covered in guano grabs the deck bucket and commences to wash down body and boat.

---

*Calypso beats her way north into the ultramarine
the crew returns to the daily routine
Celestial navigation 'n fishin' take precedence
now that our bird friends're no longer in residence*

First light reveals a spotlessly clean deck, devoid of boobies. The flying fish scattered about are cleaned up save one, which becomes bait. A hook and line are readied, the flying fish takes its final flight off *Calypso's* stern, thrown far enough so it lands beyond of the voracious herd under the boat. The line is payed out until the bait can be seen flashing in the swell, fifty or sixty feet out. Mahi Mahi appear lining up as a group eyeing the fillet fluttering in a most tantalizing fashion before them. The bait is held steady, building the tension of the unsuspecting prey. When the moment is felt to be right, a hard jerk on the line has the bait make a sudden move; a darting escape attempt.

An iridescent flash of silver, blue and green explodes from the small school of curious fish. A large mahi has reacted instantly to the darting prey, taking the lure with lightening speed. Launched out of the wave by its furious attack, it hangs in the air for an instant before splashing back into the sea.

The struggle continues, but the hook is set well, the line is held firm until the big fish has played itself out. It is now hauled aboard, being immediately prepared for breakfast at the stern where Fatlip is close at hand to gobble prime cuts as they are tossed over.

Man vs. Machine

Heavy seas continue to churn
Hector stands tall at Calypso's stern
This mechanical sailor we've mounted
keeps Calypso on course undaunted

Hector has had full control of *Calypso's* helm long enough now, unerringly in a variety of sea conditions, for the crew to bestow their trust on this mechanical wonder.

An offhand test of Hector will reveal the accuracy of this wind powered robot when *Calypso* is brought about, steering her dead downwind in twenty five knots with the main and genny set wing and wing. This is the absolute maximum wind speed where the crew carries this combination. For a true test of Hector's abilities, this extreme condition with its associated twelve foot sea running will tell the crew a great deal about what to expect when at some point, *Calypso* will run for days at a time, downwind.

She has a tendency, most likely attributed to her shallow draft, to slew around to port and starboard in steep following seas. The helm must be handled with care when running with wind and sea in these conditions, regardless under human or mechanical control. Mishandling could result in a broach, placing the boat in extreme danger. A broach many times will precede a complete rollover of a vessel. This most critical test has been on the minds of the crew since Hector was bolted onto her stern. The conditions are perfect this afternoon, with the trades pumped up and a respectable sea running to set the crew's minds at ease, or not.

Hector is switched out of service, the mizzen is doused and stowed. The helm is eased to port and the bow falls off the wind. *Calypso* swings to the southwest, the genny snaps with a wallop out to starboard when the breeze takes hold. *Calypso* is now surfing, running with the seas wing and wing, dead downwind.

A grip on one spoke of the wheel holds *Calypso* steady. An eye to the compass keeps track of the degrees she wanders to port and starboard. She is handling easily, the compass indicates a seven to ten degree maximum deviation off course, regardless whether to port or starboard. This is established as the human's best effort after a considerable amount of running. It is now Hector's turn at the helm.

Calypso is steadied dead on course, long enough to reach over and flip a switch, handing over control to the machine. The spokes are cleated port and starboard, holding the boat rudder on center with the keel. Hands are now free, one simply stares at the compass card.

Hector accomplishes the identical task, steering *Calypso* within three to five degrees of the set course. Try as one might, the human can not achieve the machine's result.

The machine's secret is the instantaneous transfer of information from wind to the windvane rudder. With the weather helm accounted for when the wheel is tied off, the vane's sail reacts to the slightest change in the boat's relation to the wind. With the movement of the windvane's sail, the trim tab piggybacked on the vane rudder moves as one with the sail, kicking the steering rudder. The potential for over-steering is greatly reduced, as Hector generally is making a series of minor adjustments. The information is passed on so fast, large adjustments are rarely needed, although Hector is fully capable of making extreme moves quickly when an extreme shift of the boats attitude to the wind occurs.

The human is simply not aware of the nuances of change from moment to moment. The delay inherent in this lack of awareness requires a bit more rudder to stay on course. This contraption is pure genius in its simplicity, as it has very few moving parts.

Hector has passed this downwind test with flying colors. The crew may sleep that much more comfortably now with their added knowledge of Hector's capabilities. Over-steering downwind is a serious concern, as this is not only inefficient, it is downright dangerous. The test completed, the crew are anxious to get back on track, *Calypso* alters course to starboard, hauls to the wind, the mizzen is set, the main and genny are sheeted tight. *Calypso* falls off to port and is charging once again, bucking the northeast trades. The mainsail and genny are now eased to accommodate the comfort of vessel and crew.

Slosh

Day after day Calypso labors to windward
Clipperton Island lies to leeward
Comes a moment in the middle of the night
crew's awakened to the sense somethin's not right

Simultaneously, the crew are awakened by a familiar sound, last heard when sailing into Belize city. The unmistakable sound of sloshing water.

Jumping up to the bilge pump there is some relief when only a few gallons, maybe ten or so, are pumped over the side before the sound of air sucking into the pump is heard. Is it possible this is freshwater leaking from a container? This seems implausible, as more than one would have to be leaking to pump this amount.

---

*Under the cabin sole there's no mistakin'
the sound of sea water Calypso's takin'
Tear up a floorboard 'n take a peek
sure enough she's opened up a leak*

Without hesitation a floorboard is pulled up, however there is nothing to be ascertained, all that can be seen are the square blocks of iron which have been painted and packed in. They are secured tightly with wedges and straps. The taste test removes all doubt, this is seawater.

A dive over the side will have to made at the first opportunity, the present conditions being too rough. The crew are not so alarmed they cannot wait a few days. A close watch will be kept on the number of times the bilge is pumped day and night for each twenty four hour period. The goal being to get a picture of the rate of flow and any gain that may occur. The best guess at present is that it may well have taken several days, possibly a week or more before the crew heard that first telltale "schlopp" against the underside of the floorboards.

---

*Ten gallons we pump out
plantin' a seed of doubt
"Not our freshwater 'cause it tastes like salt
mebbe its Hector who's at fault?"*

Suspicion is immediately put upon Hector. Has the windvane been working the transom, stressing the fasteners? Has cotton or oakum crawled from their seams? If so, it will be pounded back in.

When in Rhode Island on the beach, particularly the days when the crew was busy doing some light corking on the hull, the old grump on a neighboring boat would, without out lifting his head from his work, hum "its gonna crawl" loudly under his breath to the beat of the corking hammer. What was an irritation in Rhode Island is upgraded to a theory here in the Pacific Ocean.

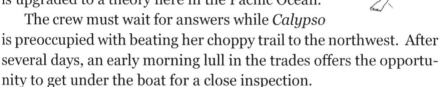

The crew must wait for answers while *Calypso* is preoccupied with beating her choppy trail to the northwest. After several days, an early morning lull in the trades offers the opportunity to get under the boat for a close inspection.

Deep Blue

Dive over the side durin' a mornin' lull
find no problem with Calypso's hull
See no damage an' the seams look tight
Calypso's hull appears to be alright

A couple thousand hours commercial diving does little to alleviate subtle fears which lurk in the back of the mind. Prior to splashing in, some time is taken to study the water immediately around the boat, keeping an eye out for dark shapes below or dorsal fins breaking the surface. Sharks. Their behavior not all that different from bears. They may be aggressive or not. They may be hungry or not. They are always unpredictable. Sharks are different from bears in that they may run in packs, like wolves. One puts aside the image of being torn to pieces before the dive over the side, buck naked into the soup. Sharks have been occasional visitors. Butterflies flutter in the stomach. A long gaze across the rolling seascape; slow deep breaths fill the lungs with fresh ocean air calming the nerves. A line is taken around the waist. Separation from *Calypso* could be disastrous. Tension felt in the neck stiffens at the thought.

One step into thin air is commitment. This instantaneous moment before crashing into the sea has all senses alert for danger. Regardless the many hours of experience, the fear-thrill of sharks dominates in mid-air. The percussive splash of the jump is a dinner bell.

The explosion of the body breaking the surface scatters small fish as they dart in panic in every direction to their hiding places. For the diver there is huge relief in not being attacked and shredded outright.

The bubbles clear quickly revealing a boat hull completely covered in a tube worm field. A month in the Doldrums is represented in this garden. Life clings to *Calypso's* hull, providing cover for a colorful contingent of tropical fish calling *Calypso* home.

Fatlip eyes the diver as the worms are cleared away. There are no immediate observable issues as the inspection proceeds. The entire stern is gone over including the transom. Fatlip seems to welcome the diver's company as he does not move from his post when the inspector comes to the spot where Hector is bolted, right in front of that battered nose. The bulbous white scar stands out, scaring little fish no doubt. He is the neighborhood thug hanging out at the street corner.

Not finding problems in the most suspicious areas, the clearing of the tube worms continues. No question, a boat's performance is compromised with a field of worms eight or ten inches long hanging from its bottom.

Nearly finished with the work, the repetitive dives and worm clearing have taken a toll. The diver stops for a moment to observe his work as well as to look down. He had intentionally avoided looking below him into the infinite blue as the work had progressed. Now, suspended in a cloud of broken worms and terrified little fish, a primal sensation consumes him. The hair raises on the back of the neck. With lightening speed he's at the bobstay and back on deck, cold blooded fear coursing through the arteries.

Pumpin' the bilge a daily routine
somethin' the crew had previously seen
Ten gallons a day we're pumpin' now
waters' leakin' from the stern somehow

Loggerhead

To the north by northwest Calypso holds steadfast
forty five days have now passed
A variety of critters entertain the crew
porpoise, whales 'n swordfish to name a few

A new weather pattern has set in since the morning of the bottom cleaning four days ago. This pattern is similar to what the crew had experienced in the Caribbean, where the wind lays down overnight. Sunrise will see light breezes which increase in the afternoon, the seas build in concert. Here in the Pacific, with its extended wave lengths and longer periods, these early mornings have seen exquisite ocean sailing. A bonus this morning with a very large, apparently social creature about to introduce itself.

A loggerhead turtle bumps alongside
Its attraction to Calypso it does not hide
mahi mahi 'n porpoise appear in the swells
behind her stern ol' Fatlip still dwells

More than just a sighting, a loggerhead turtle shows itself a short distance off in the swells. For about an hour it bobs along at two or three knots, staying even with the boat. The wind is roughly fifteen knots. The low swell associated with this light breeze is pleasant. The turtle rides easy and there is no doubt, it sidles toward *Calypso*. The crew on board are hoping for it to come alongside. An opportunity to offer it a fresh flying fish off the deck would promote this moment from a mere sighting to a full blown event.

This loggerhead is extremely large, easily three hundred pounds or more. As it continues to edge closer the flippers do not seem to be moving, yet the turtle keeps pace. Their hydrodynamic saucer shape sits pancake flat on the sea with the four flippers splayed out. Their shell is a fortress against predators. The diver can only wonder the role the shell plays in its journeys below the surface. Does it act as a weight belt, sinking the turtle to a desired depth without effort?

As a friendly greeting, the loggerhead gives *Calypso* a bump. Hands reach out to give our reptilian visitor a pat on its shell, returning the gesture. This holdover from a prehistoric age is a fascinating creature which appears to acknowledge the humans on deck.

If there are such things as good omens, this certainly would be one. Events on this scale inevitably invite conjecture on the subject.

The snowy egret certainly had; now the arrival of a turtle has the crew waxing esoteric. This loggerhead which has made a magnanimous effort to introduce itself to *Calypso* is added to this growing list of special visitors.

Flying fish are tossed in front of its beak, our friend makes no effort to partake. It appears this animal is content to bump alongside, the beneficiary of much attention from the crew. After a spell, a half hour or so, our turtle takes its leave, simply drifting into the distance off *Calypso's* stern.

Flying Fish

Tasty morsels constantly whizzin' by
the crew gives Flying Fish a try
Gathered several up that got stranded
when on deck they crash landed

Tossing fresh fish to the turtle invites another conversation which has come up periodically over the last month or so. The fish cleared from the deck each morning have been a handy source of bait. They have not been considered in creating a meal for the crew.

This morning, with an abundance of these aviators having offered themselves to *Calypso* during the night, it is decided today a few will be fried up for breakfast. There is skepticism aplenty, as a flying fish has a striking resemblance to "hooligan" (eulachon/candlefish), herring and especially smelt, one of the crew's favorites. They are much the same color, the difference being they have four wings and spend much of their time in the air between the crests of waves.

Their generous wingspan allows for long glides, mostly very close to the surface. One gets the impression some lift is gained as they appear to glide up the side of a swell. Many times in a seaway they pass by at eye level as they launch from the wave tops. Some crash shortly after take-off, most fly off arcing to port or starboard a hundred yards or so. They also "skip," making "touch and go" landings without re-entry. This skip is accomplished by a flutter of the tail at the end of a glide. The tail is first to touch the water, before the body can land, the tail flutters to a blur sending the "fuselage" another leg of the flight across the waves.

The crew can while away hours watching these entertaining aerial acrobats fly hither tither, at times in schools where there may be twenty or thirty in the air buzzing around and over the boat at a time. Predators above and below the surface constantly work the fish. Mahi mahi are spotted in the waves, frigate birds soar high, albatross swoop low. These flying fish live a harried life.

Got the estufa fired up 'n fryin'
these little fish that're done flyin'
An' when those critters are sizzlin' hot
the crew could eat them not!

A clue has been missed as to how flying fish will be at the palate when at last it is time to sample this delicacy. The crew had initially been skeptical, however they did not pay attention to the clear intuitive signal.

Calypso's library provides evidence that both the crew of *Kon Tiki* and Joshua Slocum enjoyed these plentiful fish. In the case of Joshua Slocum's "Sailing Alone Around the World," he relates a story of being chased by pirates on heavy seas. *"Spray"* suffered a broken main boom however, the pirates were dismasted, allowing Slocum to escape. He mentions gathering up a flying fish for dinner after his escape, however he was too exhausted from the ordeal to cook a meal.

The crew of *Kon Tiki* relished the fish as a delicacy, both raw and cooked. Some traditional Norwegian recipes carry strong fish aromas and flavors. Another clue missed.

The crew of *Calypso* has grown up with the milder fish of the Pacific Northwest and Alaska. King and dungeness crab, salmon, herring, smelt, halibut. cabezon, rockfish, scallops, black cod, ling cod, true cod; the list of mild fish is long in their diet.

The moment the shiny, slim fillets hit hot oil, the answer hangs in the air in a thick, acrid smoke. Tasting the result is unnecessary, yet obligatory. Gingerly a small bite is taken and immediately spit out the hatch. A swig of cold coffee swirled in the mouth follows the first bite out to sea. Possibly there would have been a different reaction, had the crew tried the first taste raw, as sashimi, however with the result in the frying pan, the crew pursues the issue no further. The best clue, so obvious now, lies in the energy this little fish must have available to survive, to hold their place in a truly hostile environment. The flying fish stores the required energy in the form of oil. The crew discovers they are the tropical equivalent of hooligan, which up north are an acquired taste. Having only developed a taste for the milder smelt and herring, flying fish are considered by the crew, unlike Slocum and the crew of *Kon Tiki*, to be undesirable.

Estufa

Too oily 'n strong these little fish
mahi mahi's our favorite dish!
An' 'bout that estufa by the way
curse that thing several times a day

Calypso has carried a variety of boat stoves aboard since leaving Rhode Island. Whenever a stove began to fall out of favor, it would invariably earn a nickname. "Estufa" became a derogatory slur, with which our current stove has recently been endowed. A bronze single burner, alcohol primed kerosene stove. This design has proved the most efficient, reliable unit to date. The base of the unit is a kerosene reservoir, which can be pressurized with its built-in hand pump. The alcohol is set alight on the metal burner which brings the temperature up to a point where the kerosene will burn clean with a blue flame.

Calypso is on her second stove of this design. This unit is made up of parts cannibalized from its predecessor and is working just fine. It is not for malfunctioning that it is now referred to as the *"estufa."*

The crew had failed in their preparations in Panama to put an adequate supply of alcohol aboard. Two weeks now without alcohol to preheat the metal flame spreader, the crews patience with the estufa is wearing thin.

Priming the burner with kerosene, rather than alcohol is a downright filthy affair below decks. The cabin fills with black smoke, the burner clogs, the stove starves for a proper mixture of fuel and air, the situation deteriorates further. The *estufa* now cooks with a sooty yellow flame.

Smokin' 'n sputterin' when set alight
an eye waterin' throat chokin' fight
An' when the fire gets good 'n hot
yer' cookin' on a fancy smudge pot!

Fried flying fish oil baked into the cabin walls adds an extra-nautical touch to the thickening grimy patina. A desperate cleaning effort produces no reward. Fresh water being a far more valuable commodity now than ever, as not one day of rain collection has occurred in nearly two months since leaving Panama. Saltwater and dish soap must suffice, the result a spiraling decay of living conditions down below.

Saltwater 'n soap's a waste of time
all that's doin' is spreadin' the grime
A black 'n gooey sticky gunge
from cabin walls we cannot expunge

Throughout the boat 'n on our clothes
greasy soot from our heads to our toes
A salt water bath or two a day
cannot keep grimy black at bay

Not necessarily an unsanitary environment aboard *Calypso*, rather, the maritime equivalent of earthy. Kerosene soot, salt water and stale fish oil enhances the ambiance of our salty little craft.

It is with certainty her interior contains a whole universe of life from the grimy underside of her cabin top, down the walls, right into the bilges. The saltwater/dish soap combination does not clean, it spreads. It provides a foundation for life to occupy and cling to every niche and cranny aboard this little boat.

Night Sky

The crew sails on to a place unseen
a timeless journey it does seem
Under constellations we so rely
Calypso's in harmony with sea 'n sky

Draped in a blanket of tiny lights
Arcturus, Spica 'n the moon offer accurate sights
With these friends in the vast expanse
Calypso's position is not left to chance

Routines keep the crew occupied as *Calypso* continues her relentless charge headlong into the northeast trade winds. Jib and mizzen hold her course off the wind a few extra points for comfort, when the wind pumps up in the afternoon. Thirty knots with an eight to twelve foot sea running on average it seems. Puffy trains of angel white clouds, peculiar to the trades are scudding past in a bums rush, late to the party beyond the horizon.

Some days, with the onset of sundown, the breeze drops by ten knots or more which allows the crew to pile on full sail. The seas relax in concert; *Calypso* is hauled close to the wind and sheeted tight. Other days the wind blows hard late into the night, sails are shortened to jog comfortably to weather. Wind, current and the power captured by the sails carry *Calypso* off to the west northwest; sheets are eased, yet she makes satisfactory headway.

"WWV" counts off each second with the light knock of a corking hammer paying into a seam. The sighted angle to the star or other body is shouted out at the exact moment the "bong" signals Greenwich Mean Time on the precise minute. This, the last activity of the days routine, is usually followed by relaxing, prone in the cockpit, gazing skyward. The constellations begin to appear as last light wanes.

Down below, the lone kerosene lamp glows, dimly lighting the cabin. The navigator works through the calculations. When finished, she douses the lamp, pops her head out the hatch, beaming. "Forty Eight!" Two miles an hour on the button. To the uninitiated, this may sound like a crawl; to the crew of *Calypso*, this is a banner day. Whenever she beats her lower upwind average of forty miles, the crew celebrates.

They do not take the credit for crafty seamanship or in the nuts and bolts of sailing their vessel. Nor do they take responsibility for astute navigation in plotting an accurate course. No, all their honors are be- stowed on their hardy little boat, and of course, Hector; staunch, standing tall at her stern, guiding her night and day with precision.

Their gratitude, like this starlit sky; boundless. Darkness descends, the constellations, most notably Orion the hunter, explode into view. Delta, Orionis and Epsilon, "Orion's Belt" stand out, pointing directly to Sirius, the "Dog Star" and the brightest bulb in the night sky.

Low on the horizon to the north, Polaris levitates. This ancient guiding star lingers above a patch of ocean circled in the "Hammond Atlas." The imaginary acre in the middle of the North Pacific where *Calypso* will tack to the northeast

---

Twelve hundred miles west of San Francisco
'bout the same distance east of Hilo
There's a patch of ocean where Calypso will be tackin'
an' to the Strait of Juan de Fuca she'll begin trackin'

The bronze bilge pump is always there, waiting to regurgitate the ocean sloshing in the bilges. An incremental increase has been observed since the dive on her last week. Pumping twenty or more gallons in twenty four hours is the new normal. The crew has been watching close; they estimate the rate approaches roughly a gallon and a half or two per mile at this point. The water is kept pumped down to avoid the irritating slosh under the floorboards.

Pump the bilge, navigation at first light on the horizon, catch and fillet a fish, feed Fatlip, create a sumptuous meal for the crew. This order of business begins a new day. On many mornings, the fish caught for breakfast is a twenty pound or larger mahi mahi. Much more than the crew and Fatlip will consume in a day. The crew has discovered a process for preserving the remainder of the fillets.

Simply cut the fillets into strips, as one would for hanging salmon in a smokehouse. The mahi are cut wider to allow for shrinkage. The strips are washed clean with fresh seawater then laid out on the cabin top. Spices are shaken liberally over the strips: garlic, red and black pepper. The result after three days drying out in the sun, a succulent jazzy jerky is produced. Fresh tuna are processed in this fashion as well, however, mainly the tuna the crew feasts on are the miniatures under the boat which leave no leftover fillets. The occasional albacore is a mild flesh suitable to the palates of the crew and large enough to provide extra to jerk.

Inventory

Closin' in on sixty days at this endeavor
takin' stock of water 'n stores not a pleasure
Of the current situation the crew is not oblivious
cause' the shortage of fresh water is quite obvious

Beans, rice 'n flour there's plenty
eggs're gettin' low, just twenty
It's quite amazin' in this tropical heat
the eggs're still okay to eat

Back in Colon, the crew had learned eggs could survive many weeks if properly handled. The simple technique yielded surprising results. The crew had been meticulously turning over the egg boxes every few days as the seasoned sailors at the yacht club had told them. Their theory being, it keeps the air bubble from attaching to the shell. Common knowledge among the seafarers was that when the air bubble sticks to one spot, the egg spoils rapidly.

Leaving Panama City, they never dreamed they would still be out in the middle of the ocean two months later. They had loaded the precious cargo in Panama City, after transiting the Canal, in order to leave with the freshest possible fruit, eggs and produce.

The eggs are farm grown, nothing added. Their yolks, after all this time, are for the most part intact, though some are already broken when cracked into a bowl; they have no odor. There are only a handful left, less than two dozen. Egg burritos, a favorite breakfast, will be soon off the menu.

The staples: beans, rice, flour and masa harina are holding well, sealed in plastic containers. Garlic, red and black pepper, cumin, various odd sauces and spices, all in abundance. Taken together with their steady diet of fresh fish, much of which is consumed raw or dried in the sun, there are no worries about sustaining the crew. The truth being, they feast on the finest maritime cuisine. Meals of such design, flavors and artistry, they could grace tables of the finest restaurants. Two months into the venture, the crew are lean and fit.

*Nearin' two months without rain
from soakin' beans in fresh water we abstain
Rationin' this precious commodity
to reduce consumption
fifty days remainin's our assumption*

Fresh water is altogether another matter. The crew has been patiently waiting for rain. Their technique for catching water had been perfected long ago in Isla Mujeres. In roughly an hour of rain squalls passing over the island, they had easily filled all their containers while at anchor. The mainsail is raised three fourths the way up the mast, leaving a trough at the foot. The boom is lowered, water is funneled off the sail directly into containers.

They had been careful with fresh water use on the journey to this point, however a glance at the "Hammond Atlas" says it all. Another two month slog against the wind, *Calypso* may or may not reach that point in the atlas. Even two months is a rough estimate, bearing in mind, the crew is using their previous thirty day average to predict the future. Realistically, "past performance is no guarantee of future results." This popular disclaimer in the financial world is applicable here.

*Twelve hundred miles sixty days at sea
Strait of Juan de Fuca no longer a possibility
Averagin' forty miles a day the crew had to balk
'cause that's 'bout as fast as we could just walk!*

Regardless of further navigational decisions, an abundance of caution has the crew taking rationing measures. Three adjustments are made to extend their self sufficiency without rain.

Saltwater bathing will no longer be followed with a fresh water rinse as has been the custom. Pasta has been boiled in seawater all along, however beans will no longer be soaked in fresh water. The crew had experimented early on with the saltwater method, but found the beans get tough, the two chefs in the galley had voted for fresh water soaking, which they had done until this day.

Lastly, one litre per day for each of the crew is allotted for drinking, which includes coffee and tea consumption. Coffee and tea has used a lot of fresh water on occasion. This in effect limits the crew to a couple cups of coffee in morning and tea in the evening. A close look at *Calypso's* position reveals she is west southwest of Socorro Island in the Revillagigedo Archipelago. Standing on deck at the bow, visualizing the coast of Mexico, Acapulco is a five hundred mile, seven day sail on a very inviting broad reach.

"Only five hundred miles to 'ol Mexico
we can run downwind for Acapulco!
Four or five days easy sailin'
we'll stop the leak an' won't be bailin'

Course Change

A very appealing alternative at first glance after two months at sea. On the surface, the whole idea is a snap. "Why not!?" So begins the assembly of negatives. Firstly, the produce would be sent to "Davey Jones' Locker," dashing hopes for a grubstake on landing ashore. Flat broke in a foreign country, no money for vessel entry fees. Visions are conjured up of two grubby urchins standing forlorn before a scowling, starchy clean customs officer. The Belize experience comes to mind. Frustrated now with this alternative, the crew looks to the Hammond Atlas and the "I Ching" for guidance. The big picture.

The atlas reveals the two closest American Ports of Call are San Diego, dead upwind and Hilo Hawaii, dead downwind. Three coins and a small pocketbook are pulled from a "Crown Royal" bag. This ritual is performed whenever the crew comes to a major decision such as this invisible crossroads in the ocean. Leaving Cuba, the three coins had turned *Calypso* for Mexico.

The coins are tossed, the results tallied. The crew reads aloud passages in the book, arising from the toss of the coins. Funny how these things work. There it is this morning in black and white. "Go west and cross the Great Ocean."

Sloshin' bilge, shortages 'n slow speed
for Calypso's crew its decision time indeed
"Crossin' the Great Ocean's best" the I Ching reports
"Hawaii's thirty seven hundred miles west!"
The navigator retorts

Chapter 16

DOWNWIND TO HAWAII

May - June 1981

Running Free

Douse the mizzen 'n slack the mainsheet
helm to port 'n quit this upwind beat
Out to starboard the genny flies
under pearly white clouds
scuddin' 'cross blue skies

Slidin' down twelve footers wind at her back
for Hawaii Calypso's on the right tack
Sails're set runnin' wing 'n wing
if only this little boat could sing!

Calypso responds as though she shares in the adrenalin rush, sailing pellmell down the face of steep seas with abandon. A bamboo whisker pole is hooked into the bowline at the genny's clew, the inboard end is secured to the bitts. This "preventer" will keep the sail from flopping inboard, when she takes wind on the backside as she rolls in the bottom of the trough. Sailing all day in this fashion it becomes apparent, the whisker pole is overkill.

The genny holds her shape throughout, never once showing a tendency to collapse. With no violent action aloft, the whisker pole is removed. It accomplishes nothing other than distract attention and irritate. Possibly the preventer will be used in light winds, should that ever occur here in the trades.

---

*Calypso has an easy motion
rollin' with the Pacific Ocean
Stars floatin' past the hatch at night
this run for the Islands feelin' just right*

The chop disappears as the wind eases to less than twenty knots in the early evening. The jib is hauled in, replaced by the mainsail to port, balancing beautifully with the genny out to starboard. A transformation has taken place. For the last thirty days the crew has been riding *Calypso* as a thoroughbred mare, relentlessly charging headlong six hundred miles into wind and sea; this day, she has sprouted wings and fledged. She is a graceful seabird swooping down a seaway. She is Pegasus.

As the sun drops below the horizon, sights are taken, the bilge is pumped clear; the leak has picked up some since changing course nine hours ago. The surprising amount of water gushing over the side has the crew taking mental note.

Whenever one of the crew is at the pump, it has become habit for the other to put an ear to it as well. A rehashing of theories often begins when there is a noticeable change in the average. To date, these discussions have never come to a satisfactory conclusion. The single standout clue is the wet planking above the floorboards throughout her stern quarters, port and starboard. The verified truth of the issue remains a mystery.

This night is different, a significant increase in the leak receives nothing more than mutual shrugs and shakes of the head. The crew is not about to let this nuisance ruin the magic of the day.

After dinner and tea they are pasted to the deck on their backs gazing deep into the universe above, while each and every wave is felt as it passes below. Her hull slices through the water with a soft whoosh, backed up by intermittent wooden thuds in the forepeak when her bow greets the bottom of the trough. The breeze has the sails full and taut. Gentle rocking and dipping to the long, smooth seaway lulls the crew into silence. With the harmony of all these elements, a sense of timelessness pervades.

The pair turn in rather late this first night. Looking up through the open hatch, the universe swings back and forth. Their guiding stars and planets peek in and out of view. Hector can be seen, standing tall to the wind, the helm held firm reinforcing the sense of security in their decision.

Eyelids grow heavy with their boat's easy downwind motion, the pair drop into deep sleep. *Calypso*, under Hector's steady hand, runs free for Hawaii.

---

*Navigation's way more fun
takin' sights of stars, moon 'n sun
Lines of position showin' headway
Calypso's makin' a hundred miles a day!*

Waking in advance of the pre-dawn light, the eyes focus on the hatch. The gaff boom can be seen sweeping an arc across the constellations to port and starboard. The mainsail is taut. Water is whooshing smoothly yet softly by, while the thuds on her hull up forward are light; light to the point of being a comfort.

A glorious Pacific dawn in the making has the crew up, sextant in hand with "WWV" knocking and bonging away. The smell of fresh coffee fills the cabin, a cursory view out the hatch reveals the slightest hint of the horizon backed by a few short rays of the sun.

Breakfast Fish

Flying fish are gathered up, several buckets of seawater flush the decks clean. The bronze bilge pump spews gallon after gallon over the side. The sun rises, an accurate sight is taken when the globe ascends above fifteen degrees. The angle recorded on the sextant at the "bong" is shouted out to the navigator sitting below decks, already busy working out the first light sights on Venus, Vega and Altair. The sun sight will combine with the morning star sights and the previous evening's lines of position gained from Spica and Arcturus and Antares.

Breakfast this morning is caught while the navigator works out *Calypso's* position. The bamboo fishing pole is quietly slid into the water alongside the hull. This simple, specialized fishing tool has exceeded expectations.

Unlike the glass smooth Doldrums where fish can be seen crowding the pole, out here in the deep blue, sailing along at a good clip, fish cannot be observed so easily, for the exception of Fatlip about a foot under the surface in the eddy at the stern.

The pole is held for only a minute or so, fish are imagined in the "mind's eye" to be gathering around. A quick jerk, the pole is pulled up quickly and swung over the deck. A single fish, of the miniature tuna variety is flippity flopping at the business end of the pole. The fish in residence have turned west with *Calypso*.

The two fillets this little fish provides have separate destinations. The first is cut into sushi strips, the second is left whole as bait for the hand-line hook. Before fishing for a morning mahi the mini-tuna strips are taken aft. "One for you, one for me" is sung out as the first piece is dropped to a waiting Fatlip who snatches the morsel on impact with the surface. The strips are shared, devoured quickly by fish and fisherman alike. The second fillet goes to work when it flies out from the boat off the stern. A swiveled, banana shaped trolling lead is tied in about a fathom ahead of the bait. The lead hits the water first, the baited hook flies on for the length of its leader, then splashes in. The line is payed out, the bait can seen flashing, pulled just under the surface by the sinker seventy five or a hundred feet away.

Several indiscernible fish are seen near the bait, "it won't long" is the thought when "One hundred five miles!" is shouted out from the cabin; in the same fraction of a second a fish hits the lure, hurling itself skyward in celebration then crashes into the sea, violently thrashing at the surface.

After a brief struggle, a fifteen pound mahi mahi is brought aboard. Attention turns immediately to the navigator's wonderful news; the pair pour over the "Universal Plotting Chart" and make a light pencil point approximation in the atlas. A banner day for *Calypso*. It has been two months since *Calypso* has made one hundred miles in twenty four hours.

Seaborne Circus

Continuin' on with her entourage
a thousand Dolphins leapin' n' twirlin' is no mirage
Sharks join in a frenzied feast
on the remains of some poor hapless beast

Swordfish circle 'n whack their prey
mahi mahi's the catch o' the day
An' speakin' of fish on the bite
good' ol Fatlip's still hangin' tight!

The circus has made the turn to the west with the boat, all the performers continue their routines above and below the surface. *Calypso* is the center of this traveling spectacle which continues to delight the crew.

This particular morning proves no exception when they are treated to a special, albeit extremely dangerous visit by a creature which had previously only been spotted at a distance. Positive identification had eluded the crew as the sightings were indistinct for the exception of observing they were a billfish of some sort.

A blue marlin sidles up to *Calypso*. From the deck, this silver beast appears as long as the boat while its girth confirms, this is an exceptionally large animal, well over a thousand pounds. The concern, for which it seems nothing can be done, is for the real potential the marlin may begin whacking the residents under the boat and ultimately the hull with its bill. Should it work itself into a frenzy, anything is possible including severe damage to the boat. The crew simply sit quietly above the fish; a dazzling display of a myriad of colors, dominated by deep blue, magenta, purple and the brightest imaginable silver when reflecting light. So stunning the iridescence, the moment so intense, the pair each wrapped in their sense of silent wonder, are motionless.

As quietly as the marlin had approached *Calypso*, the big fish idles off after fifteen or twenty minutes in a most leisurely fashion. A few slow-motion sweeps of the scimitar-like tail, takes it out of sight to the northwest. The deep blue color runs the entire length of the upper third of the body, camouflaging it in short order as it swims away in this navy blue sea.

There has been great pleasure for the brief time the blue marlin was at *Calypso's* side. Now, an equal amount of relief on its departure.

Before noon this day, white caps begin to appear. The crew, out of an abundance of caution, drop the mainsail, raising the jib in its place to run wing and wing with the genny. *Calypso* has been making good time this morning however, will they see gale force trades today?

By mid-afternoon, the freshening trades settle in at a moderate twenty five knots with a six foot sea. Overhead, puffy white clouds coast along against a pastel blue backdrop.

The crew feels this day is perfect to gain some latitude, as their position is currently several degrees south of the Big Island. Hector is clicked off, *Calypso* is hauled into the wind, the crew taking note; the wind is stiff when taken full on in the face. They are happy not to be beating into it any longer. The previous thirty days had been a taxing slog.

The jib is doused, the mizzen is set, the helm put down to port, taking wind and sea on the starboard quarter. Sheets are hauled in as the bow falls off, the helm secured when she is balanced on a broad reach. Hector is clicked in and goes to work; *Calypso* barrels along to the northwest in perfect harmony under genny and mizzen.

They are confident sailing conditions are such that they will not be sailing beyond their boat's comfortable stress levels. Nothing is to be gained by driving hard, other than a heightened risk for boat and crew. This has been the rule since embarking on this venture in Rhode Island. It was assumed back then, there will be numerous times when stress levels on the boat will be exceeded. That is the nature of maritime endeavors in general, therefore the crew strives to reduce wear and tear at every opportunity.

After enjoying this pattern for a steady week with all but two of the seven days topping one hundred miles, the crew feels their decision to run for Hawaii has not been only a correct decision, it has handed them a fresh adventure on a silver platter.

This exhilarating week is capped by a seaborne extravaganza shortly after the morning sight. Thousands of spinner dolphins simultaneously appear. A three hundred sixty degree show to the horizon has the crew agawk. These acrobats command the attention of the crew with their airborne antics. A display of communal exuberance so contagious, the crew are caught up. All activity ceases on deck; the sheer joy of these animals with their wry smiles has the crew bouncing around, chortling with delight.

Gradually *Calypso* sails out of the pod, leaving them in her wake; the show fades off to the southeast. The crew returns to the routines of the day. The bilge has priority as a heavy slosh is climbing up the interior wall on her lee side. Fatlip shares a meal with the crew after a few small tuna are brought aboard with the bamboo hook pole. *Calypso* continues to behave famously on the quartering tack, making terrific time.

A couple of days following the spinner dolphin event, the thrashing of sharks, their heads and tails spotted in a boil of white water is seen at a distance too great to make out what the ruckus is all about. An approach to the melee does not appeal, therefore, the victims' identity remains a mystery.

Seventy three days out
the crew has no doubt
Life at sea with all the critters around
is truly a life of freedom unbound
Pumping Seawater

L ife for the crew has improved ten fold with this run for the Big Island. Not to say that it is entirely carefree, the irritations are small, but persistent. There is sail cloth beginning to rot and fail. Water rationing prevents proper bathing and the beans are tough. Most importantly, and more than a mere irritation, there is the ever present leak.

Pumpin' day 'n night now the chore
cause' Calypso's leakin' more 'n more
A pesky leak increasin' as we make our way
Calypso's takin' eighty gallons a day!

The crew has not been keeping a record. Yesterday at the first light pump, an estimate had been jotted down. This continued throughout the next twenty-four hours whenever water was pumped over. This morning, with the twenty fourth hour pump, the estimation alarms the crew somewhat. Not so much the eighty gallons tallied; of greater concern is the creep factor.

The habit of the crew is to give the pump a few pulls whenever one is handy to it. A natural reaction at all hours is to grab the handle in passing for a few pumps until air is heard sucking in. A few gallons here, a few gallons there, not much mind is paid to it.

The leak is still on the crew's minds when NPR is turned on for some evening news as is the custom. The conversation revolves around the eighty gallon surprise and the fact, *Calypso* is fast approaching one hundred twenty degrees in longitude, another milestone. The nightly news puts in proper perspective the problem of the substantial increase in *Calypso's* leak.

Over the shortwave radio
world news continues to flow
The Pope 'n President've both been shot
but to the crew of Calypso it matters not

Cause we're at sea in a sinkin' boat
no idea how long we'll stay afloat
Popes 'n Presidents're not our concern
Calypso's got water pourin' in from the stern!

May fourteenth, a second hunger striker in England has followed Bobby Sands in death. Sands began the hunger strike on March first, the week prior to *Calypso* departing Panama. Yesterday, Pope John Paul II had been shot in an assassination attempt. This follows the attempt about a month ago on the life of President Reagan.

Big news. But, what of the crew and their little boat, sinking in the middle of the Pacific Ocean? No one will know details, there will only be those empty words, "went missing at sea."

For whatever reason, the crew are not disturbed by the prospect of sinking here. This salty world is home, complete with the vibrant life which surrounds the pair who have become fundamentally at peace with life as it is. Possibly, they have indeed become comfortable with their niche in Wolf Larson's "yeasty ferment."[5]

---

5 From Jack London's "Sea Wolf"

Playin' backgammon 'n throwin' dice
makin' tortillas, beans 'n rice
Days are all kinda serene
even sinkin' seems routine

Bumper Crop

The supply's low an' there's a need to replenish
that produce for which the crew has a fetish
A serrated knife leaves the bumper agape
so it's patched up with glue 'n duct tape!

The herb put aside in Panama for consumption en route has run out, requiring a reopening of the cache. This must be done with great care in order that nothing will appear amiss after the procedure. The sharpest serrated knife is used to pierce the bumper. A tiny slit is started in the longitudinal seam which proves to be constructed of very tough material. It takes considerable force to slice neatly along the seam. Now, an untimely roll of the boat and the blade runs wild; it leaves a foot long half moon incision in the side of the bumper. This error revives the conversation of what to do with it, now that the careful work to conceal its contents has been compromised. A difficult repair is attempted by gluing the jagged, irregular edges of the gash. The initial effort fails to hold. A second attempt is successful when duct tape is used to reinforce the repair.

Rehashing the options, there is nothing new to add to the three originally conceived. The navigator is firm, the bumper should be thrown in the bow, with piles of boaty stuff. The first mate wants to hide the thing in plain sight where it should be seen while docking. The navigator counters with the standard "but it's oversize, it doesn't look right." The discussion always comes to loggerheads here.

The crew both agree, as the captains of *Calypso* share the responsibility, the third answer remains a possibility; to set it adrift, and be done with it. Most likely this would mean working on a dive boat rather than lounging on "easy street" when finally reaching the mainland. Both captains agree to kick the question down the road, until the decision becomes critical.

Fatlip Chocks One Up

Right after the routine mornin' sight
always taken at the crack of first light
Lean over the stern check on that fish
that narrowly avoided our supper dish

An'' ol Fatlip's always there
lookin' up with that mournful stare
Never gives the bait a second look
ever since he flipped off that hook

Fatlip has set a record of sorts since he was targeted for the dinner plate two months ago. The only record within *Calypso's* library that speaks to fish following a boat long distance, is Joshua Slocum's mention of a dolphin fish (mahi mahi) that followed *Spray* a thousand miles. Fatlip has doubled the feat.

Slocum spoke of feeding the fish, identifying it by its scars. As he says, "Fishes will always follow a foul ship." *Calypso* certainly meets the criteria. The garden cleared following the Doldrums drift has reestablished itself, providing a haven for hitchhikers. Sharks can be seen on occasion during the day idling by, while speeding trails of phosphorescence in the night are telltale signs they are on the hunt under the boat. Hector is Fatlip's shark shield.

Every time a fish gets caught
for scraps he's johnny- on-the-spot
Thousands of miles' ol Fatlip has swum
this hardy little mackerel's not so dumb!

Fresh Water 'n Sun Rot

For a deluge the crew's been a wishin'
a tropical downpour's the only thing missin'
Freshwater showers'd make life even better
'cause salt water 'n sun's turnin' soft skin to leather

El Sol has been burning hot every day since departing Panama. Today, in celebration of another week maintaining an average of one hundred miles a day, and as a reward for the water conservation which has gone much better than expected, the crew has decided that a fresh water rinse will be rationed out following the afternoon buckets of saltwater when the decks and bodies all get a thorough soak.

This liberal fresh water shower, using about a gallon and a half for the pair is evidence of the confidence they have in reaching their goal. Calypso is under their feet, hurtling down the face of these trade wind driven seas; she is rocking and rolling in the happy way sailboats do when running free with the wind. Barreling for the Big Island they sense her happiness, her harmony right through to their bones.

This brief rinse of fresh water is beyond luxury, a softness not experienced in so long, it is not even remembered as such. The simple feel of freshwater caressing sun tortured, salt toughened skin is a reward which leaves the pair lounging in quiet ecstasy. Conservation will continue as before, however, the crew resolves to look for another opportunity to have a fresh water rinse.

The mainsail's cause for concern
as that tropical sun continues to burn
Haul it in an' make repairs
durin' early morning's lighter airs

The Dacron mainsail shows serious sun rot, while the cotton genny, being relatively new is holding up quite well. The Dacron jib, stowed much of the time while the genny is in use does not suffer near the wear as the mainsail.

Early mornings the pattern has been for the wind and sea to have calmed some overnight. The lighter trades offer some time to work on sail repair. The crew takes the opportunity to swap out the main for the genny.

Quartering on the starboard tack eeks out a bit of latitude while under genoa and mizzen. *Calypso* slides down the easy swells at a comfortable angle of heel. This allows the sail repairs to be made without interruption from the severe moves she makes in higher wind with choppy waves.

Patches are cut from leftover cotton sail material purchased in Belize for the genny. Some are a foot or more square to cover a rotted area surrounded by sail strong enough to hold a stitch. This is the moment the "palm" is retrieved from the sail repair kit. This vital little tool makes easier the work of forcing the needle through the heavy Dacron mainsail. The work is tedious and difficult; the finished product, less than pleasing to the eye as the cotton sail material has not escaped the grunge that has accumulated down below.

Patchin's hard work 'n takes some time
then hoist the main 'n get 'er back on line
Calypso goes chargin' ahead, sailin' full tilt
lookin' like Cosmic Chris an' his patchwork quilt!

Racin' along at breakneck speed
exhilaratin' ridin' our trusty steed
Seven hundred miles covered in a week
a thousand gallons pumped
stayin' ahead o' the leak!

Fifteen hundred miles under the keel since the sheets were thrown and the helm put down for the west. *Calypso* rides a wind and current which has carried sailing vessels down these sea lanes for centuries.

One imagines a flotilla of tall ships with their clouds of sail, transiting the Pacific Ocean under the spell of these trade winds. *Calypso* is rocking easily at this moment as she mimics the lumbering roll of the heavily laden square riggers. This thought interrupts the reverie, *Calypso* is wallowing like a square rigger because her bilge is full of water. The pump remedies the situation in short order. Her sluggishness gives way to the familiar downwind happy dance that is so much her style.

Makin' our way to the twentieth parallel
eighty days at sea 'n all's well
Food 'n water still holdin' out
plenty of fish swimmin' about

Hilo sits just south of twenty degrees latitude, the crew has decided to approach Hilo Bay from the twentieth parallel, an extra margin clear of South Point on the Big Island. Over two thousand miles distant, there is no immediate necessity to gain latitude, however when the wind and seas are comfortable, the crew sets her on a quartering tack until the wind freshens and a chop develops. On the return of strong trades, they turn back on the downwind course, flying main and genny wing and wing.

Trades pump up considerably in the afternoon
fillin' Calypso's genny like a big white balloon
Guidin' her through the night is Hector
tirelessly trackin' the trade wind's vector

Sinking

Still stayin' ahead of the water comin' in
determined not to let it win
But what if the pump should give out
an' the crew can no longer hold out?

Twenty-four hours, one hundred ten gallons estimated. Two fifty five gallon drums full is a new record as *Calypso's* leakage history goes.

The crew remains pragmatic; they are managing well with a single hand pump, they are making excellent time toward their destination and they continue to keep the water below the floorboards. That, for the present, is sufficient.

The cause of the leak has still not revealed itself. The seams look fine. Cotton is not pushing out; no outward damage is evident. Hector, being the newest element remains the number one suspect. This is because its extra large rudder, hanging outboard, may be putting severe torque on the transom. Not a convincing argument, but for the time being, it is enough. The remedy revolves around keeping the bronze pump busy and maintained.

A contingency plan is radical, but then again, sinking out of sight in the middle of the Pacific Ocean is a dire situation requiring extreme measures.

The solution to this months long irritation has been sitting in plain sight on the library shelf.

"There's a ton of ballast in the bottom of the boat
we'll just toss it all overboard an' still float!
The idea's really not daft
after all, Kon Tiki was just a raft!"

Inside Ballast

Newport Rhode Island had introduced the crew to inside ballasted sailboats. This detail had escaped the would be sailors when first looking over sailboats in New England harbors. The image of outside ballasted sailboats sailing sharply upwind is so ingrained, until boarding *Calypso*, alternative designs had not been considered.

This did not deter the crew when they learned of her configuration. Experience fishing in rough ocean conditions or crossing dangerous bars on the coast had taught the crew some weight in the fish hold (in effect, "inside ballast") makes a better ride. This added to the prospect of sailing in shallows around fragile reefs, where her draft of only three feet would be an advantage, seemed more than enough compensation for whatever compromise in her ability to sail upwind has been made.

Her shallow draft, achieved by placing the iron or steel ballast inside the hull, proved effective when she rode the breakers over the Yucatan Barrier Reef. A ton of lead bolted to the bottom of the keel would have planted itself firmly on the reef, allowing the breaking seas to grind *Calypso* to splinters.

Sailing the shallows behind the Barrier Reef of Mexico and the entire length of Belize, then winding her way through the reef nests of the Bay Isles in Honduras, her shallow draft again allowed her to survive passage where deeper, outside ballasted boats would have often found themselves in jeopardy.

Sinking in the Pacific Ocean, with plenty of time on their hands during the process, has given opportunity to consider alternatives to Davy Jone's locker. *Kon Tiki* comes off the library shelf for inspiration, if only to look at pictures of a "boat" floating at deck level. Not the happiest of circumstances, however, minus the weight in her bilge, is there any real difference between *Calypso* and *Kon Tiki*?

The process is visualized in total. Life would be very different living at sea level, literally. Minus her ballast, the theory being only wood and nails are left, which will provide an excellent platform when sunk.

Waves washing over *Kon Tiki* were tolerated, the crew of *Calypso* will do likewise. In the minds of the two optimists, the empty water containers will be placed strategically under side decks, transom and in the fo'csle. Hector, it is theorized, will ride lower however the sailvane will remain above sea level high enough to (possibly) continue guiding *Calypso*. A bit of an unknown here, the helm will still be accessible although it will be underwater in the cockpit.

With the mainsail aloft in the trades more extreme measures are conjured up. There is an image of a top heavy, sunken *Calypso*. There may be a danger of her rolling over in the seaway; at this moment, it is simply unknown, but must be considered a possibility. When the ballast is being jettisoned, care must be taken to see *Calypso's* reaction. Should the crew feel she is becoming too "tender" they plan to hold on to some ballast and pause to asses the situation.

A plan forward is not clear, but alternatives are whirling in the minds of the crew. Eliminate the gaff boom then cut the mainsail to a Marconi rig is thought will be the first step. If she steadies up, more ballast, little by little will go overboard. If not, possibly the main boom will be removed, Both booms will stay with the boat and added to the bunks that have been torn out and stored for constructing a shelter of sorts on deck.

The most extreme measure in their bag of tricks will be cutting the mast down by half or more and jury-rig the existing stays at the new masthead. That should steady her up enough to toss the rest of the dead weight. She may still want some ballast, the last of it will be removed slowly, with great care to observe her reactions.

All the food will have been moved up on deck, their water tight containers should be fine. Bunks will be cut to pieces in order to fashion a table and stowage bins on deck. Only ballast will go over the side, everything else stays. There will be plenty of scrap sail plus the booms to construct a shelter.

Timing is an unknown element. The crew is unsure of when to commence these extreme measures. Possibly, when unable to keep the water below the floorboards any longer. That's as far as theory takes the crew. All that will be left to do is let her sink. A silver lining; the crew won't have a bilge to pump.

With that comfortin' thought Calypso sails along
an' with the daily routines, the crew carry on
Closin' in on a thousand miles to their destination
they tend their pump without hesitation

The daytime sky's filled with aids to navigation
thousands of people flyin' to the Islands on vacation
Contrails from all the major cities are convergin'
to a point over the horizon
where Hawaii will be emergin'

The AM radio's comin' in handy
as a direction finder it's a dandy
Pointin' out stations on Hawaii 'n California
correspondin' what the stars
sun 'n moon're tellin' ya

Closing in

Except for the love of navigation, taking sights and making calculations is no longer necessary. There is so much information available on the a.m. radio and in the skies to the north of *Calypso*, one would have to be blind and deaf to not find Hilo.

In reality, the contrails are a nuisance, an interruption of the ambiance, slicing through blue skies above the clouds. An interference in the crews navigation routine; they simply do not want the additional information giving them clues.

They are very happy identifying favorite stars, taking accurate sights, working out their lines of position; generally immersing themselves in the process as they solve the problems involved in finding their way across this vast undulating expanse.

The contrails so frequent, one may look aloft and see them all day long and guess fairly accurately which island they are bound for. The Big Island being the easiest to discern.

The A.M. radio band on the short-wave radio is directional. Simply holding the radio perpendicular to the horizon, sweeping through the compass, San Diego, Los Angeles and San Francisco are picked up in the eastern quadrant. To the west are the islands of Hawaii. Held in the direction the bowsprit points, KHLO booms in.

It is true, the age old quote "a prudent mariner will not rely solely on any single aid to navigation." With these wise words as the rule of thumb, the crew begrudgingly suffers the intrusion.

For the exception of two incidents since leaving Panama, the crew have enjoyed months of "aloneness."

The first being the freighter heading for Panama steaming by, giving the crew a scare, followed by the entire ship's crew on deck waving their hearty greeting.

The second, so brief, yet so memorable. Lounging on deck, south of the Baja Peninsula when *Calypso* was beating her way north, the crew was alerted to an odd sound, one not ordinarily heard so far offshore. A "whirlybird!"

The tiniest of such creatures, a bubble dome with two people inside taking a close look. The crew jumps to their feet to wave to the visitors in a way that would let them know they are having a good time and in no trouble. The pilot and spotter return the salutations, then buzz off, presumably in search of tuna. The chopper being part of an unseen commercial seine operation in the neighborhood.

Miles high in the sky, it seems unlikely folks in the commercial jets above, without a visual aid, would be able to spot *Calypso*. She is camouflaged by her months at sea. Her sails, no longer bristling white, are mottled with a brown grunge. Her once bright yellow hull, now drab, dulled by a thick coating of sea scum.

A wonderful sail we really don't want to quit
"We'll put on food 'n water 'n refit
stop the leakin'' 'n patch the sails
then follow the trade winds
an' the Humpback Whales!"

The nearness of civilization is unsettling, the crew is quite comfortable with the natural world surrounding them. If not for the horrendous amount of water pouring in, Hawaii would be a short stay for provisions. Possibly they would cruise up the chain, then the current, and most ambitious idea, is to continue on for Japan.

A very inviting route is a great circle from Hawaii to the Philippines, then island hop north to Japan. This route follows the trades dead down wind, down current. The great circle direct to Japan will find more variable winds and cooler temperatures. The prevailing current will turn adverse as well, sometime after leaving the Hawaiian chain and remain so the remainder of the distance.

Fresh sails, some hull work as yet to be determined, renew sheets. The list grows as *Calypso's* condition is surveyed; much more involved than first envisioned. There are some unknowns it is true, however, plans are being readied for arrival, right through to departure.

There is the thought jobs may need to be acquired to finance a haulout, repairs, sails and provisions. *Calypso's* advantage again, she's a "pocket cruiser." Mostly thought of as referring to a small sailboat, in reality for the crew, she's easy on the pocket. A part time job or two should provide enough income to deal with expenses and continue on in a reasonable amount of time.

Mahi Mahi

Closin' in on these Islands of the Pacific
the Ocean sends a message humorous yet specific
Got slapped in the face by a fish leapin'
an' 'leavin' this sailor thankfully weepin'

A school of mahi mahi iridescent 'n bright
appear in a wave bathed in mornin' light
Eye to eye with these beautiful fish
one could hear the Oceans' wish

An incident occurred which can be too easily cast off as a coincidence; to the crew of *Calypso*, it is certainly not so simple. An illustration of the ocean's critters, even the ocean itself as part of a collective consciousness is perceived when literally slapped on the face, while a healthy chunk of mahi jerky rides in the jaw like a chaw of tobacco. A flying fish, chased from the sea had flown across the deck to make the strike, square on the cheek. Recovering from the surprise, eyes focus on the seas passing under the boat.

Just a few fathoms off to starboard, a half dozen mahi are grouped tight, keeping pace with *Calypso*. The fish are grinning. A mischievous grin as if they are a pack playing a juvenile game while staring this sailor down, eye to eye. Overwhelming emotion arises, the jerky chokes down at this exchange; the sailor breaks, tears flood the deck.

The mahi mahi have sustained the crew all these months since leaving Panama. Locked in this mutual stare their eyes continue to bore deep. As tears and emotion subside, a solemn promise is made to our ever present companions.

The message to the crew's loud 'n clear
these wonderful creatures have been very dear
A debt of gratitude there will always be
for these most magnificent mahi mahi

So now beans 'n rice the mainstay
an' a small tuna or two a day
An' still waitin' for scraps with that soulful stare
good 'ol Fatlip's still there

With this heart wrenching experience, the pact is set in stone. No more mahi will be taken for the dinner plate. There is an abundance of food under the boat, this certainly will be no hardship on the crew.

Over the stern, Fatlip follows along. He is informed there will be no more mahi scraps, but there will be plenty of tuna coming his way. When having a conversation, eye to eye with Fatlip, there are always extra wags of the tail in acknowledgment. So it is settled, our hitchhiker has wagged his approval.

The Leak

That' ol bronze pump ya work by hand
the crew's pumpin' to beat the band
Throughout each night' n all day long
somethin' down below's gone way wrong

Slosh...slosh...slosh...KERSPLOSH!
slosh...slosh...slosh...KERSPLOSH!
Calypsos' bilge alarm's the motion
of a rhythmic rollin' heavin' ocean

The horizon is not yet visible when the crew are awakened in the early hours with the familiar sound of water calling out to wake up and pump the bilge. "It's ankle deep!?" is shouted out when bare feet are surprised by water over the floorboards. A new high water mark has been established. An extended deep sleep by the crew allowed more water than "normal" to begin filling the boat.

The pump is worked with renewed vigor. The water recedes to the tune of "Well we overslept and its not as bad as it looks," followed by soothing words to *Calypso* that "your doing fine girl, we're not going to sink you now." The glass is always half full aboard *Calypso*. The lightest, brightest brainstorm is inevitably put forward in every situation, always alert for the positive in problems and their solutions.

There is no panic, there is only business as unusual. Happily sailing along in a boat, sinking mid-Pacific and discussing future dinner plans with a fish certainly qualifies as unusual business. This water over the floorboards incident is treated as a "one off" for the time being. A couple hours yet until first light, the bunks are dry, the crew returns to sleep until the morning sight.

As Calypso approaches her destination
the leak's still cause for consternation
These gallons we're pumpin' we no longer count
the crew only knows it's a huge amount

Calypso has maintained her one hundred mile daily average since altering course for Hawaii. The crew is up early this morning, light on their feet with a milestone crossed at midnight.

Three solid months, ninety days at sea. The Big Island, now somewhere just over the horizon, calls for a fresh water rinse celebration. With Hawaii only several days off, three gallons is allotted, attesting to their absolute confidence in completing the voyage safely. The trades remain consistent. Mornings see Calypso charging toward the twentieth parallel. Afternoons she is hurtling down a steeper, chopped up seaway, wing and wing. The navigator calculates five or six days to Hilo. Another degree north is desired for the approach, Calypso works each morning toward that final track which will take them down wind, down current into Hilo Bay.

Eyes're now scannin' the horizon'
cause soon there'll be land arisin'
Pumpin' seawater we'll do no more
we'll have showers, pizza 'n beer galore!

Crossin' the hundred fiftieth meridian today
more 'n more contrails're pointin' our way
Sailin' the twenty north latitude line
a followin' sea 'n makin' great time

Contrails are no longer a nuisance, rather, they now elicit excitement in the crew. Approximately three hundred fifty miles to Hilo. Jet planes streak across the sky. Their angles of approach beginning to converge toward a point beyond the bowsprit as they home in on the Big Island. There is a noticeably light step in the crew. A subtle exuberance pervades; visions of ice cream, fresh fruits and vegetables along with a thorough cleansing of body and boat. Images of land; mostly, green hills and the feel of cool earth underfoot.

Approaching land is serious business. The crew must be on their toes. Vessel traffic should pose no issues. The potential of managing a gusty thirty knot onshore breeze against a rugged coastline which the crew has no local knowledge of, is real. They spend extra hours resting down below in preparation for arrival. There is comfort in a chart of the Big Island, which shows a generous, gaping entrance to Hilo Bay.

---

*Day ninety-three at first light
get up 'n take the mornin' sight
Throw 'ol Fatlip a breakfast snack
sit in the cockpit 'n kick back*

This morning begins as any other over the last three months. The bamboo pole is put to work which takes three small tuna in short order from the garden for breakfast. The "garden" is flourishing, sporting a forest of full grown tube worms with a wonderful compliment of associated flora and fish too small to identify. The crew has ignored the growth. *Calypso* will drag the whole mess into Hilo. Most likely, H.M.S. *Resolution* approached the Hawaiian Islands with an identical garden two hundred years ago. The crew of *Calypso* enjoys the luxury of knowing there is an island chain ahead. Captain Cook had only clues that South Sea Islanders had been trading somewhere in this area of the ocean. He was sailing blind across a seemingly endless ocean in search of the "Northwest Passage."

The *estufa* belches out another blanket of grime while at the same time producing flash fried fillets and fresh flour tortillas. The *estufa* is destined for an extremely short half-life on arrival.

Breakfast and morning duties complete, a savory morsel of fresh tuna saved for Fatlip is tossed over with the usual greetings. With a second cup of Panamanian coffee (the carefully rationed supply has held all these months), the crew settles back to relax sailing wing and wing to a lightly rolling sea and equally light early morning breeze.

Wind freshens considerably in the early afternoon. The swell lumps up. A hearty chop is now visible across the heaving deep blue expanse. The genny is doused and stowed, replaced with the jib. The mainsail is not reefed, *Calypso* balances just fine; not over sailed, where she would be diving into the trough. The long period of the Pacific swells allows this, where in the short chop of the Caribbean, the mainsail sail would be shortened now.

She races comfortably at hull speed toward her destination along with the broken patches of puffy white clouds, which seem to be in an exceptional rush this afternoon. Her downwind happy waddle is in full swing.

Calypso's risin' 'n fallin' in a heavy seaway
a ten foot swell runnin' today
From top of one of these rollin' blue hills
a sight on the horizon gives the crew chills

Climbin' the riggin' to get a better view
smiles 're glowin' on Calypso 'n crew
The unmistakable sight of land poppin' up 'n down
gettin' intermittent glimpses of Mauna Kea's crown

Chapter 17

HILO, HAWAII

June 1981

Land Ho!

The mountain's presence now dominates
that small nob in the distance captivates
Calypso's sailin' as if possessed
the crew's sailin' as if obsessed

Yesterday at the top of a swell something out of the ordinary had caught the eyes of the crew. "Did you see that?" Whatever it was, it did not reappear at the tops of the following waves. "A Humpback!?" A Humpback would most likely show itself again, as the tail did not stand-up, signaling a deep dive.

Not reappearing, the usual scramble half way up the mainmast for a better look is hard work in the seaway. Concentration on the horizon ahead is broken by the effort to hang on, gripping with white knuckle fists in the rigging while squeezing the mast tight between thighs and ankles. The cheek is scrunched against the mast, the eyes shut tight from the strain of the head grip through the snap rolls.

A pause through a slow roll allows a look around. An attempted shout is choked out, unheard below. Tears well up, blurring the vision, a second attempt blurts out an over-excited classic. The

352

cracking, high pitched, "land ho!" is acknowledged below with a wide grin, sparkling eyes and an arm wave in the direction of the knob

Back on deck, exuberance reigns; they had done it. Tears and laughter punctuate the day as does the continual straining to see the knob when it momentarily peeks up above the horizon. The rest of the day the crew plays hide 'n seek with Mauna Kea until nightfall closes the curtain.

Today, since mid-morning, the mountain is just there. It is so "there," it takes extra effort to keep from locking on with a stare, ignoring the three hundred sixty degree view around the boat. The morning sight determines the current has a considerably strong set to the southwest. This was first noticed the morning before. They take note, Hilo Bay is now due west of their present position; they are a bit south of their intended approach.

We discover where land 'n sea meet
the whole experience bittersweet
Caught in conflict with the notion
of leavin' this wondrous Pacific Ocean

L and. The initial enthusiasm has worn away overnight. Mauna Kea's presence dominates the scene as well as the mind's of the crew this morning. Reality sets in; we are leaving home.

The crew will step off their floating oasis to encounter busy streets, people bustling madly about, noise, polluted air; as the list grows, to say they are intimidated understates their apprehension.

Were it not for the dire needs of *Calypso*, this would surely be a short stop for a quick haulout, fresh bottom paint, sail repair, maintenance and provisions. Her persistent leak and rotting sails preclude further thought of sailing on any time soon.

Two days more the mountain's standin' tall
Calypso will soon arrive at her port 'o call
After ninety-six days we'll make our way
into the arms of Hilo Bay

Pinto beans soaked in fresh water turn creamy, the first since tacking west. The delightful beans and tortilla breakfast is complimented with extra cups of coffee, for this is the day they will sail into Hilo Bay.

There will be fresh water showers after the daily saltwater washdown of the decks. There has not been a single day of rain since leaving Panama, however, there is still an untapped six gallon jug aboard. At a minimum the crew will appear well scrubbed, although the same may not be said of *Calypso*, her nautical condition will have to do.

Trade winds had eased through the night. Two miles offshore of the Big Island at dawn, *Calypso's* light morning breeze tapers off to a glassy calm. One imagines the trades sweeping across the Island high aloft, leaving light breezes and a low swell along Hawaii's windward shoreline at sea level.

With land so close and almost zero moving air, it is plain to see without consulting the charts, the current here flows southwest. On hindsight the crew would have been much better off if they had worked harder to maintain a course to the north of Hilo Bay. They had been lost in their reverie since Mauna Kea first appeared, paying little attention to their approach. Why bother? There's the Island, big as life.

Nightfall sees *Calypso* continuing the struggle far offshore to allow some sea room from the rugged coastline. Ominous thoughts creep in with the darkness. The crew is very aware of the charts lying open on the bunk. One is an oceanic wind and current chart which plainly maps out *Calypso's* dangerous situation. The memory of the idyllic drift in the Doldrums is now a black cloud casting a shadow on *Calypso* and her crew.

Coastline Struggle

Nearin' our goal winds get fluky
the current's strong 'n situation spooky
Cause' without headway there's a danger here
from the Island chain Calypso will be swept clear

Throughout the night
Calypso 'n crew endure this fright
Aware of this precarious pinch
Calypso's scratchin' 'n clawin' for every inch

The landmass falls away to the southwest. An airless drift away from the Big Island will carry *Calypso* beyond the Hawaiian chain. If she is unable to beat her way upwind against the current on the return of the trade winds, she will have an open ocean all the way to the Philippines.

The security of the sea room is abandoned, as the chances of a drift into the far beyond is much more likely than it will be with *Calypso* close by the shoreline. There will be options as well near the island. She may have an opportunity to surf into a beach on the low swell. A more extreme measure will be setting some sort of signal fire without lighting up the entire boat.

The crew works dangerously close in, white flashes accompanied by the sound of crashing surf has nerves stretched taut. This torture persists through the night, a zig zag pattern, using whatever intermittent puffs she is able to make use of, keeps *Calypso* clear of the breaking water without venturing offshore into a swift current. First light finds *Calypso* has held her ground quite well, Cape Kumukahi is still roughly five or six miles distant. Eyes strain against the shore to observe the drift direction and speed. After a long stare, it is determined there is a light counter current taking her in the direction of Hilo Bay.

An exhausted crew continues the tacking, made easier now with daylight. Light breezes are now seen on the water rather than felt on the cheek or the eye catching a sail pooch with a puff in the dark.

The decision to hang tight to the Island has paid off. Upper atmosphere clouds appear to be moving well to the southwest, yet a calm persists next to the mountain at sea level. This appears to be the result of the bulwark effect. Mauna Loa and Mauna Kea stand to face the full force of the Trade Winds.

Cape Kumakahi, lies fifteen miles to port, Hilo Bay, just five miles north up the coast. The crew, by early evening had lost ground to the Cape, even though they had struggled the whole day with wispy breezes, chasing catspaws wherever they are spotted. The effort proves exhausting, though it has been marginally fruitful. *Calypso* is now very close to shore, Cape Kumukahi is plainly visible at about ten miles.

Tackin' back 'n forth close by the shoreline
Calypso catches a counter current in the nick of time
Mid-afternoon of her ninety seventh day
she's sailin' into Hilo Bay

Fatlip's Farewell

"**P**erseverance furthers." Those wise words first heard on the deckof a fishing vessel, uttered by a partner during a difficult fishing venture. Breakdowns and slow fishing plagued the effort, however the crew always pressed on. Rounding Leleiwi Point, *Calypso* picks up a half knot current flowing into Hilo Bay. "Perseverance furthers!" The words ring out loudly on the completion of their voyage, with *Calypso* chasing zephyrs on her drift into the Bay.

The crew is animated, giddy; laughing loudly. They jump to the bilge pump happily taking turns pulling water from *Calypso's* thirsty hull for the last time. The celebration is interrupted with a glance ahead, a couple hundred yards. The pump is abandoned mid-stroke, the bilge not yet cleared of water. "Fatlip?!"

Up ahead a color change causes concern
the crew scrambles to look over the stern
To say goodbye to 'ol Fatlip, our friend the fish
who never wound up on the supper dish

Tossin' scraps to 'ol Fatlip always brought smiles
this little mackerel swimmin' thousands of miles
Strainin' to get the very last look
at our little friend who outsmarted the hook

The crew are on hands and knees, looking over the stern. Fatlip is on station, a series of tail wags greets the pair. The question arises, how to say goodbye to a fish? A small bite of tuna jerky is tossed over,

Fatlip snaps it up. This is odd, Fatlip doesn't like jerky, trial and error has shown, he prefers fresh sushi fillets.

Is this little fish aware of the implications of Hilo Bay and the nearby harbor? Does Fatlip sense the change? Even more curious, is Fatlip communicating a message in taking the snack?

The crew must assume it is so. Lime green water is only yards away, a stark line, where clear water disappears. Fatlip as well will be lost to the opaque water when *Calypso* crosses the line. This is how their long friendship comes to a close. The water around th boat clouds up, swallowing Fatlip. *Calypso's* hardy little sidekick we'll see no more. The crew voices a hope, Fatlip will find a comfortable new home here in Hawaii. "Keep well Fatlip, stay safe."

Hilo Bay

In Hilo bay the wind quits
givin' the crew the fits
Wonderin' " can this really be?"
Calypso's driftin' back out to sea!

Catspaws disappear, Hilo Bay is glass calm. The harbor is still a good distance off, a mile at a minimum. Possibly the meager Hawaiian tide has begun to ebb; the crew observes *Calypso* is losing ground at a startling pace for the amount of tidal change.

Has the current switched outside the Bay? If so, in all likelihood, it will be flowing south. Possibly the fast moving water near shore is sucking water out of the Bay. An instant fear arises in the crew. Thoughts of sweeping past Cape Kumukahi with no wind, resulting in the identical predicament they had just spent the last twenty four-hours extricating themselves from.

The crew is desperate for a solution: even before the thought of tossing an anchor is acted on, the red entrance buoy catches their attention. *Calypso* had just passed the marker which now lies very much in the path of their ebbing drift. A line is made ready, *Calypso* only needs a nudge to starboard to pass close by.

Appears Mauna Kea's offerin' Calypso a gift
the entrance buoy's in the path of her drift
A favorable puff of wind an' on the first try
gotta line round that buoy as we're floatin' by

Catspaws are spotted ahead, the helm is put down, the mizzen boom is shoved to port. Lightly rippled water sweeps around *Calypso*, sails catch the wayward zephyr, she spins, her hull now broadside to the buoy. She crashes awkwardly into the steel, the clapper responds with a resounding clang. The line is hurled over the top, a wrap of the tail end taken on the bitts. She hauls around in the current, pulling up with a rude jerk; the maneuver punctuated with a series of lighter clangs of finality. *Calypso* has arrived in Hilo, Hawaii.

The immediate threat of being swept out to sea averted, the crew takes stock. First off, it is illegal to be tied to a navigation aid. The crew are concerned this will attract the unwanted attention of the Coast Guard. They have no idea how long they will have to wait for wind or a favorable change in the direction of the current.

There is one concern, actually, an immediate threat that must be attended to before the Coast Guard boards *Calypso*, should that occur; at this moment, it seems a real possibility.

Hangin' off this giant red anchor for survival
a pitiful scene, our momentous arrival
However it gives the crew time to make a plan
of what to do 'bout Mr. Customs man!

Bumper Business

The crew has kicked the bumper argument all the way across an ocean without resolution. The vision of the Coast Guard crawling all over *Calypso* searching every nook and cranny as they did in the Atlantic injects an urgency into the conversation. The crew goes to their corners and come out defending their positions, which has not changed in three months over these six thousand miles.

Dug the bumper from outa the bow
ponderin' "whadda we do now?
We can set the thing afloat
or hang it over the side of the boat?!"

The idea to set the bumper adrift now is abandoned after careful consideration. How far will the bumper drift? It is very large, visible from a great distance. Where will the current take it? It may still be floating nearby when the Coast Guard shows up, the variables stack up quickly. The same two alternatives remain. Stuff it in the bow or hang it in plain view over the side.

When we're tyin' up to the dock
that 'ol bumper's gotta take up the shock
The pressure's a heavy load
that duct taped' bumper's gonna explode!

he navigator's argument prevails; the bumper is oversize, it will stand out. It is in a weakened condition, the duct tape may well let go on contact with the dock. The bumper will remain in the bow piled in with empty water jugs, life preservers and paraphernalia.

The entire smelly mess has a thorough coat of *Calypso's* pedigree patina. The crew counts on a lesson learned from all previous encounters with customs officials. As uniformed representatives of their countries, their tidy, well scrubbed appearance precludes a hands-on search of a filthy boat.

Good Samaritan

A Good Samaritan sails in from the west coast
Calypso gets a tow line an' invited to a pig roast!
A crowd's gatherin' 'n helpin' out
"That's the missin' boat!"
a Coast Guardsman shouts out

ood fortune befalls the crew before the Coast Guard makes an appearance. A large sailing vessel out of California arrives in

Hilo Bay. As she sidles up to *Calypso*, the first words heard from another human in three months ring out. "We're twenty eight days out of San Diego!" "Ninety-seven days out of Panama, can you take our line? We have no engine!" All goes quiet on deck of the big boat.

Their exuberance fades, dumbfounded stares is all that remains of the greeting. The captain breaks his frozen crew loose, throws his boat in reverse, barking "Take their tow line!"

A wrap is taken off the bitts and let go, *Calypso* falls back with the current away from the buoy. The loose line is coiled then quickly tossed over to our host. Their crew makes *Calypso's* tow line fast to a stern cleat, the captain engages his motor, the line comes taut. *Calypso's* sails are stowed as she is underway into the harbor. Her work, for the time being, is finished.

A sizable crowd has gathered to greet the new arrivals. *Calypso's* tow line is tossed to the folks on the dock, she is hauled in and secured in a slip in short order. The crew are overwhelmed by the attention. "We're having a barbecue, free food to the boat with the longest time at sea!"

The gathering is made up of nearby sailors in the harbor, most of whom have arrived within the last couple of weeks from the mainland. They begin shouting out a variety of days at sea, to which the crew chimes in with their ninety-seven, winning the contest hands down. The crew are looking forward to a variety of foods, other than raw fish, beans and rice.

Questions begin to come rapid fire at the pair, but are hushed by a young Coast Guardsman shouting in disbelief. "That's the missin' boat! THAT'S THE MISSIN' BOAT!" His voice cracking as it blows through the high end of his range.

The Coastguard's in a dither
up 'n down the dock runnin' hither tither

Hilo, Hawaii

This alert young fella's in the know
Calypso'd been reported missin' two months ago!

This announcement takes the crew by surprise. Their families had come up in conversation periodically. The crew were concerned of the worry they had surely caused, their last communication had been letters mailed from Colon before transiting the Canal. The subject would usually trail off, as there was nothing to be done. With this bit of the information the crew are now anxious to get off the boat to make phone calls home.

Protocol dictates only the captain may disembark on entering a country from a foreign port. This will not be necessary, a Customs agent can be seen working his way through the growing throng on the dock. The crew waits aboard in respect of the formalities. Phone calls to family and friends will be first on their agenda when Customs has finished with *Calypso*.

Mr. Customs Man

Mr. Customs man arrives impeccably dressed
lookin' down at Calypso visibly unimpressed
Gingerly he steps aboard our floatin' hovel
grime so thick he shoulda' brung a shovel!

An audible sigh of relief accompanied with rolling eyeballs is shared privately between the crew at the gentleman's initial reaction to *Calypso*. This fellow, it is plain to see, is very hesitant to board *Calypso*, however, with a shrug of resignation, he asks permission to come aboard.

The crew drops into the cabin, with an invitation to the officer to join them down below. The officer is using extreme caution in seeing that his uniform, the white cuffs especially, touch no part of *Calypso* as he descends into the cabin. It is all the crew can do to hold back their laughter at the sight of this poor fastidious man, doubled over at the waist for lack of standing headroom, looking about as if he'd fallen into an outhouse. His face pale, it seemed he was about to puke, pass out, or both right there.

The crew, rummage for passports giddy with excitement, they cannot sit still which further distracts our guest. The mood of the crew is buoyed even more now that it is clear to them, this customs agent will not be crawling forward to search the fo'csle.

While the gentleman is busy filling out his paperwork with passport information, the crew take the opportunity to exchange furtive glances forward at the bumper which is in plain sight. When their eyes meet, they share their amusement in silence.

Preoccupied with stayin' clean
he's gingerly surveyin' this grungy scene
Makin' a couple notes in his book
never givin' that ol bumper a second look!

The customs officer hurriedly scribbles information, then turns for the hatch, politely taking his leave while grinding out a tight lipped "Aloha, welcome to Hilo."

Formalities completed, the crew returns topside, hop into the crowd gathered on the dock and make haste for land; the pair are anxious to feel terra firma under foot. They are not disappointed when finally stretching their legs with bare feet brushing through cool grass.

Potluck

Steppin' off the dock onto dry land
the crowd gives the crew a big hand
Calypso's arrival's cause for celebration
an' the barbecue's fired up for the occasion!

The folks're full of questions now
of what where when 'n how?
The crew explain the journey as best they could
an' these world sailors 'n locals understood

Curiosity overcomes the folks, questions come rapid fire. The crew toss out answers as quick as possible without long winded explanations. To a remark concerning *Calypso's* sea-worn condition the crew responds they are desperate for a haul-out. "*Calypso's* sinking. She'll sink right where she sits in a day or two." Admittedly, an exaggeration, it would be more like three or possibly four days before she goes under.

At this, the folks are alarmed, then energized; out of a buzz of inaudible mumblings a voice is heard to say, "I'll get hold of Sam." Another voice pipes up, "there's a grid over there," the person pointing to a cement seawall across from the docks.

Everything is happening fast. Too fast. The pair hurry to the phones, spreading huge relief among family and friends back home. A cigarette is offered. Not having even thought about smoking a cigarette for months and without even a slight craving, the smoke is stupidly accepted.

Tables're piled high with food, beer 'n wine
these folks know how to have a good time
Pizza 'n poki 'n cake 'n ice cream
everthin' a sailor could dream!

Mouthwatering. An absolute extravaganza unfolds before the crew. The vessels and their crews tied up in Hilo represent a wide variety of countries. The feast which adorns these tables reflects a mind numbing number of cultures from around the globe, as well as the Hawaiian favorites "poki, "lomi-lomi salmon," "poi" and "Laulau." There is baked ham, prime rib roast, baked and mashed potatoes, as well as hamburgers, hot dogs and kebabs on the grill. Cans of spam, loads of ice cream, gallons of wine and beer; the list goes on.

The crew had not witnessed such a display since the fishermen in Isla Mujeres created the most artful arrangements of the finest fare Mexico has to offer.

Burgers 'n dogs sizzlin' on the grill
we're gonna eat our fill!
Pilin' a plate high with goodies
'n grabbin' a glass of wine
Calypso's crew sits down to dine

A few small bites into this feast we take
start feelin' the 'ol belly ache

*What at first we thought a real treat
all this food we cannot eat!*

Nausea overcomes the crew after only a few bites taken from the plates they had packed. Uncomfortable, exchanging glances of discomfort, they have only blank stares for the food. As hungry for this delightful meal as they are, it does not stay down very long. Pain etched on their faces, they double over.

The unmistakable taste of bile creeping up the throat has this sailor bolting for the head. An embarrassing moment our fellow sailors find quite amusing, while they offer sympathetic condolences.

---

*When out at sea we thought we'd eat like hogs
now we're tossin' burgers to the dogs!
When before we thought we were payin' a price
now we're missin' our raw fish, beans 'n rice!*

Chapter 18

BEACHED

June - August 1981

Mystery Solved

*First order of business when the tide goes out
find what this miserable leak's all about
The crew examines her hull all around
at first glance she appears sound*

Day two on land, the crew wakes with renewed energy and sense of urgency. Rolling out of the bunk at first light, bare feet splash onto the cabin sole. A rude reminder of the business at hand. Between the wonderful Aloha yesterday and the deep sleep which followed, the bilge had not been pumped.

An early riser on the neighboring boat is aghast at the amount of water the crew pumps overboard exclaiming "wow, how much water was that?!" "Oh, maybe eighty gallons, give or take."

The tide will be low soon, dropping about three feet. The crew waste no time; the bilge is given a thorough pump, jib and mizzen are set then the lines cast off. *Calypso* glides quietly out of her slip, the intermittent wisps of air is all she needs to sail across to the "grid." Not a formal tide grid as found on the mainland, there are no heavy timbers to rest a vessel on, there is only a flat bottom next to the cement seawall, wide enough to set a small vessel through a tide change.

Calypso is tied to a light pole, sails are stowed then the *estufa* is fired up for the very last miserable time. The crew now puts together a much anticipated egg burrito breakfast while waiting for the water to drop.

Folks were very generous during the celebration, *Calypso's* fresh food larder has been replenished. The eggs were included in groceries that had been dropped off and are pounced upon this morning.

Scrambled eggs doused with hot sauce then rolled up in a fresh made flour tortilla fill the sensitive bellies. The crew are ravenous this morning, breakfast is over in short order, done in by a few quick, wolfish bites.

The tide recedes so secretively when *Calypso* touches bottom, the crew does not notice. Only when returning to the deck, the light pole line is seen to be taut, the boat does not move; it no longer feels like a boat. It feels as though it is a structure built on land. *Calypso* is hard aground. About two hours more the tide will be low, when her bottom will be visible for inspection.

Lookin' inside the boat again
"Yup! The waters' still pourin' in!
No visible damage anywhere
but there's water comin' in everywhere!?"

Tide is dropping fast. Two feet of her red bottom paint is showing now. There is still an hour more water to lose when the crew tears up floorboards then opens access to the transom wherever possible. The cockpit sole and surrounding hatches are removed as well as the steering gear cover. The interior of the entire stern is now exposed to some degree.

With so much of the planking and heavy members visible, it is very plain to see where water has been seeping in. All the seams below the waterline have darkened the planks. Water soaked wood reaches forward from the transom timbers a full third of the inside of her hull. The seams on the transom face are dry above the waterline.

The navigator has put her wood boat surveyor cap on and is rowing slowly alongside *Calypso* examining the outer hull in a dinghy she has borrowed from a neighboring yacht. The pair shout their findings back and forth.

Along the seawall above *Calypso*, a sizable group of folks has gathered, coffee mugs in hand to observe and chat while this curious crew go about the business of making a diagnosis.

Calypso's boat stripe's painted blue
an' here's where Pat finds a clue
With close observation she becomes wary
"What're these tiny little holes?" is her query

Naval Shipworms

"Worms!" A voice booms out from the group of onlookers. Murmurs of agreement ripple through the folks above. "I'll call for the crane." This startling announcement comes as a surprise, even though the crew had an idea this was coming. They simply are not prepared for such an abrupt, convincing declaration of both the problem and solution in one fell swoop.

"You're in good hands now!" A new voice is heard to shout followed by another murmur of agreement. The crew had no idea who they were referring to other than the name "Sam" was tossed about. This is taken as a very positive development.

A painfully obvious realization is, the crew had not come to this conclusion at sea. There were many more characters performing in *Calypso's* traveling circus than met the eye. These unseen devils were busy chewing their way through the hull since before the leak was first detected over two months ago. It dawns on the crew, the worms entered when *Calypso* was adrift in the Doldrums. The bootstripe does not protect the hull, as it is a painted line above the protective bottom coating.

Leaving Panama, this line was submerged, as *Calypso* was heavily laden with water and supplies. The free floating larvae attached then bored into the unprotected bootstripe.

Proddin'' n pokin' prove our worst fears true
when the knife just pushes right on through
The bootstripe served as an open hatch
where parasites could happily attach'

Haulout

Calypso is just bumping the bottom lightly as the incoming tide begins to lift her. The crew sits on deck chatting with the folks as they wait to raise sail. A message is passed along to the crew: "Sam says sail around to the park by the fish market at high water, a crane will meet you there." A great relief to the crew, Calypso will be safe ashore, no longer needing the constant attention she's required all these months at sea.

Sail 'round to the public park on the risin' tide
where a crane shows up 'n takes Calypso for a ride
On terra firma the crew stands with a solemn stare
at their sweet little Calypso way up in the air

High water finds *Calypso* tacking back and forth in front of a quiet looking park adjacent a very busy fish market, complete with a buying station crowded with boats from the Big Island mosquito fleet. They are taking on ice, delivering their  catch; going through the familiar motions which has brought this crew so many miles.

 A truck mounted crane eases into the park, pulling up to an embankment which runs along the beach. A small group gathered wave *Calypso* in, the crew brings her close by, leaving room for the slings to be lowered ahead of her bow. Sails are stowed, a long pole reaches out hooking the bobstay. This enables the folks on shore to pull *Calypso* into the slings. When in position, the slings are tied off fore and aft, preventing them from sliding out from under the boat.

The crane operator gently lifts *Calypso* about two feet, carefully moving her toward the embankment where the crew is able to jump off. This done, he takes her up several more feet, where she is clear to swing over the land. Blocking comes off the truck then placed under the hull, fore, aft and amidships. She is lowered onto the blocks, braced in position, then wedges are driven wherever needed between the braces and the hull. This secures *Calypso* in position to begin work.

---

*A shady spot's found to park it
right by "Suisan Fish Market"
Sam Kumukahi takes the crew under his wing
An' his gang of friends who love to drink beer 'n sing!*

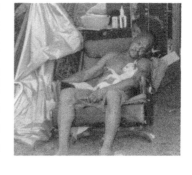

Calypso has been placed next to what appears to be a permanent encampment in the park. A hooch built of Army surplus tarps, manila lines, olive drab barrels and water cans; all items representative of the nineteen forties. The crew are introduced to Joe Jack, overseer of the enclave and the park's sole permanent resident.

Once settled, the crew are introduced to "Sam." They are a bit startled when he is introduced as Sam Kumukahi, which they instantly relate to Kumukahi Point, the point of land they had struggled with to make Hilo Bay.

Sam, a bigger-than-life Hawaiian individual, extends a huge hand accompanied by a wide, warm grin and a booming "Welcome to Hilo, Hawaii!" It is apparent, Sam is a very well respected member of the gathering who have surrounded Joe Jack at the fire pit.

He wastes no time, prodding about the hull, stern to bow. When finished, he proclaims "you were lucky, your boat's planking is gone in the stern quarters, both port and starboard, if they had gotten into the bow, you would not have made it." Pointing with his knife at the affected planks, "there is nothing here." He then shoves the knife clean through the plank, right up to the hilt with no effort whatever.

The plank he has stuck his knife into looks fine, about half way between the waterline and the keel. The crew are well aware, the inside of that plank looks fine as well. When Sam removes the blade, water pours from the hole. The immediate reaction is "damn!" in near disbelief. Stepping up for a close look, a closed fist strikes the plank between two frames where the knife hole is leaking water. The punch, not near hard enough to break knuckles blows through a spongy board, the arm buries all the way to the elbow.

A second punch breaks out a chunk of the adjoining plank which is discolored to a dirty gray black from its original creamy white. Close examination of the piece and the oak frame it was nailed to reveals some fascinating information about this deadly worm. Most obvious is that it avoids breaking the skin of the boat inside and out. Another curiosity are the light gouges in the oak frame where the worms ran into the hardwood. The tunnel turns back into the softer, straight grain pine with no real damage to the frame.

Naval Shipworms had been makin' tunnels
from Calypso's keel to her gunnels
Bi-valves with a shell on their head
this is the critter wooden boats dread

With our boat worms're havin' a great time
'cause they're dinin' on sweet New England White Pine
Our tough little vessel in 'n outa so many jams
an' now poor Calypso's got the clams

While blocking *Calypso*, the only boat in the park, a crowd of locals stop by out of curiosity. By the time this initial work is completed, most have moved on, however a group of eight or ten around the fire pit have settled in. They chatter away, occasionally pointing toward *Calypso*. Laughter and animated conversation trail off when the folks break into song. Traditional Hawaiian lyrics backed up by ukulele, accompany the hammer which now falls into the rhythm as it beats wormwood out of the bottom of the boat

---

Surrounded by this Aloha atmosphere
The crew jumps into high gear
With a vengeance that's feelin' real good
rippin'' n tearin' worm eaten wood

Planks so thin the impression they give
Calypso's become a seawater sieve
Teredos have kept the crew pumpin'
now their gettin' a real good thumpin'!

66 **N**aval Shipworms", A free floating pestilence which lurks unseen in the sea, came within days of sinking Calypso. They have had three months to whittle and scrape through the relatively soft planking of her hull. They had been at work almost two months when the blue marlin was alongside. Calypso was compromised by that time, it would have taken very little on the part of the billfish to send her to the bottom.

Bashing the planks with a light steel mallet breaks up what remains of the wood. The chunks are feather light, just over or right at one inch thick. They resemble pieces of cardboard torn from a box. Not much is seen of the critter itself, only its tiny cutting shell at the head. A bit of black slime dangles from the single shell; disgusting as it is deadly.

Once this critter completes its cycle from its entry as a larva, then matures to a full fledged shipworm, it begins devouring wood. A characteristic of this seagoing tunneler is the integrity of the outer and inner walls of the tube. Water is pumped through the tunnels by the surge motion of the boat. This aids in propelling them forward and carrying away waste.

An irony which saves *Calypso* and crew is the clam's creation of a sturdy, efficient tunnel system. Here is a symbiotic relationship, of sorts, in that regard.

Calypso provided a home and food, while the critters obliged by not eating their way directly through the side of the boat. A nod, albeit with reservations, is given these teredos. After all, they were simply the keepers of the tunnels of terror, a silent sideshow in *Calypso's* seagoing carnival.

Repair and Refit

*Cuttin' out bad wood doesn't take long
fourteen planks completely gone
Saws 'n planes, chisels 'n drills donated
nails, screws 'n goopucky preferences debated*

*Pick up the lines with a spile
mahogany boards waitin' in a pile
Makin' patterns 'n cuttin' out planks
to Sam 'n his gang we owe so many thanks!*

"Ya, but what're ya gonna do about those garboards?" The familiar irritating refrain rings loud on the back swing. The mallet will strike the "first broad" the plank adjacent the garboard plank. "THUD." Surprise! This plank is made of oak, the mallet does not dent the hardwood. "A.A. Bernard, yes sir! YES SIR!" Another, even harder whack on the plank, "Boatbuilder!" Aim is taken at the center of the garboard plank between two frames and given a hard shot. "THUD." Now comes a furious spate of exuberant hammer hits all along the two planks at the bottom of the boat from the transom to the stem, port and starboard. "Solid as a rock!" On cleaning off the exposed upper edge of the first broad plank reveals the teredos had made only scratches, as were evident on her oak frames. Silence falls at the fire pit as the mallet takes a final shot at the garboard with that very pleasing, heavy "THUD." There is a protracted moment, no one speaks, then "A.A.Bernard... BOATBUILDER!"is blurted out from the fire pit in near unison.

Beers are raised, people chant and sing, destruction moves to the starboard side. The hammer swings, now trained, make quick work of the seven planks which are virtually gone from the transom forward eight or ten feet. This first day ends. *Calypso* has her frames exposed by the two gaping holes in her bottom. The holes are surrounded by good planking above the water line, below by the first broad and the forward two thirds of the hull. Sam is driving off to the dump with a load of what had been the bottom of our boat.

Joe Jack's is busy late. By the end of the evening, whatever tools are needed, they have been offered. Theories on all things boat repair are bandied about through the hours. All the while, coolers full of beer and pupus continue to arrive at the fire pit.

---

*Work slows some to a relaxin' pace
'cause in Hawaii life isn't a race
But storm winds of September will soon prevail
an' for the North Pacific Calypso must sail*

The next weeks are spent visiting with family and getting word out on the mainland that *Calypso* has arrived in Hilo, Hawaii and the crew are now making preparations to continue to Port

Townsend. There is widespread relief as *Calypso* had gone out as missing on the airwaves.

Sam arranged for the lumber yard to "give them whatever they need." In short order, straight grain Mahogany boards along with boxes of bronze screws and a latest, "state of the art" concoction; "Microballoons." Sam insisted this is an absolutely bombproof underwater seam sealant.

The crew are skeptical, as being of the "two part" variety, it is not, to their knowledge, commonly used in plank boat construction. There is however, no resisting Sams's insistence while under the spell of his warm, winning grin. His boat, *Kuuipo II*, a thirty six foot carvel planked powerboat, fifty odd years old, had the product applied years earlier. Needless to say, Sam's *Kuuipo II* is immaculate.

Family arrive, namely Dennis's mother and brother who had been suffering the worry and torment over the fate of the missing "kids." She tries to convince the crew to sell the boat and fly back. This bears no fruit. Instead, she finds herself here in Hawaii doling out the money for materials so they can do it all over again to her. She resigns with her usual shaking of the head while mumbling a low "mumma mia" to help out. This clears the bill at the lumber yard.

Pat's family arrives, their generous support is accepted with a heavy heart. Their grandson, our nephew, Rex John aged eight, drowned in Puget Sound shortly after *Calypso* arrived in Hawaii. In light of the concern they had carried for the crew of *Calypso*, the irony of this tragedy looms.

---

*The corkin' hammer rings nearin' works' end
returnin' to sea's right 'round the bend
Drivin' oakum 'n cotton into her seams
paintin' the bottom of this boat of our dreams*

J uly and August have slow progress to show in the rebuilding process. Life in the park is quite comfortable. The social gatherings, virtually every day beginning early afternoon, stretch to about ten p.m. when Joe Jack is fast asleep on his lounge chair. Fishing trips with Sam and tours of the Big Island punctuate the work.

Hawaii's weather is so pleasant, it does not offer a hint of the coming change of seasons as one feels in the northern latitudes. However, the crew are well aware, the Equinox is not far off. This first week of August sees an uptick in the pace of work on *Calypso's* hull.

When the last of the fourteen boards is fitted, work ceases for the afternoon. This is the "whiskey plank" and cause for celebration. A gathering in the evening similar to that on *Calypso's* arrival has come together with much merriment as the board is clamped, drilled and fastened into place. There is  much comic ceremony around the final screw. Once the clowning plays itself out, the fastener is driven half way.

A pause is taken, firelight laps at her portside, the revelers fall silent. A nod of thanks to Sam, then the screw is driven home. Singing erupts like Mauna Loa, punctuated with whoops, cheers and bare-fisted pounding on the hull.

Early the following morning, light tapping wakes the crew. The unmistakable sound of a knocking corking hammer paying oakum and cotton into a seam. The crew are up and out the hatch before the pounding begins. The noise will be unbearable when the material is driven home on the next pass of the corking iron.

Hopping to the ground, the crew are introduced to a mid sixties, sinewy Hawaiian fellow sitting on a short stool under the boat. He has been corking boats since the war, where he began his career pounding oakum into aircraft carrier decks at Pearl Harbor. It is good fortune for *Calypso* to have an expert doing the work as there are a good number of wide seams left by the inexperienced boat repairman.

When the hull has been corked, just a days' work for the master, the new planks receive a final light fairing with the plane, then sanded to recapture her fine lines after which the crew plug screw holes and putty the finished seams. Her hull above the water line is given a primer coat. Below the waterline she receives a thin coat of anti-fouling paint, followed by a second heavy coat. The bottom paint is brought up well above the waterline as an extra measure of protection where the teredos had originally entered.

The original blue color she had when found at the boat show in Rhode Island is chosen for her new color in the northern climes. With two coats applied, *Calypso* is ready to launch.

The big day soon arrives
time for Calypso' n crew to say their goodbyes
Friends gather in the Aloha Way
Calypso sails quietly outa' Hilo Bay

Chapter 19

NORTH PACIFIC OCEAN

August 1981

Launch Day

Early on the morning of August twenty-fifth the crane eases up to *Calypso*. The trades have been pounding the eastern shore of the Big Island incessantly for days. This has the crew in high spirits. There is good sailing in the offing. Less than a month until the Equinox, time must not be wasted, they are already late in leaving for the mainland.

One last check of a mental list of provisions finds nothing lacking for the journey. Preparations had begun a month in advance, time enough to have double and triple checked every item on the boat. The cabin interior has been scrubbed clean and painted, the *estufa* replaced with a two burner "Coleman" stove. The water containers are lashed down, lining the cabin sole as before, stealing what little headroom the crew enjoyed in the park. They will want for nothing on this leg.

Joe Jack has been up puttering since before first light. The crew had been up as well, fumbling around in the dark in their excitement, stowing lines, clearing the decks and lashing down anything that may move. With daylight comes the rumbling of the crane truck, Sam follows close behind.

As straps are secured, folks begin arriving, many carrying flowers and leis. The crane then gently lifts her a few inches where the supports are knocked away. She is now free to swing over the embankment, where high tide waits to receive her.

She is guided over the edge with helping hands then lowered to where her deck level is even with the ground. Folks crowd around the crew, leis are placed over their shoulders as they step aboard. A lei is placed on the end of her bowsprit. They wish the pair fair winds while throwing flowers on the boat and in the water.

Calypso is lowered, the crew works her out of the slings, drifting clear. They raise full sail to the light inshore breeze. The freshly patched main poofs out with a muffled "womp" to the initial puff. She heels gently, bearing away from shore.

New braided "Dacron" sheets are soft, coiling easily; a pleasing sensation in hand as main, jib and mizzen are sheeted in. There is the

familiar gurgle as *Calypso* gains speed on this first tack. The helm is put down, sheets fly, she turns on her keel for a sail-by and a final wave to the folks gathered on shore. She glides out of earshot, the people ashore give their last waves as they disband. The colorful lei swings happily on the end of the bowsprit which points to the red entrance buoy and the Pacific Ocean beyond. The leis come off the shoulders and tossed into the water as the ocean swells lift *Calypso's* bow.

---

*Returnin' to life at sea 'n familiar routines
it's that thing of storybooks 'n daydreams
Not pumpin' the bilge its dry's a bone
chargin' over blue seas 'n headin' home!*

Calypso labors to windward as she works her way out of Hilo Bay. The sea is up with a refreshing chop, slapping the bow at the wave tops. Pepe'ekeo Point, a prominent headland is off her port bow. Once rounded, the island chain falls back to the northwest. Her heading will be due north from the Point. Several southeasterly tacks have her in position to clear the headland when close hauled. Sheets thrown, helm down, the bowsprit swings obediently through the eye of the wind. Sheets are hauled tight, the helm steadied and the new course is tied off. Hector is clicked in, taking command of the helm. This last tack, projected to be one thousand miles, ignites a renewed excitement which courses through boat and crew alike. Unleashed once more, free on the open sea, Calypso gallops to windward as she passes the headland. No more than two miles pass under her keel when Hector is clicked off, sheets slackened, the helm eased, then tied off when the compass points due north. Sporting full sail, a final adjustment of the sheets spills copious amounts of wind to maintain a speedy, comfortable ride on a blustery beam reach.

Hector is re-engaged. There is a familiar feel underfoot as she bounds through the seaway. She's a spirited pony, back on the open range in perfect harmony with her environment. The crew sway to the easy rhythm of their trusty steed. Glorious.

Pickin' up the trades roundin' the headland
spirits soarin' 'n the crew's feelin' grand
But for Calypso somethins' missin'
it's for 'ol Fatlip she's a wishin'

Her tag along sidekick for so many miles
followin' Calypso through so many trials
Hopin' her best friend's found a new home
an' wonderin' if 'ol Fatlip still has an urge to roam

Two Worlds

A peek over the stern can not be resisted, just to be sure, even though common sense says otherwise. Many thoughts crowd the mind. The memory of their faithful friend; always there with that penetrating stare, always happy to share a meal or listen to a one sided conversation.

The small eddy behind the transom, next to Hector, is vacant. The vacancy extends to the heart in concern for Fatlip's wellbeing. Was he able to safely re-locate? Did he return to clear water? The questions that arise in quick succession are unanswerable.

Hawaii should be fine for Fatlip. He will have adjustments to make, the loss of his sushi chef for one. He will have to return to his previous life as a hunter-gatherer. Will he be pelagic, or will he find a rock to call home. There are a variety of options along this rugged eastern coast, or he may take up residence in the calm waters of Hilo Bay, right where we left him. There will be other mackerel to befriend and certainly the waters are still warm enough. The humans continue on with life in their world, Fatlip will do likewise in his. This is the one thought that gives some real comfort, knowing Fatlip will not follow *Calypso* into the icy cold waters of the North Pacific. That would seem a cruel end for our warm water friend.

Due North

Sailin' along Hawaii's windward side
Calypsos' havin' a great ride
A beam reach in fine weather
all dried out 'n light as a feather

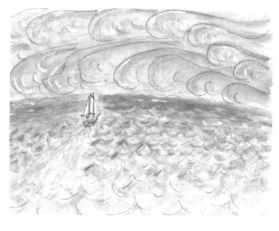

The crew has re-gained their sea legs by the following day. The wind veered slightly south overnight, enough that *Calypso* is carrying full sail on a sizzling broad reach. She feels especially buoyant, having dried out in the park. Fourteen new mahogany planks have her quick and lively at the wave tops, she darts into the troughs then scrambles out, crashing through the chop at the top of the next wave.

The morning sight leaves a very encouraging line of position on the plotting chart north of Pepe'ekeo Point. By the time the evening sight is worked out, an accurate distance made will be calculated.

This does much to boost the crew's confidence on this first day of their final leg of the journey. The great circle line they have drawn measures over three thousand miles, to allow for best sailing conditions with the prevailing winds and currents.

The projected line drawn runs due north before turning east. This will bring *Calypso* to somewhere in the neighborhood of eight or ten degrees south of the Strait of Juan de Fuca where they will tack to the east northeast. The crew are working on a theory which takes a vessel north of the North Pacific Gyre, where they could be stalled in the high pressure with light and variable winds. A sufficient gain in latitude will have *Calypso* in position to take advantage of the prevailing westerlies which will allow her to scoot toward the Strait along the northern reaches of the predicted location of the Gyre.

More'n fifteen degrees north latitude gained
Polaris risin' higher as if unchained
A thousand miles an' the trades're holdin' steady
ten days out 'n the crew's rough 'n ready

Ten days out of Hilo, *Calypso* has still not adjusted course. Hector has held her nose to the compass with an eye to Polaris whose declination has been rising more than a degree each day.

The North Star has guided vessels for thousands of years. Most likely, it played an important role in the discovery, populating and ultimately the establishment of a trade route to Hawaii, becoming

Polynesia's northernmost neighbor. It would be well over a thousand years before this remote group of Islands are discovered by western explorers. Captain James Cook being credited with the discovery, however some historians point to earlier contact.

The discovery of Hawaii is intriguing, specifically when looking at a chart of the entire North and South Pacific Oceans. The extremely remote location of the Hawaiian Island chain would seem a discovery by chance. However, it is known Cook sailed from the Society Islands.

Navigators of the Societies held the secrets of those Islands to the north. Did Cook gain information of their existence? His route, would suggest the possibility that he was not quite "flying blind."

Cook's vessel, *Resolution*, made a beeline on prevailing winds and currents, from the Societies to Hawaii. At a point somewhere south of the Equator, a lookout posted high in a crows nest may have been the first to observe Polaris rise at the horizon.

As Cook's *Resolution* pressed northward, Polaris would be observable from deck level. The helmsman would begin steering by this star the rest of the way to Hawaii.

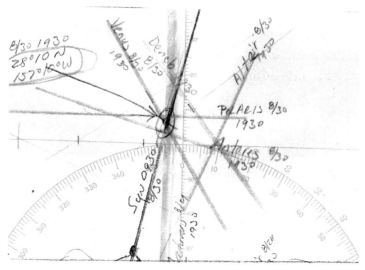

T he crew of Calypso watch Polaris gain altitude in the same fashion sailors have done all these thousands of years. Polaris ignites that deep sense of timelessness, so often felt on these crystal clear ocean nights.

Gotta mention it ain't flowin' like a creek
but Calypso's opened up a new leak
Maybe the transom's got Teredos
them miserable microscopic torpedoes!

W ater sloshing under the floorboards, a familiar, unwelcome sound wakes the crew in the pre-dawn hours of day twelve. *Calypso* has been driven hard since leaving Hilo. With the exhilaration of setting off on the passage, the crew had given her the reigns. Hector worked effortlessly as she charged ahead. The steady twenty-five knots blowing across a six or eight foot seaway has had her dashing up and down the choppy hills, mimicking the exuberance of her crew.

"Worms!" is the first thought flashing in the mind as the pump spews a puny half dozen gallons over the side. Realistically, it is much too soon for another attack to show a leak of any significance. An alternative explanation is having kept sail piled on, sailing her at full tilt for almost two weeks, she has most likely taken on water as the planks had not soaked enough from her time drying on the beach. Driving hard into the troughs, the planks above the waterline in the bow are very dry. They may just be taking their sweet time swelling tight.

This is a common, non-threatening result which the crew passes off with a laugh. "SEA TRIALS!" is blurted out in unison. A joke the crew shares which refers to launching a vessel after repairs or refit then taking short day trips in calm waters to soak-up and work out bugs. A common practice. However as fisher folk they rarely had the spare time for fiddling around in a bay. Emphasis is placed on attention to details ashore. When the boat hits the water it is "turnkey," ready to fish. *Calypso* had the basics covered when she was launched, however she did not have the luxury of time to soak up and swell tight. A more pressing issue had to be given priority; the Autumnal Equinox.

Wakin' to a change in the weather
tossin' boat says it ain't changin' for the better
Wind's outa the northwest today
deep blue seas now battleship grey

Weather Change

Sixteen days out of Hilo the easterly wind subsides sometime after midnight while the crew sleeps. *Calypso* rolls deeply in opposing swells. One does not need to look out the hatch to observe this phenomenon, it is felt and visualized while braced in the bunk.

From her port side, jumbo swells can be felt to shove *Calypso* to starboard with authority. The long deep rolls are interrupted by the sharp chops of shorter seas from the opposite direction. The crew suffers this buffeting through the dark hours, rising when there is light enough to see the horizon. This morning, as light comes on, the hatch is pushed back to reveal a low darkly overcast sky. There will be no morning sight. *Calypso* wallows awkwardly in heavy twelve footers, however, the cross sea is nowhere to be seen. A northwesterly swell has dominated the easterly swell entirely. This lumbering grey ocean is accompanied by a light, slap in the face cold breeze. Not only is there a sea change, the chill has the crew donning warmer clothes.

An abundance of caution has the main and jib stowed, the mizzen set with a reef. A "wait and see" approach is taken this morning; a hearty breakfast of soft boiled eggs smothered in heavily buttered corn meal mush topped with salt, pepper, cheddar cheese and hot sauce; "grits 'n eggs."

A cold weather favorite conjuring memories of sailing the calm waters of the Intracoastal Waterway; of waking to frosty decks in quiet anchorages, the water, mirror still. This comforting meal will hold the crew in good stead for the signs are clear enough. It is big weather pushing these seas. No surprise here in the middle of the North Pacific Ocean on the cusp of the Equinox

This cold wind it's bitin'
a rough ocean Calypso's fightin'
Increasin' now gale force blowin'
two hours more 'n the storm's still growin'

Seas continue to gain bulk through the morning hours. By noon the wind has yet to measure twenty knots. The crew are back on deck, lashing everything tight. The helm is checked for center, re-lashed, the main and mizzen booms receive the same attention. When the crew are satisfied all is secure on deck, they return below to double check that her opening ports and hatches are tight. Lastly, all loose paraphernalia is stowed. The open shelves and cubbies are then secured with small mesh net.

Late in the afternoon, the wind can be heard to freshen, a chop slaps at *Calypso*. The tension of waiting is relieved. The crew can feel her darting and dashing as the weather comes up. A very brief peek out the hatch reveals an ocean where the waves are now twenty-footers sporting heavy combers at their tops.

Storm Riders

Hove to under reefed mizzen
hurricane force 'n seas have risen
Every breakin' wave Calypso catches
water blows through portholes 'n hatches

Darkness falls with a heavy foot. Curiosity has the hatch slid back enough to poke the head out momentarily, to gauge wind and sea. The wind tears at the face, stinging it with salt spray. The blackness is such that all that may be observed are pearly white combers close by. *Calypso* weather-vanes to the wind, rocks wildly to port and starboard in the troughs followed by snap-rolls in the chop at the tops of mountainous seas. A rough estimate of sixty or seventy knots is made, the hatch is then shut and secured.

Deficiencies show themselves in a most rude fashion, when presumably, *Calypso* takes a comber on deck. Almost as if the port holes are wide open, gallons of water fire-hose the bunks. The cockpit must have filled, as the companionway is dumping a bathtub full of water into the cabin. Water is pouring through the louvers in the companionway hatch. The forward hatch is draining into the fo'csle as if the boat is underwater. The crew had thought the Tehuantepecer could not be matched in its ferocity. Tonight, *Calypso* is challenged by wind and sea which dwarf what they had witnessed in the Gulf of Tehuantepec.

They don full raingear as sleepwear this night, the foam mattresses are now fully absorbed sponges. Water sloshes but is still contained below the floorboards. The weather is nothing short of wicked.

Rather than go out on deck to pump the bilge, an attempt at much needed sleep is made. Tossed around, often violently all day and now a cold water washdown have taken a toll. The crew are exhausted.

Wedging into the bunk in the fetal position so as not to be thrown to the floor, a modicum of comfort is gained. Violent moves are countered when asleep with automatic isometric responses against the sides of the bunk and hull.

Hoods are up on the rain coats as the pillows are water soaked. The crew are in good spirits, chuckling in their misery over "Shackleton's Boat Journey," as told by the navigator Frank Worsley.

Conditions inside *Calypso* must be similar in many ways, however they are not having to endure the far more extreme conditions as were experienced by the crew of the *James Caird*. Six people crammed into a twenty-two foot lifeboat in an Antarctic hurricane.

Great comfort is found in Worsley's account of their misery, for it makes this encounter with the elements seem a cakewalk by comparison. Much of their casual attitude is also attributed to their absolute confidence in *Calypso's* ability to "take care of you when you can no longer take care of it." Surprisingly, with the wet-cold, tumultuous conditions, sleep still comes to the crew.

The Great Wave

Calypso's bein' tumbled 'n trashed
crew's hunkered below soakin' cold 'n thrashed
In the middle of the night wake to a scare
floatin' off the bunk weightless in midair

T he mind works at light-speed mid-air as the body is tossed out of the bunk. It sees *Calypso* being hurled with impunity from the top of a gigantic wave. She then free falls through blackness into an unseen trough far below. The scene plays out to its tragic end where poor *Calypso* explodes into ten thousand shards of splintered wood when she belly-flops back into the sea.

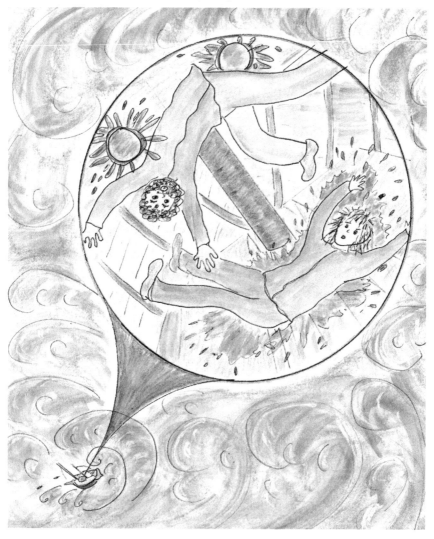

While Calypso's free fallin' in space
the minds's thinkin' "we're gonna leave no trace!"
A fifty or hundred foot wave the truth be told
"when we hit the trough she's gonna explode!"

"Gonna be the end of this madness!"
as Calypso plummets through the blackness
When back into the ocean she crashes
onto the cabin sole this flyin' sailor splashes!

Splashes?!"Cold water on the face instantly clears a groggy, dream cluttered mind when the body slams onto the cabin sole. The shock of a water landing sets off a string of instantaneous thoughts, the first being vocalized in a howl of victorious defiance to the ocean; "SHE HOLDS! MICROBALLOONS!" One can feel Calypso's strength right through to the bones at this moment. The exuberance is cut short when the inner bilge pump alarm goes off. There is no putting off the pumping any longer, Calypso has

continued to flood from the decks down rather than the bottom up while the crew "slept."

The hatch is slid back gingerly as *Calypso* continues her wild gyrations. Wind and spray tear at the face when stepping into the cockpit. One arm wraps the mizzen mast while the other shuts the hatch. Hugging tight to the mast, the pump handle is worked furiously at first, the cadence interrupted by the toss of a wave where both arms are needed to wrap the mizzen.

A line is taken around the mast at the waist to prevent being thrown over the side and allow the pumping to continue at a more measured pace. The work is tiring, as forty or fifty gallons are pumped before air is felt to be sucking in. A great relief to slide open the hatch and retreat below. Wild as it is down below, it is out of the wind and relatively dry. Comfort is measured by degrees of discomfort.

Now this soakin' wet mattress feels real good
protected by this bundle of nails, screws 'n wood
Thinkin' "this is gonna be one to remember
this Equinox storm of mid-September"

Three days more weather stays foul
wind simply will not cease to howl
A relentless march of greybeard waves
reminders of Calypso's many close shaves

C aught in the grip of this weather, there has been no opportunity for sights on sun or stars. Days spent struggling to
either hold oneself in position in the bunk, moving about the cabin
or preparing a hot meal take a toll. Not only is this physically exhausting, the sense of time and space without navigation for this
extended period has the crew in a netherworld with nothing but
these tossing walls which surround them, keeping eternity at bay.

The crew are numb, weary in the extreme; their mood remains
light, fiercely so. They cling to their wit as if it were a fuzzy warm
teddy bear; their barrel of wry humor is bottomless.

On this fine mornin' of the sixth day
The greybeards have finally gone away
Wind's twenty knots outa the northwest
Calypso survived her North Pacific test

T he storm subsides with a sigh. In the darkness as the crew
lay awake, all goes quiet; eerily so. The lumps of water
passing under the hull no longer hurl *Calypso*. She can be felt
to ride up a wave, smooth at its top, then waddle easily down the
backside.

Without the snap-rolls, the crew drops into a deep sleep,
waking with sun streaming through the portholes. "Coffee," the

first thought. Water is put on to heat, the companionway hatch is slid back to a cloudless blue sky.

Jumbo seas lumber by, the wind is a cold, delightful fifteen knot northwest breeze. A light chop dominates the seascape with the occasional comber rolling lazily off the tops of the heaviest waves. The deep blue this morning invites the crew to set full sail for a romp in these grand rollers.

Murphy

Emergin' from our sea soaked abode
the crew's back into sailin' mode
Fresh winds fillin' the genny 'n main
sun's shinin' 'n there ain't no rain

The mainsail is set, the halyards belayed, the genny explodes when it snaps full and tight with a solid "hooWOMP." *Calypso* responds on a broad reach, heeling into a full gallop across the ocean, diving into valleys then bounding over hills. The crew catches *Calypso's* fever, the mizzen reef points are loosed, the halyard gets away from the hand. Murphy is right there to snag it.

Shakin' out the reef 'n raisin' the mizzen sail
it's the mizzen halyards' turn to fail
Gotta repair it before the next storms arrival 'cause
its Calypso's rig for heavy weather survival

Mis-handling the mizzen halyard allows the line to jump out of the sheave. A minor detail overlooked when on the beach, the mast should have been repaired to prevent this from happening. This is the same predicament the crew had suffered months ago in the Gulf of Tehuantepec. With the more pressing issue of a sinking boat, this obscure detail at the mizzen top was easy to miss, the consequence of which is this interruption of what promises to be a magnificent sail, conditions being what they are.

The mizzen sail had only begun to rise when the line jumped, however, far enough that the reef points can not be tied when weather comes up. This being unacceptable, as well as being nearly useless now as a balancing sail in optimum conditions. The problem must be dealt with without hesitation. This little sail is vital to the comfort, even the success or failure of the journey.

---

*Once before the mizzen was scaled
an' that attempt miserably failed
But pullin' the mast down was a difficult chore
so it's decided to climb the mizzen mast once more*

Calypso is hauled into the wind, mainsail and genny stowed. She is now allowed to drift free. The crew take time now to assess the situation. Should they begin loosening the stays? The ordeal months ago is still fresh in their minds, as well as the failed attempts to scale the tiny pole. The nature of the seas here are different, however it is difficult to ascertain how they will affect either climbing or dropping the mast. There is a much longer period between crests and the walls of the waves are not as steep. The seas for the most part here are smooth rollers, combers being few and far between. The one standout difference, the seas in this neck of the woods are huge. In the trough of a big set, the top of the mainmast which is thirty feet, is about level with the wave tops, the seas being double or better than those in the Gulf of Tehuantepec.

The decision is to repeat the initial exercise by initially making an attempt to get to the top of the mast. If this can be done, the repair may be made quickly. The line will either be pried or cut loose. Preparations are made. A replacement line is slung loose at the waist, a screwdriver for prying and a knife for cutting is all that are needed.

The crew studies the seaway waiting for a noticeably large set to go by, though it is difficult to tell the difference between big and bigger until "humongous" shows up and passes by. A couple of its hefty mates are let go by as well, then a leap from the cabintop begins the scramble to the masthead.

Timin' moves with the boat's roll
made it the top of this skinny pole
While gripin' stays with white knuckles
the mizzen mast whips snaps 'n buckles!

C linging apelike to the port and starboard stays, legs wrap the mast tight at the thighs and ankles. A deep roll to port at the bottom of the trough forces one to freeze in this position. As *Calypso* takes her righting moment, a shinny scramble combined with arm pulls, one on a stay the other on the halyard, makes quick progress, until the boat reaches the peak of her righting. One must grip the wire stays with bare hands while bear hugging the mast, cheek pressed tight, through the next deep roll. With each opportunity several feet are gained until the sheave is within reach.

The mast strains now with the added weight at its top. A desperation grab pops the line free at the moment *Calypso* topples off the top of a mountain. "Curaack!" The mizzen mast snaps like dried spaghetti, frayed wire rope rips open the skin as hands are torn from the stays. When the mizzen whips in the roll, the body pancakes the deck.

The stays keep the mizzen mast standin'
on deck this sailor makes a hard landin'
Got the mast lashed 'n sistered
with hands all bleedin' 'n blistered

Only after the mizzen is set properly are injuries, which are surprisingly numerous, tended to. The hands require bandages to stop the bleeding while splints must be made for the mizzen mast. The stays have held the mast in place but it has suffered a clean break just above the level of the cabintop which is the obvious lever point. The break is not a long fracture as one would expect, its a near perfect ninety degrees. Two twenty inch pieces of scrap mahogany are hollowed to fit either side of the mast. They are placed over the break and lashed securely with seine twine.

Bringin' the mizzen back on line
we accomplish in the nick of time
Only a few hours sailin' toward our goal
the crew can see it's a sucker hole!

The crew are uncertain of the weather conditions. The skies are clear and the swell has come down, however, it still runs a persistent fifteen or twenty feet. The barometer too has not budged, it remains stuck in the mid nine hundreds. The crew pile on sail, as present conditions still offer good traveling, but they are wary, the signs are not all that good.

"Batten down the Hatches"

With reefed mizzen 'n helm lashed tight
Calypso's readied for the next fight
Skies darken 'n grey seas return
there's dirty weather brewin' off her stern

Steadily the ocean lump's beginin' to grow
cold northwest wind startin' to blow
In black clouds Calypso's soon cloaked
down below bunks're cold 'n soaked

Intuition proves accurate when a haze appears during the late afternoon hours in the distance off *Calypso's* stern. The swell continues to build. There is no discussion or hesitation. Hector is disengaged, main and jib stowed, the mizzen reefed. The mizzen mast stays are given close attention, all four being tightened equally. All is readied for the next blow, as it is surely coming, and soon. The crew retire below, they had hoped to get the mattresses out to dry however this sucker hole has only offered a short respite.

Black bean burritos with scrambled eggs are made up in preparation for the severe weather. Burritos are one of the crew's classic "comfort foods." The crew are well seasoned now, not made ill by the extreme motion, but a full belly is the best defense in preventing seasickness.

Coffee is put on in anticipation of a long sleepless night. Loss of sleep will be aggravated by worry over the mizzen mast's ability to withstand the weather. The makeshift repair will be tested this night, that is a certainty.

It's a wonder how Calypso behaves
bouncin´´ round in these giant waves
White capped crests constantly smackin' her hull
the crew patiently waits for the next lull

The crew returns to the deck for one last pump of the bilge, as well as another check of the mizzen. The small mast takes the strain put on it by the combined stresses of sail and tossing boat. The repair appears to hold firm.

The assumption now, this is not your garden variety sucker hole; it would fool no one. When storms line up, marching in succession, they are often separated by a patch of clear weather. The next system sneaks in to pack another punch. Fishermen are quite familiar with this common occurrence. The Fall season especially, separate storms may line up, striking one after another for a month or more at a time.

This tempest is a horse of another color. The barometer remains in the basement, the swell is still up, the wind increases steadily, again. Coupled with the ferocity of the previous days' winds of seventy, eighty knots or more, this is not the approach of a second weather system.

The mizzen holds *Calypso* to weather, her bowsprit points due west. The crew go about double checking that the forward hatch is secure as well as booms and helm all lashed tight. They know well what they are in for; round two of a bout with one of those unnamed hurricanes of the North Pacific. The crew take one last long look at the fast approaching "back wall," before retiring below. *Calypso* is about to leave the eye of the storm.

The crew hunkers down three days more
no chance to dry out 'n gettin' bedsore
Sun greets the mornin' on the fourth day
set full sail 'n get Calypso underway

Raingear is donned, the crew brace themselves in the bunks for the initial strike; they do not have long to wait. *Calypso* can be felt to dive deep into a trough. On ascending the wave to its top, a terrific blast of wind is taken right on the nose, she then dives into the next trough.

The mizzen has done its work setting the boat to the wind. So it begins. Listening to the wind tear at their boat, feel the deep rolls and high hops as she negotiates one wave at a time. By the time the first three waves have gone by, the wind could be felt and heard to back off to a steady storm force.

Calypso sings in ranges when the wind rises above a full gale. The winds of this hurricane howl and scream at an earsplitting pitch taken to an intensity where the entire hull is shaken on its frames.

A comber rakes her decks, gallons of water gush in from the topsides, blasts through ports and hatches. The mattresses drink their fill. Squishing and squirting with every move, the big sponges ignite contagious fits of gut wrenching belly laughs as the crew embrace their misery.

Days and nights run together to a point there is no differentiating the two. Meals happen whenever one of the crew has the energy to haul themselves off the bunk and wedge in at the stove.

Cooking is a challenge, however the fire is hot and dependable. The crew has enjoyed their choice of stoves for this leg of the journey. Meal preparation at sea is difficult enough; the previous *"estufas"* took much of the joy from creating tasty meals. Thankfully they are not dealing with one of those stoves here in these conditions. If one could even keep the *estufa* lit, the flame was so weak, the simple act of boiling water might not have been possible.

Handling hot food, boiling water and such in a tossing pocket cruiser is a necessary art. Spaghetti boiled in water then refried with spices and a tomato sauce finish is the chefs choice this first morning breakfast. Misery is relieved substantially when this "hot 'n spicy" dish is served up. For this brief moment in time, the elusive sense of sanity accompanies the hot meal. A big pan full of leftovers will be there for cold snacks throughout the day.

Three days and nights in a wet, cold washing machine, has the crew hunkered and numb. Sometime in the pre-dawn hours of the fourth day the shrill, mind-numbing din, subsides. Huge seas can be felt to pass under the boat; devoid of the hard chop, boat toss and deep dive into a trough. This brings the crew on deck. Stars are visible, including Polaris. The horizon is not quite visible yet, but the height of Polaris is encouraging, allowing a rough estimate of forty-five or fifty degrees without a sextant; very near the latitude of the Strait of Juan de Fuca. A line of position from a noon sight while in the eye of the storm is the sole navigational aid captured since the weather turned. Not much to go on. The crew estimates a fifty or sixty mile storm drift each day. There is no way to be accurate, however dead reckoning says *Calypso* has made reasonable progress toward her destination. The wind has been steady from the west to northwest quadrant.

From her progress northward, it is assumed *Calypso* rides the *kuroshio* current, a favorable stream which runs directly to the West Coast. They wait in high anticipation for the appearance of the horizon when the sights will reveal lines of position to add to the noon sight taken days ago. The result will be an accurate picture of where *Calypso* is in relation to her goal.

One thing for sure it's goin' our way
this nasty weather's headed to Neah Bay
Weather's gearin' up for the season's change
the Strait of Juan de Fuca's straight downrange

First light shows the thin line of horizon. Polaris being the initial target, as the angle measured will yield *Calypso's* latitude with an error of a meager sixty miles or so. Forty-four degrees ten minutes puts her somewhere off the the Oregon coast in the proximity of Tillamook. Calculations with sights from Antares, Polaris, Altair and the morning sun sight will mark *Calypso's* longitude and exact location.

The wind is twenty knots. The west southwest vector invites the crew to set main, genny, douse the mizzen and run with wind and current due east, wing and wing. Hector takes over the helm, showing masterful skill holding course with a steady hand as *Calypso* does her happy downwind waddle in these overgrown storm seas.

The behemoths are round, smooth for the exception of a light chop; they are running twenty-five to thirty-five feet. From their tops, one can see a great distance. The ocean has turned from grey to dark blue. The occasional snow white comber breaks off, then crashes down in an avalanche on the wave's face. World class sailing at its very finest; the reward for enduring the creation of this magnificence.

In the ways she finds to tantalize
the ocean never ceases to surprise
This blue Pacific mornin's no exception
when she toys with the crew's visual perception

Psychedelic Ocean

Light bathes the sea turnin' it blue
revealin' a spectacle to the crew
Far as the eye can see on every swell
she casts her magical spell

The pair stand waiting on deck this Equinox morning as the orb rises unseen, still hidden by earth, its first rays cast golden light over a black, undulating expanse. An oddity has captured their attention, as yet, unexplained. Colored lights have begun intermittently winking at them, holding their gaze in wonderment. The scene which surrounds them is a mystery unfolding, shrouded in the quarter-light of dawn.

The sun approaches that curved line of our planet, long fingers of light sweep the waves, setting the twinkling lights afire. More lights appear as the sun rises. When it breaks the horizon, the mystery is solved.

Bedecked, bedazzled bejeweled 'n ballooned
with colorful glass fishin' floats she's festooned
As many as practical the crew collected
these ocean gifts so unexpected

An amazin' sail which has come to be
a magic carpet ride on this slow rollin' sea
Risin' sun sets glass floats afire
psychedelic sailin' through the North Pacific Gyre

Fishermen and beach combers of the west coast and Alaska come upon these jewels on occasion, however, a scene such as this must certainly be a rarity. Japanese fishing floats, commonly referred to as "glass balls" may be found in abundance on coastal beaches. On the fishing grounds, they are generally found one at a time, occasionally laying alongside the corkline of a net.

Calypso is sailing full tilt, the first good traveling since the short hop in the eye of the storm. As much as they desire to load the boat as they had in Bahia de la Ascension with coconuts, the crew are loathe to take the time for a serious harvest. Lacking a dip net, there is no way to scoop them up. *Calypso* must be brought into the wind, slack the sheets, then drift down on the float.

C hoosing a jumbo float, the crew maneuver the boat upwind, drop the mainsail and genny, raise the jib and mizzen, then begin a downwind drift on their target. With reduced sail, *Calypso's* drift is adjusted by sheeting jib or mizzen as needed. She is worked alongside where the crew can get their hands on the prize.

Attracted by its large size initially, they had not related the size of the float to the size of the net. The lime green globe is shrouded in fishing gear. The heavy web is either from a seine or trawl of the high ocean variety. Ships, not boats carry this equipment which represents a very controversial industry. By-catch from this gear includes schools of dolphins and porpoise.

The net hangs deep, out of sight below the float. It is loaded with tube worms and kelp along with tons of unidentifiable life. The mess must be cut away to retrieve the glass ball.

The work proves far more difficult than it had appeared at first. The web is thick and tough to cut; nearly an hour passes before the float is free. The loss of sailing time irritates the crew, however, there is another large prize a short distance off. The crew make for it, sidle up and begin the chore of cutting it free, along with considerable grumbling over the valuable time lost. Impatience cuts the harvest short. The pair decide to abandon the gathering of the jumbo variety, opting to resume sailing on course for the Strait. There is such an abundance, the revised plan is to scoop small floats into the boat while sailing by. This too proves very difficult. Some success is had with the gaff hook on small floats which have material dangling below. Occasionally one would be just right and brought aboard easily. This balances the desire to collect the colorful bobbles while making tracks for home.

Gotta sun sight right at noon
got another on the moon
Calypso's averaged seventy-five miles a day
just eight hundred miles to Neah Bay

Exquisite sailing on a broad reach, the occasional glass ball comes aboard, delighting the crew on every successful capture. Navigation too resumes. Following the evening sight, *Calypso's* position is marked seven hundred, eighty-three miles from Neah Bay. It is determined this glass ball event is the result of *Calypso's* course taking her through the North Pacific Gyre.

This expansive area of ocean is well known to sailors for its summertime calms, the result of the circular patterns of prevailing winds and currents. Floating objects gather, due to the whirlpool effect created on an oceanic scale.

The seas gradually subside with the wind as it backs to the west, blowing now at fifteen knots. The genny replaces the jib, the mizzen is hauled in, the helm eased. The genny takes the wind on the backside, slapping over to port. *Calypso* surfs wing and wing on smooth eight to twelve foot seas, dead downwind.

Calypso's world's surreal for three days
while bathin' in a bright suns' rays
Nights're crystal clear 'n crisp
at the horizons' edge a low lying mist

The seas' rise is almost imperceptible
then grow quickly to a size quite respectable
The shift in the wind's very slight
an' it still carries that cold northern bite

Neptune's Rage

Mattresses are damp, no longer wringing wet, having been out on deck during the previous two afternoons. The cabin has recovered to a reasonably orderly state. The mizzen fix is holding strong. The crew are counting the miles to home at this point with full knowledge and confidence, it is within their grasp. They have sailed out of the Gyre, at least the portion where the glass balls had gathered, for there are none to be seen on this third day.

The wind veers to the northwest in the late afternoon along with a gradual increase in the swell. When the breeze freshens, the crew waste no time in their response. Mattresses are brought below, genny and main are doused. The mizzen is set with a reef, booms are secured, the helm is lashed on center.

Barometer's fallin' like a stone
wind's chillin' the crew to the bone
Top of the waves white caps appear
in the crew of Calypso this raises no fear

After two years sailin' the crew has learned
Calypso's a tough little boat an' our respect she's earned
The crew hops to an' gets the deck squared away
gonna be driftin' on a reefed mizzen today

"Risin' seas, fallin' barometer," the old adage rings true with the suspect dark grey fog hanging in the northwest quadrant. The distant cloud is low, reaching right down to the deck, threatening in a way that has the crew making preparations for a long night at sea. Once the deck is squared away, they retire below to prepare a meal. A large quantity of rice and lentils are boiled together then fried with garlic, onions and spices. This should hold the pair for a couple days.

A final check of the deck finds everything in order. Strong wind whips the wave tops into a frenzy. Even more unsettling than the wind, an unwelcome cloud formation has crept up on *Calypso* while the crew were below enjoying their dinner.

Top 'o the waves wind stings the eyes
at the troughs bottom the cold wind dies
Risin' seas whisper "more wind's a comin' "
the riggin' chimes in an' starts a hummin'

A low grey cloud appears
the wind cranks up as if changin' gears
The anvil arrives with its leadin' edge
an' it's like gettin' hit with Neptune's sledge

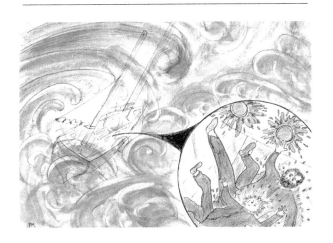

The initial blow lays Calypso on her side
sendin' her slidin' down the waves' backside
The blast is hurricane force
an' it's blowin' Calypso right on course

C alypso takes a sucker punch in a dark alley. The crew are thrown against the starboard hull when the mizzen snaps the agile little boat to weather at a wave top. A deafening scream accompanies the toss, then comes a dive into the trough with a few precious seconds of quiet stillness at its bottom. The next wave heaves up, the wind howls, Calypso bucks the wave to its top where she takes another tremendous blow from the leading edge of the storm.

The crew hang tight to the bunks through the next seconds while the wind has its way with the little boat. She bobs and weaves in defiance to being hurled at will by this howler.

Thankfully, the duel is short lived. The leading edge passes, the wind settles back to storm force. The crew steel themselves for what follows; a storm of unknown duration.

The mizzen sail sets her bow to weather
Calypso floats on this ocean light as a feather
The anvil quickly passes by
an' like a thief steals the blue sky

Hove to three days before the weather breaks, the crew is weary from the tumbling; their tiny world in constant motion as Calypso rocks, rolls, climbs and dives. She endures angry wave tops as they slap at her with impunity. Down below the crew brace themselves through the violence. Relief is fitful, coming only in those moments where Calypso is completely still, hanging motionless for fractions of a second or a little more before the next series of wild gyrations resumes.

This blow passes pre-dawn. The seas continue to remain heavy. They do not subside with the wind today. Grey skies only allow a morning sun sight through the cloud cover. This has the crew on edge, alert and watchful for the next system which is surely on its way.

Time is not wasted. The twenty knot westerly breeze has the genny set with the mizzen: the course is adjusted to the northeast to gain latitude. Hector is clicked in, leaving all hands free to go about other business, specifically, making a hot meal with plenty of left overs to carry the crew through another day. When underway, every mile made while conditions allow, doubles the mileage made drifting under a reefed mizzen. Even so, by the time *Calypso* makes Neah Bay, she will have drifted somewhere in the neighborhood of a third of the total distance from Hilo to the Strait of Juan de Fuca. It is safe to assume she has drifted one thousand miles on this leg of the journey, beating her Doldrum drift by four hundred miles or more.

One after another marchin' in succession
the storms of September in a grand procession
On leavin' Hilo the crew never had the notion
they'd be sailin' backwards 'cross the ocean

Closing in

Navigation since *Calypso* made the turn east has been a mix of celestial and dead reckoning. This short reprieve from the weather provides no clear skies for a brief peek at Polaris which would give an estimation of latitude. Two weeks of storms and lulls since the last accurate position taken on the Equinox, when it was fixed at forty-three degrees, thirty minutes north latitude by one hundred-forty degrees thirty minutes west longitude; eight hundred miles offshore.

Cloud covered days 'n dark stormy nights
two weeks waitin' for those precious star sights
Not takin' navigation by chance
sailin' by compass 'n seat of the pants

Dead reckoning on the chart has a circle drawn surrounding an area roughly two hundred miles in diameter. The crew estimates *Calypso* is now in the neighborhood of three or four hundred miles offshore. They are also of the opinion they have gained enough northward latitude to be southwest of the Strait, about equal with the Columbia River, give or take a hundred miles.

Wind and sea conditions have *Calypso* bounding along under her trusty jib and mizzen combination. A restless night is spent, checking and rechecking conditions as under Hector's steady hand, she continues to barrel blindly through the darkness. Choppy waves snap at her from the tops of a sea running a tolerable eight to twelve feet. The crew stand ready all night to douse the jib and lay to weather. They are sailing *Calypso* on the knife edge of sanity, rabid in their hunger to chew up the remaining miles to the shelter of Neah Bay.

After midnight, stars begin to show between broken clouds. A sizzling sail in these boisterous seas is not reigned in. The crew can smell the barn.

At long last a break in the weather
a change in this pattern's for the better
Sights're taken right at dawn
then lines of position carefully drawn

Aldebaran, Capella and Polaris provide intersecting lines of position with the morning sun sight. The skies are breaking clear with a chilly breeze blowing out of the west northwest at a pleasing twenty knots. A light chop ruffles the tops of an easy eight foot sea.

The mainsail is set, the wind is taken on a beam reach, as there is good news from the navigator's table. *Calypso* is due west of Westport, Washington, two hundred eighty miles out. Her position is outside of their dead reckoning circle to the north and east. She has made outstanding progress toward the coast, much better than the crew had calculated in their estimation. With this knowledge, the decision is made to gain the rest of the latitude before approaching land while the wind is favorable. They will meet the Strait head on, possibly even from the north if these conditions hold. Should the wind veer to the north, the Strait will be an uphill slog, extending their days at sea.

Ninety miles are logged over the next twenty-four hours, forced to reduce sail to jib and mizzen during the afternoon, they are able to pile sail back on in the evening. The mainsail, genny and mizzen carry her through the night.

Before the sun rises, the first sign of land greets the crew. A lone shearwater swoops a half circle around the boat in the early morning half light.

Thirty-five hundred miles outa' Hilo
Storm petrels n' Shearwaters're greetin' Calypso
A mere two hundred miles to the West Coast
Of a tough Equinox crossin' Calypso can boast

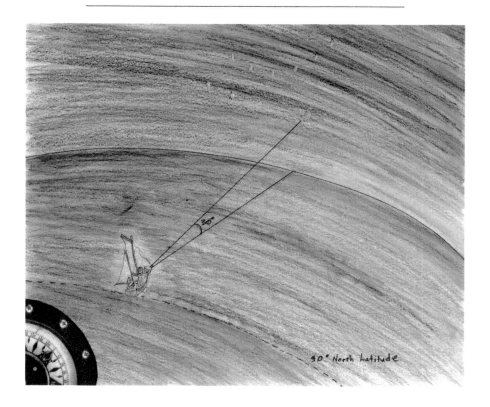

Chapter 20

A JOURNEY'S END

October 1981

Continental Shelf

Where ocean turns from blue to green
the Continental Shelf is clearly seen
Gulls're now circlin'' n swoopin' nearby
to the North Pacific Ocean we'll soon say goodbye

C lear weather holds overnight, the wind remains steady at twenty knots. The morning sights have *Calypso* just over one hundred miles offshore. Cape Flattery lies unseen, off the starboard bow.

A prominent seamark reveals itself to the crew this day. The afternoon light is perfect to observe this wonder of planet earth. *Calypso* is sailing in clear blue water. Green water is visible to starboard, defined by a line running north and south as far as the eye can see.

This is the thousand fathom drop-off, the edge of the North American continental shelf. The helm is put down lightly to starboard as the sheets are slacked, taking the wind on the stern quarter. Hector is clicked in, giving the machine the honor of crossing the demarcation zone.

Her position is fixed off the Strait of Juan de Fuca on the

Vancouver Island side. The present tack will take her across the La Perouse Bank from where she will drop into American waters. The wind, if it holds, will carry her straight to Neah Bay.

Puffins and terns are among the next birds spotted as she works her way toward shore. This part of the ocean is familiar from commercial tuna fishing days. Curious gulls circling, crisp Autumn air and emerald green water; the neighborhood feels like home.

Thick mornin' fog on day thirty-seven
starts breakin' up just after eleven
Olympic mountains're lookin' grand
curtain's liftin' on an evergreen land

Fog Bound

After midnight, the lights of the first vessel since leaving Hilo are sighted. Shortly after the vessel passes, a bulk carrier headed north up the coast, the Cape Flattery Light flashes into view. The crew is not asleep this night, excitement will not allow it. The Light is re-mindful of the distraction created by the "knob" of Mauna Kea when first sighted. The eyes keep diverting to the flashes, the brain counts the seconds. This prominent marker is visible from fourteen miles which tells the crew they are on approach to the Strait of Juan de Fuca.

The freighter too is an indicator of the bottleneck where commercial traffic will converge from multiple directions. *Calypso* being no exception, must negotiate any number of fast moving vessels as she crosses the mouth of the Strait into U.S. waters.

The wind has held from the west northwest, however it wanes dramatically before dawn, down to a wispy five knots. The skies above are clear, while a haze has settled allowing only occasional glimpses of the Light. The breeze turns flukey, unpredictable wisps from various directions tease the crew. The sails flop with the listless rolling of the boat on a glassy three foot swell.

First light has Cape Flattery shrouded in fog. Fog. Of all the torments one encounters on the seas, regardless of inside or outside waters, fog is certainly among the most unwelcome and dangerous of nature's elements.

The crew has noted the compass course to the Light. Their speed is zero to two knots at best. Before full daylight, *Calypso* too is draped in the wet blanket, visibility is down to a few yards around the boat.

A leisurely breakfast of fresh made flour tortillas and refried beans smothered in a hot chili sauce comforts the crew bundled in the cockpit. Their world is a special kind of quiet, one in which the only sound is that of a light shlopping of water against a plunging hull. Thick fog such as this muffles sound. Still the dull pounding of another freighter in the distance can be felt as much as it is heard.

The morning wears on, the shroud covering *Calypso* begins to lighten above the mast. A slow process of the thinning of the cover continues until the mast points to a patch of blue. Gradually, more blue sky is exposed as well as visibility at the deck level around the boat. A few yards from the boat has grown to a quarter mile or more. The fog lifts off the ocean while it burns away overhead. The tops of the Olympic Mountains rise above the cover; the first land sighted after thirty-seven days.

Terra firma visible to the north 'n south
the Strait of Juan de Fuca's gapin' mouth
Glassy calm 'n ebbin' this afternoon
the tide'll be turnin' 'n floodin' soon

Sun burns last of the fog away
tide turns at the end of the day
The crew can hear the current's gurglin' whoosh
when Calypso goes driftin' close by Tatoosh

L ow fog is persistent, not so the fickle little breeze the crew has been contending with all morning. This late afternoon the waters of the entrance to the Strait remain glassy. The ebb tide takes a windless *Calypso* to the southwest. She drifts across the border before dark when the fog is just beginning to reveal Vancouver Island to the north.

A pod of killer whales usher *Calypso* into the night. Her drift is not all that disadvantageous. She is crossing the Strait, bringing her closer to Neah Bay. At the same time she is being dragged away by the tide.

Goin' with the flow on this windless drift
this flood tide's nature's gift
A panorama of lights replace the daylight
when Calypso goes driftin' into the night

Nightfall

C *alypso* is virtually right under the Cape Flattery Light at Duntz Rock when the tide turns. The combined light wind and drift takes her close by Tatoosh Island, back into the Strait from the ocean.

Darkness settles in. The lights of the village appear, then, one by one disappear as the drift takes her past the mouth of the bay.

Nothing to be done until some wind makes up. The night is cold and clear, the sails lifeless.

The Strait of Juan de Fuca is a beehive. The lights of tugs towing barges and massive container ships moving through the traffic corridor are visible along with those of commercial fishing vessels and speedy little sport boats.

The incoming vessel traffic lane is just one mile north. The drift is taking *Calypso* clear of the inbound lane by a substantial margin giving some relief to the crew. Lights appear to the north on Vancouver Island, to the east down the Straits and south along the Washington shoreline.

A myriad of lights nearly overwhelm
the lookout steadfast at the helm
Shippin' lanes're real busy
so much traffic the crew's gettin' dizzy

Tugs 'n barges 'n ships all about
great difficulty sortin' all the lights out
Bright lights ashore add to the confusion
of what's real 'n what's an illusion

Logship!

With a long night ahead, the crew take shifts at the helm; one to have a nap while the other waits for wind to get *Calypso* underway and her anchor down somewhere.

After weeks on an empty ocean, the crew would rather sleep at anchor this night than work through the dark hours staying clear of traffic. As it stands, *Calypso* will ride the flood another two hours when the ebb will begin taking her back toward Neah Bay.

Down below, the exhaustion of the journey surfaces. Sleep comes quick, not hampered by the soggy bunk. The rhythmic pounding of ships engines are muffled, as the sound waves pass through the hull. The gentle rocking sweeps this sailor into a dreamless deep sleep.

On deck, the navigator stares into the night, sorting out the lights which number into the hundreds now. Their numbers are amplified by reflections on the glassy waters of the Strait. The flood tide reveals more lights onshore as *Calypso* drifts east at a knot and a half or two.

The shoreside lights are a distraction while searching for the flashing green light of a buoy at Clallam Bay which should be showing up low on the water to starboard. Straining to pick out the elusive light, a green light catches the eye, but something is not right, it is not at deck level. It appears to be a green light at an intersection on land, until its mate, the red port side light pops into view.

Two lights appear of a ship previously unseen
most definitely they're red 'n green
At first just a twinklin', a couple minutes later
Pat's yellin' " It's a freighter!"

The moment's shattered with her shout
"Get life preservers 'n flashlights out!"
Driftin' in a dead calm Calypso has no recourse
'cause she's on a deadly collision course!

"Log Ship!" Turns two sailors to stone for a long instant at the sight of those nav lights bearing down. A freighter departing Port

Angeles for the ocean is on a collision course with *Calypso*. Most likely a log carrier on a secondary commercial traffic lane between shore and the incoming lane a mile to the north.

Life preservers and two flashlights are dug out and tossed up on deck. The navigator was alert to pick out those two ship's lights among the confusing array around them. In addition, she had a plan and was already letting sheets go on the mizzen and main sails to expose more sail to the ship. *Calypso's* kerosene navigation lights seem puny, woefully inadequate in the present situation

*Middle of the night her big engines pound
hearts are racin' at the sound
Black steel towerin' in the night
this homecomin's an absolute fright*

*Freighter's bearin' down, crew's standin' transfixed
on the sails flashlights are fixed
After thousands of miles 'n so many trials
we're gonna end our trip
on the bow of this big 'ol ship!*

The pulsating of the beast's engines builds in a painfully slow search of a crescendo when she will turn *Calypso* to kindling with one fatal blow. On deck the crew has scrambled to the mainmast with their life preservers and flashlights in hand. They hug the mast and each other while casting their lights wildly on the sails.

Calypso lies windless on glassy waters, dead center between the ship's lights. The big engines pound hard, shoving the heavily laden hulk through the water. The crew feels every rotation of those big propellers underfoot on the cabintop.

The black shape, its menacing green and red lights locked on the crew, are growing larger, brighter. The pair at the mast make a decision to jump ship together the second the vessel strikes *Calypso*, not before. Should *Calypso* survive the strike, they would suffer the consequences, whatever they may be, in the water when they would have been better off to stay aboard. Seconds pass like minutes.

*The crew's hangin' onto the mast ready to jump
the instant Calypso takes that first big bump
Time slows to a crawl as the last moments passed
starin' at that bow where Calypso will be dashed*

A great wave rolls off the ship's bulbous bow. The massive hull, fully loaded, is pushing tons of water out of its way to get at *Calypso*. The lights on the sails are increasingly frantic in the attempt to gain the ship's attention.

*Ever so slight the lights give a shudder
when the helmsman hits hard-over on the ship's rudder
Those red n' green lights go cockeyed
as that ship heels over on her starboard side
Musta' rolled the crew right outa their beds
an' sent the capt'n runnin' for his meds!*

The ship so close now, there is just the blackness of the hull between the two lights up high. A black hole with white water churning at its base in a neat curling wave, above *Calypso's* deck level.

The crew, their senses acute, do not miss the subtlety of the ships navigation lights when they tremble. The lights shiver then freeze. They hang before the crew, askew at thirty degrees or so. The next instant, the ship is on top of *Calypso*.

*In the black of night the world's surreal
when the bow wake takes Calypso by her keel*

The crew holds tight at the mast as *Calypso* is rolled steeply by the bow wake. They are poised to spring as the wave picks up their boat, holding for that instant when metal smashes wood. *Calypso* is knocked down, but the hard demolishing strike never comes.

A sickenin' surge from under her port side
then that wave just tosses Calypso aside

The pair are nearly thrown from the deck, but they clutch the mast and each other with a lifesaving grip. *Calypso* feels as though she has been thrown clear of the water when she splashes down hard, rights herself then rocks wildly. A wall of black steel towers above them as it races close by, engines pounding.

Thanks to the helmsman's quick thinkin'
Calypso's not dashed to pieces 'n sinkin'!
The ship leaves Calypso floppin' in her wake
not a scratch on Calypso does it make

The crew sit silent, stunned as they watch the ship suffering deep rolls, to port and starboard; the slow motion mnemonic reaction to her extreme maneuver. *Calypso* too rocks wildly behind the ship, then, as fast as it all happened, it is over.

Calypso settles back into her lazy drift. The muffled drumming of the ship's engines can still be heard. The night sky is mirrored in the waters surrounding her.

The crew held on 'n didn't jump ship
that'd been a lousy end to a pretty good trip!

It would have been a spectacular death under a magnificent starlit sky. As it turns out, it is simply another glorious night to be alive.

Calypso's sails fill with an early mornin' breeze
into Neah Bay she tacks with ease
After thousands of miles 'n two years
the crew's at anchor sharin' laughs 'n tears

From the Log of Calypso

SATURDAY, October 10, 1981

Calypso glides into Port Townsend Bay with a light wind and flood tide. A quiet sail from Seiku, a spectacular rainbow, killer whales frolicking in a Fall sunrise welcome her home.

Afterthought:

Oh! That little business venture?
Just another misadventure!
Thought we'd fill the coffers to the top
With our Panamanian bumper crop

Months at sea did not serve the contraband well
Makin' seaweed impossible to sell
When all was said 'n done in PT 'n Hilo
Calypso never peddled a single kilo!

Made in the USA
Columbia, SC
05 July 2022